EXERCISES IN INTRODUCTORY PHYSICS

EXERCISES IN INTRODUCTORY PHYSICS

R. B. LEIGHTON
R. E. VOGT
California Institute of Technology

ADDISON-WESLEY PUBLISHING COMPANY
Reading, Massachusetts
Menlo Park, California · London · Amsterdam · Don Mills, Ontario · Sydney

Reproduced by Addison-Wesley from camera-ready copy
prepared by the authors.

 Printed in the
United States of America. Published simultaneously in
Canada. Library of Congress Catalog Card No. 73-82143.

ISBN 0-201-04215-0
EFGHIJKLMN-AL-89876543210

INTRODUCTION

These exercises were compiled by the authors for use with Volume I of The Feynman Lectures in Physics in the first year introductory physics course at the California Institute of Technology, and they are accordingly arranged in the same order as to subject as the Feynman Lectures. Within each topic or chapter, the exercises are subdivided into categories according to degree of generality or difficulty. In the order in which these appear in a given chapter, these are: proofs or generalizations, easy exercises, intermediate exercises, and more sophisticated or elaborate exercises. Usually, the proofs and generalizations supplement the discussion given in the Feynman Lectures, and the results are intended to be understood and used by the student. The average student should have little trouble solving the easy exercises, and should be able to solve most of the intermediate exercises within a reasonable time -- perhaps ten to twenty minutes each. The more sophisticated exercises generally require a deeper physical insight or more extensive thought, and will be of interest principally to the better student.

The individual exercises were contributed and critically evaluated by many people. A substantial number were originated by R. B. Leighton in connection with the original Feynman Lecture series; some are reproduced by permission from an extensive set compiled by Foster Strong; many were adapted by R. E. Vogt from examination problems used in the introductory course. To the many contributors, known or anonymous, the authors express their sincere thanks.

The authors regard the present work as far from complete. It is hoped that in the course of time they, or others at Caltech, will refine the present material and add new exercises and explanations so that a self-study workbook may eventually result, whose utility might extend beyond the present limited range.

CONTENTS

PART I

PART II

PART I

CHAPTER 1

Atoms in Motion

Refer to The Feynman Lectures on Physics, Vol. I, Chs. 1 to 3. Use the ideas outlined in these chapters, together with your own experience and imagination, in analyzing the following exercises. Precise numerical results in most cases are not expected.

A-1.

If heat is merely molecular motion, what is the difference between a hot, stationary baseball and a cool, rapidly moving one?

A-2.

If the atoms of all objects are perpetually in motion, how can there be any permanent objects, such as fossil imprints.

A-3.

Explain qualitatively why and how friction in a moving machine produces heat. Explain also, if you can, why heat cannot produce useful motion by the reverse process.

A-4.

Chemists have found that the molecules of rubber consist of long criss-crossed chains of atoms. Explain why a rubber band becomes warm when it is stretched.

A-5.

What should happen to a rubber band which is supporting a given weight, if it is heated? (To find out, try it.)

A-6.

Can you explain why there are no crystals which have the shape of a regular pentagon? (Triangles, squares, and hexagons are common in crystal forms.)

B-1.

You are given a large number of steel balls of equal diameter d and a container of known volume V. Every dimension of the container is much greater than the diameter of a ball. What is the greatest number of balls that can be placed in the container?

B-2.

How should the pressure P of a gas vary with n, the number of atoms per unit volume, and $\langle v \rangle$, the average speed of an atom? (Should P be proportional to n and/or $\langle v \rangle$, or should it vary more, or less, rapidly than linearly?)

B-3.

Ordinary air has a density of about 0.001 g cm^{-3}, while liquid air has a density of about 1.0 g cm^{-3}.

a) Estimate the number of air molecules per cm^3 in ordinary air and in liquid air.

b) Estimate the mass of an air molecule.

c) Estimate the average distance an air molecule should travel between collisions at normal temperatures and pressures (NTP). This distance is called the mean free path.

d) Estimate at what pressure, in normal atmospheres, a vacuum system should be operated in order that the mean free path be about one meter.

B-4.

The intensity of a collimated, parallel beam of K atoms is reduced 3.0% by a layer of A gas 1.0 mm thick at a pressure of 6.0×10^{-4} mm Hg. Calculate the effective target area per argon atom.

B-5.

X-ray diffraction studies show that NaCl crystals have a cubic lattice, with a spacing of 2.820 Å between nearest neighbours. Look up the density and molecular weight of NaCl and calculate Avogadro's number. (This is one of the most precise experimental methods for N_0.)

B-6.

Boltwood and Rutherford found that radium in equilibrium with its disintegration products produced 13.6×10^{10} Helium atoms per second per gram of radium. They also measured that the disintegration of 192 mg of radium produced 0.0824 mm^3 of Helium per day at STP. Use these data to calculate:

a) The number of helium atoms per cm^3 of gas at STP.

b) Avogadro's number.

Reference: Boltwood and Rutherford, Phil. Mag. 22, 586, 1911.

C-1.

Rayleigh found that 0.81 mg of olive oil on a water surface produced a mono-molecular layer 84 cm in diameter. What value of Avogadro's number results?

Note: Approximate composition $H(CH_2)_{18}COOH$, in a linear chain. Density 0.8 g cm^{-3}.

Reference: Rayleigh, Proc. Roy. Soc., 47, 364 (1890).

C-2.

About 1860, Maxwell showed that the viscosity of a gas is given by

$$\eta = 1/3\ \rho v\ \ell$$

where ρ is the density, v the mean speed, and ℓ, the mean free path. The latter quantity he had earlier shown to be $\ell = 1/(\sqrt{2}\ \pi N_g\ \sigma^2)$, where σ is the diameter of the molecule. Loschmidt (1865) used the measured value of η, ρ(gas), and ρ(solid) together with Joule's calculated v to determine N_g, the number of molecules per cm^3 in a gas at STP. He assumed the molecules to be hard spheres, tightly packed in a solid. Given $\eta = 2.0 \times 10^{-4}$ g $cm^{-1}s^{-1}$ for air at STP, ρ(liquid) ~ 1 g cm^{-3}, ρ(gas) ~ 1×10^{-3} g cm^{-3}, and v ~ 500 m s^{-1}, calculate N_g.

C-3.

A glass full of water is left standing on an average outdoor windowsill in California.

a) How long do you think it would take to evaporate completely?

b) How many molecules $cm^{-2}s^{-1}$ would be leaving the water glass at this rate?

c) Briefly discuss the connection, if any, between your answer to part a) and the average rainfall over the earth.

C-4.

A raindrop of an afternoon thundershower fell upon a Paleozoic mud flat and left an imprint which is later dug up as a fossil by a hot, thirsty geology student. As he drains his canteen, the student idly wonders how many molecules of water of that ancient raindrop he has just drunk. Estimate this number using only data which you already know. (Make reasonable assumptions regarding necessary information which you do not know.)

CHAPTER 2

Conservation of Energy, Statics

Refer to The Feynman Lectures on Physics, Vol. I, Ch. 4.

1.

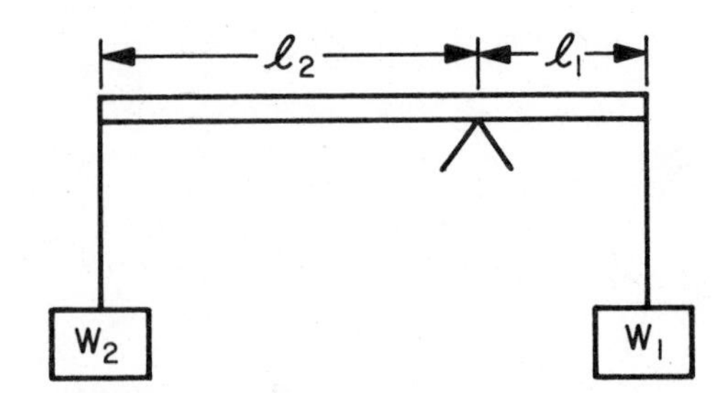

Use the principle of virtual work to establish the formula for an unequal-arm balance: $W_1 \ell_1 = W_2 \ell_2$. (Neglect the weight of the cross-beam.)

2. Extend the formula obtained in the previous exercise to include a number of weights hung at various distances from the pivot point:

$$\sum_i W_i \ell_i = 0$$

(Distances on one side of the fulcrum are considered positive and on the other side, negative.)

3. A body is acted upon by n forces and is in static equilibrium. Use the principle of virtual work to prove that:

a) If $n = 1$, the magnitude of the force must be zero. (A trivial case.)

b) If $n = 2$, the two forces must be equal in magnitude, opposite in direction, and collinear.

c) If $n = 3$, the forces must be coplanar and their lines of action must pass through a single point.

d) For any n, the sum of the products of the magnitude of a force F_i times the cosine of the angle $\triangle_i$ between the force and any fixed line, is zero:

$$\sum_{i=1} F_i \cos \triangle_i = 0.$$

4.

Problems involving static equilibrium in the absence of friction may be reduced, using the Principle of Virtual Work, to problems of mere geometry: Where does one point move when another moves a given small distance? In many cases this question is easily answered if the following properties of a triangle are used:

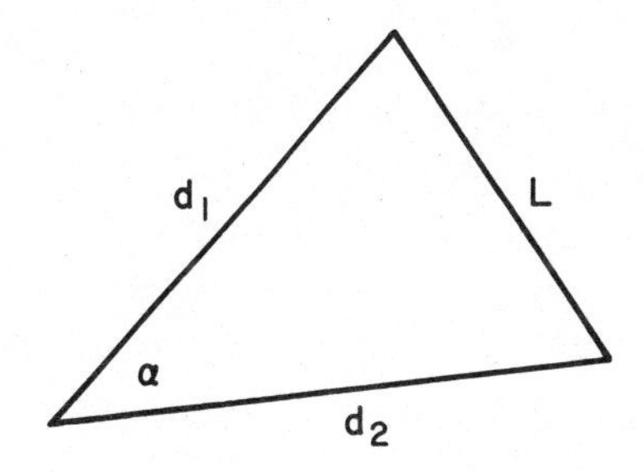

a) If the sides d_1 and d_2 remain fixed in length, but the angle α changes by a small amount $\triangle\alpha$, the opposite side L changes by an amount $\triangle L = \frac{d_1 d_2}{L} \sin\alpha \triangle\alpha$.

b) If the three sides a, b, c of a right triangle change in length by small amounts $\triangle a$, $\triangle b$, and $\triangle c$, then $a\triangle a + b\triangle b = c\triangle c$ (c is the hypotenuse) Prove these formulas.

A-1.

A uniform plank 1.5 m long and weighing 3.00 kg is pivoted at one end. The plank is held in equilibrium in a horizontal position by a weight and pulley arrangement, as shown. Find the weight W needed to balance the plank. Neglect friction.

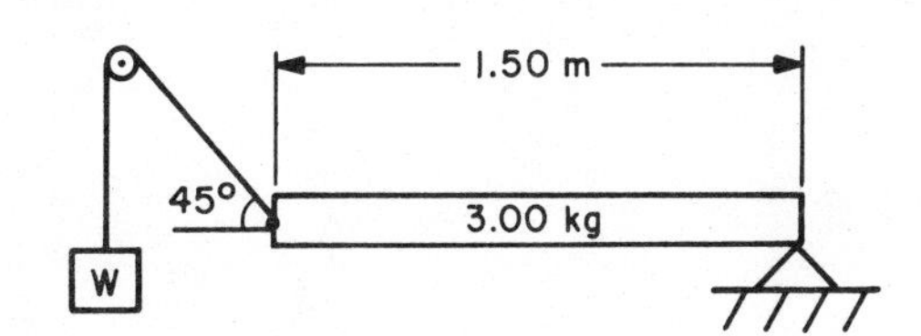

A-2.

A ball of radius 3.0 cm and weight 1.00 kg rests on a plane tilted at an angle α with the horizontal and also touches a vertical wall. Both surfaces have negligible friction. Find the force with which the ball presses on each plane.

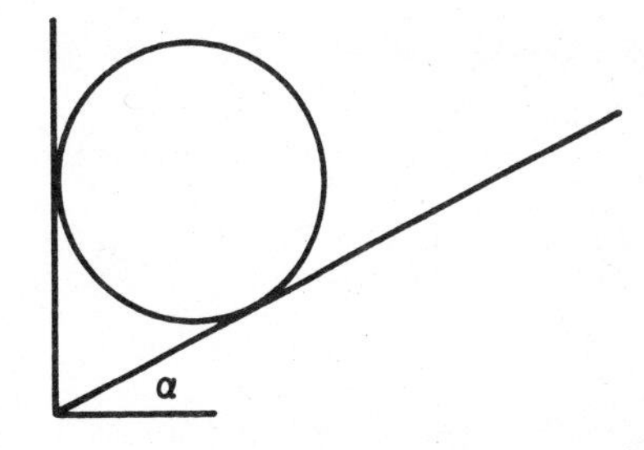

A-3.

The jointed parallelogram frame AA'BB' is pivoted (in a vertical plane) on the pivots P and P'. There is negligible friction in the pins at A, A', B, B', P, and P'. The members AA'CD and B'BGH are rigid and identical in size.

$$AP = A'P' = \tfrac{1}{2}\,PB = \tfrac{1}{2}\,P'B'$$

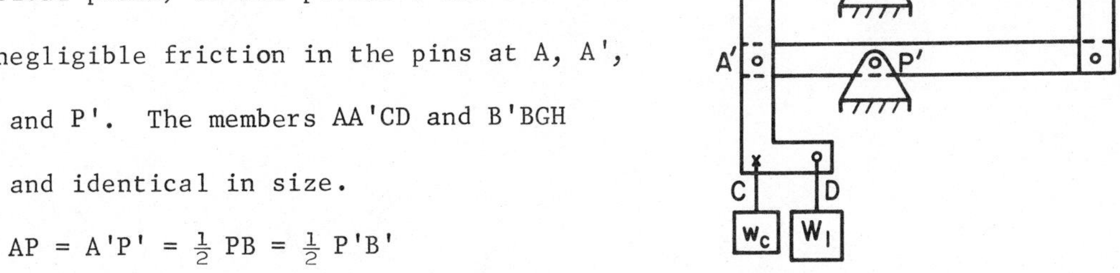

Because of the counterweight w_c, the frame is in balance without the loads W_1 and W_2. If a 0.50 kg weight W_1 is hung from D, what weight W_2, hung from H, is needed to produce equilibrium?

A-4.

The system shown is in static equilibrium. Use the principle of virtual work to find the weights A and B. Neglect the weight of the strings and the friction in the pulleys.

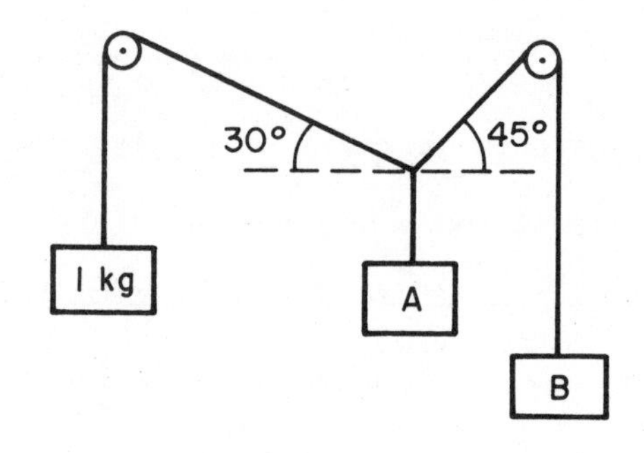

A-5.

A weight W = 50 lb. is suspended from the mid-point of a wire ACB as shown.

AC = CB = 5 ft. AB = $5\sqrt{2}$ ft. Find the tension in the wire.

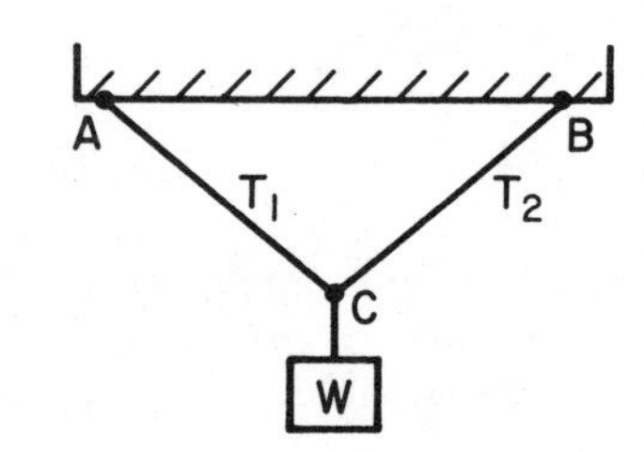

A-6.

The truss in the figure is made of light aluminum struts pivoted at each end. At C is a roller which rolls on a smooth plate. When a workman heats up member AB with a welding torch, it is observed to increase in length by an amount x, and the load W is thereby moved vertically an amount y.

a) Is the motion of W upward or downward?

b) What is the force in the member AB (including the sense, i.e., tension or compression)?

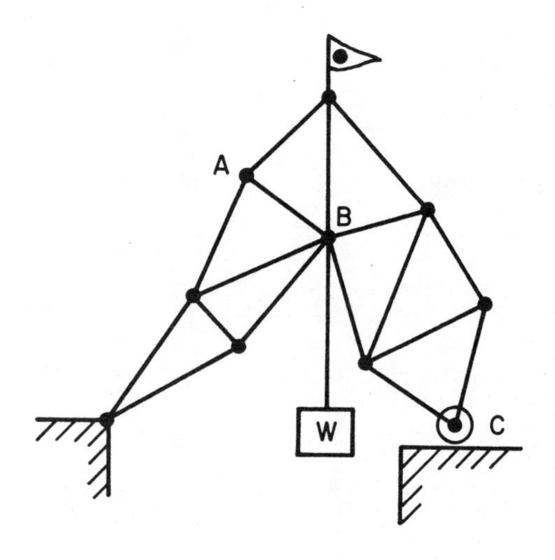

A-7.

What horizontal force F (applied at the axle) is required to push a wheel of weight W and radius R over a block of height h?

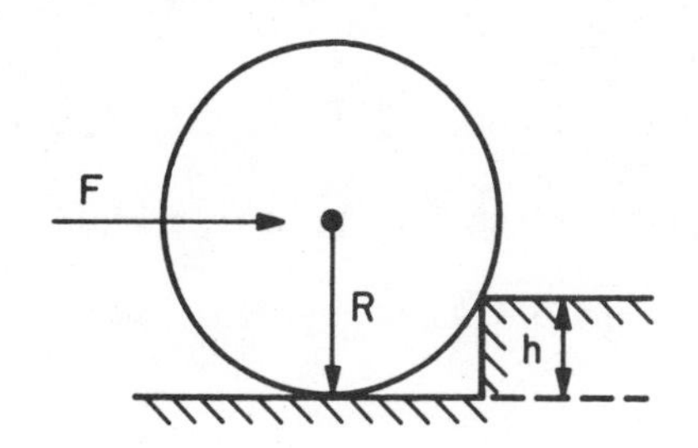

A-8.

A horizontal turntable of diameter D is mounted on bearings with negligible friction. Two horizontal forces F in the plane of the turntable of equal magnitude, parallel to each other but pointing in opposite directions, act on the rim of the turntable on opposite ends of the diameter.

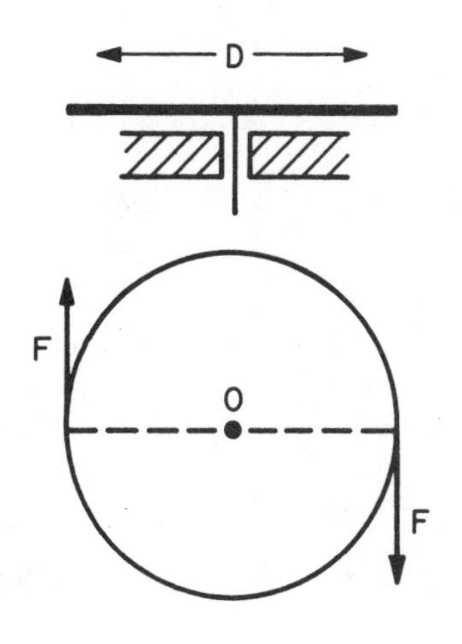

a) What force acts on the bearing?

b) What is the torque (= moment of this force couple) about a vertical axis through the center 0?

c) What would be the moment about a vertical axis through an arbitrary point 0' in the same plane?

d) Is the following statement correct or false? Explain. "Any two forces acting on a body can be combined into a single resultant force that would have the same effect".

In framing your answer, consider the case where the two forces are opposite in direction but not quite equal in magnitude.

A-9.

A flat steel plate floating on mercury is acted upon by three forces at three corners of a square of side 0.100 m, as shown. Find a <u>single</u> fourth force which will hold the plate in equilibrium. Give the magnitude, direction, and point of application along the line AB.

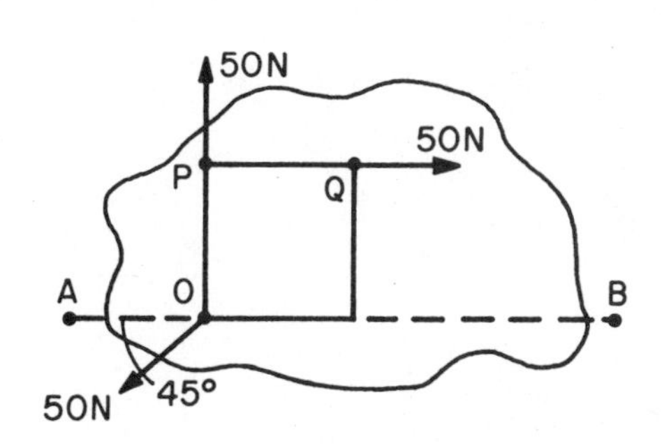

A-10.

In the absence of friction, how fast will the weights W_1 and W_2 be going when they travel a distance D, starting from rest? $(W_1 > W_2)$

A-11.

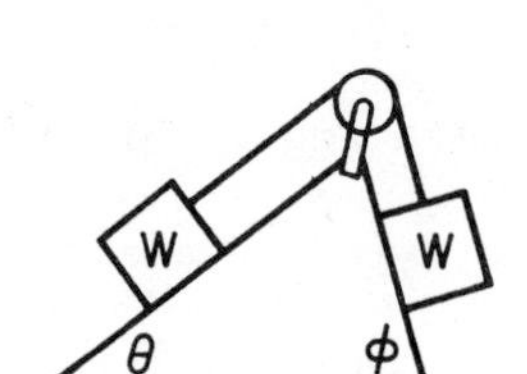

In the figure, the weights are equal, and there is negligible friction. If the system is released from rest, how fast are the weights moving when they have gone a distance D?

B-1.

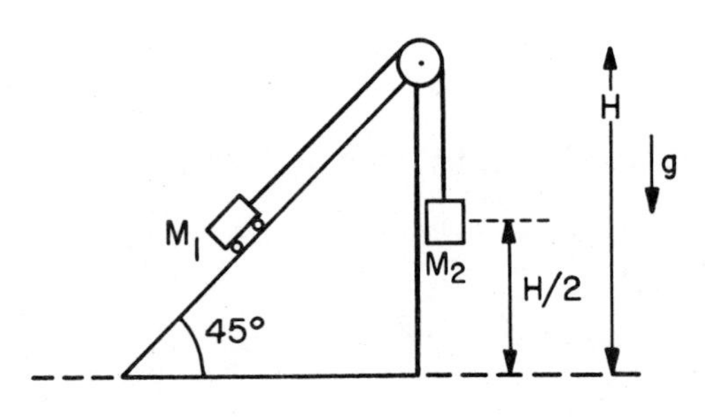

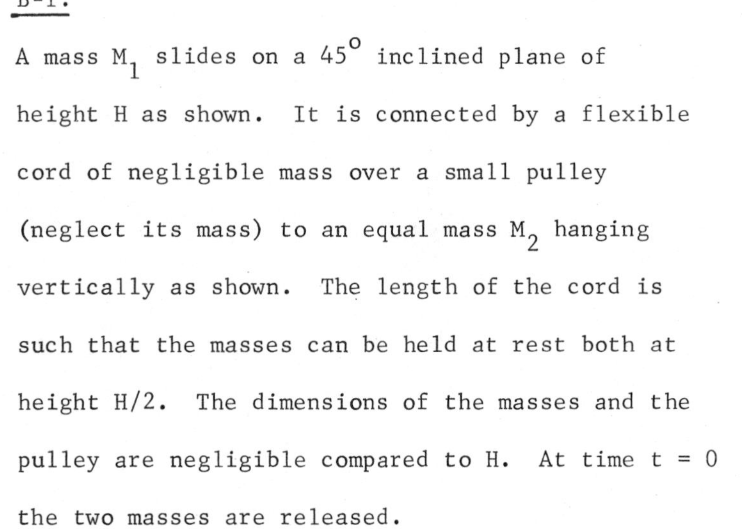

A mass M_1 slides on a 45° inclined plane of height H as shown. It is connected by a flexible cord of negligible mass over a small pulley (neglect its mass) to an equal mass M_2 hanging vertically as shown. The length of the cord is such that the masses can be held at rest both at height H/2. The dimensions of the masses and the pulley are negligible compared to H. At time $t = 0$ the two masses are released.

a) For $t > 0$ calculate the vertical acceleration of M_2.

b) Which mass will move downward? At what time t_1 will it strike the ground?

c) If the mass in (b) stops when it hits the ground, but the other mass keeps moving, show whether or not it will strike the pulley.

B-2.

A derrick is made of a uniform boom of length L and weight w, pivoted at its lower end. It is supported at an angle θ with the vertical by a horizontal cable attached at a point a distance x from the pivot, and a weight W is slung from its upper end. Find the tension in the horizontal cable.

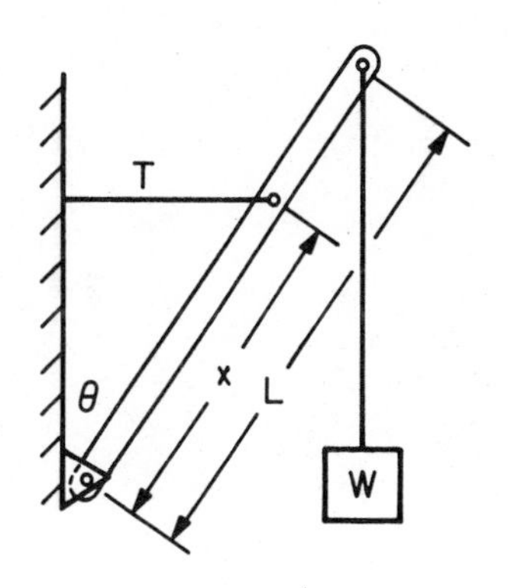

B-3.

A uniform ladder 10 ft. long with rollers at the top end leans against a smooth vertical wall. The ladder weighs 30 lb. A weight W = 60 lb is hung from a rung 2.5 feet from the top end. Find

a) The force with which the rollers push on the wall.

b) The horizontal and vertical forces with which the ladder pushes on the ground.

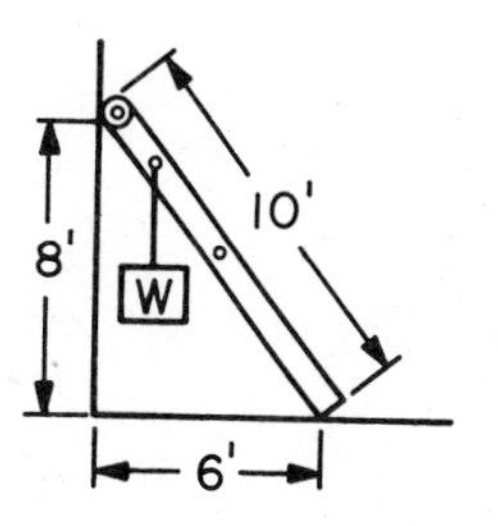

B-4.

A plank of weight W and length $\sqrt{3}$ R lies in a smooth circular trough of radius R. At one end of the plank is a weight W/2. Calculate the angle θ at which the plank lies when it is in equilibrium.

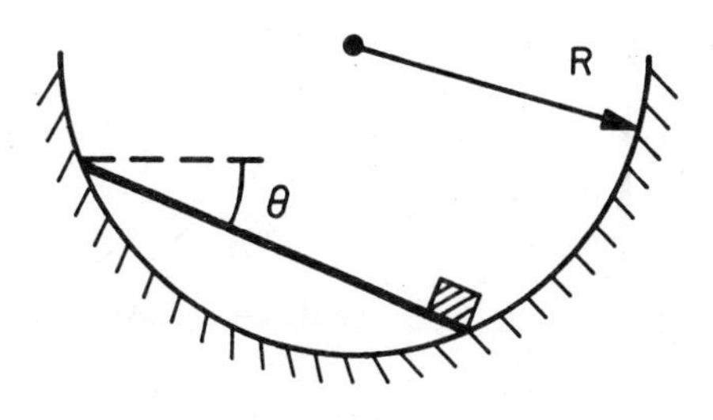

B-5.

A uniform bar of length ℓ and weight W is supported at its ends by two inclined planes as shown. (Neglect friction.) From the PVW find the angle α at which the bar is in equilibrium.

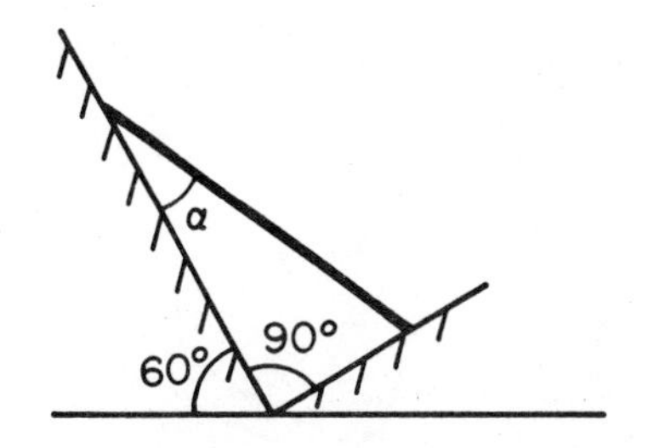

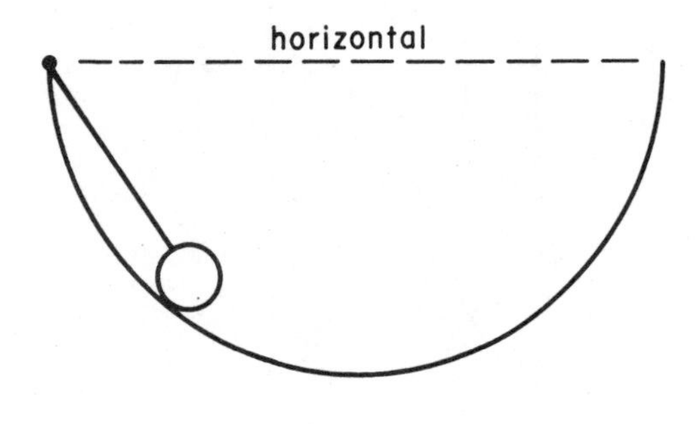

B-6.

A solid small sphere of radius 4.5 cm and weight W, is to be suspended by a string from the ends of a smooth hemispherical bowl of radius 49 cm. It is found that if the string is any shorter than 40 cm, it breaks. By PVW what is the breaking strength of the string?

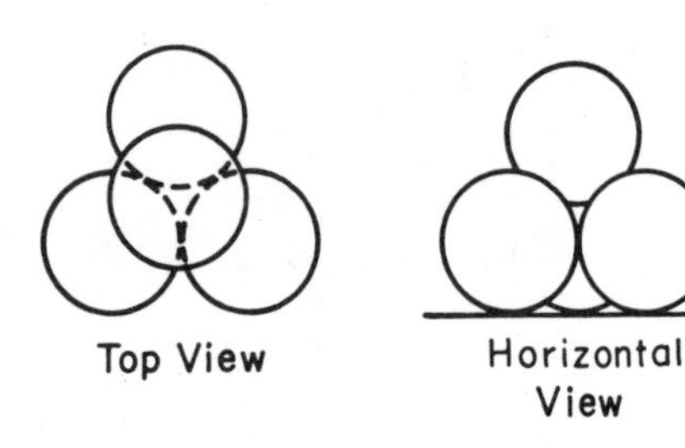

B-7.

An ornament for a courtyard at a World's Fair is to be made up of four identical, frictionless metal spheres, each weighing $2\sqrt{6}$ tonwts. The spheres are to be arranged as shown, with three resting on a horizontal surface and touching each other; the fourth is to rest freely on the other three. The bottom three are kept from separating by spot welds at the points of contact with each other. Allowing for a factor of safety of 3, how much tension must the spot welds withstand?

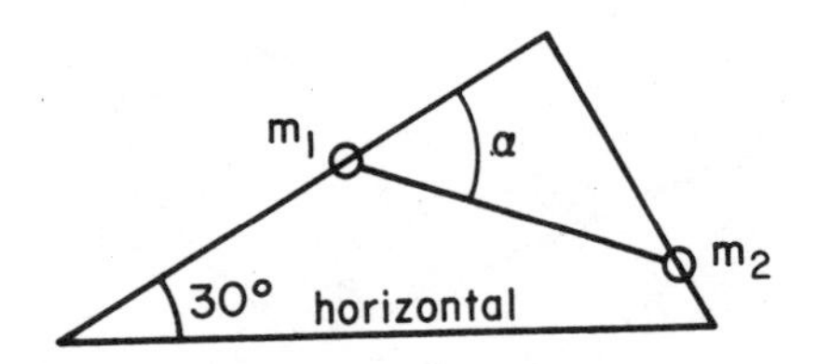

B-8.

A rigid wire frame is formed in a right triangle, and set in a vertical plane as shown. Two beads of masses m_1 = 100 gram, m_2 = 300 gram slide without friction on the wires, and are connected by a cord. When the system is in static equilibrium, what is the tension in the cord, and what angle α does it make with the first wire?

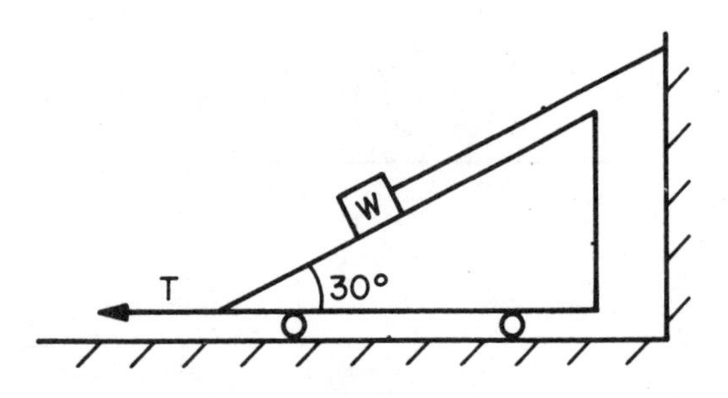

B-9.

Find the tension T needed to hold the cart in equilibrium, if there is no friction.

a) Using the principle of virtual work.

b) Using force components.

B-10.

A bobbin of mass M = 3 kg consists of a central cylinder of radius r = 5 cm and two end plates of radius R = 6 cm. It is placed on a slotted incline on which it will roll but not slip, and a mass m = 4.5 kg is suspended from a cord wound around the bobbin. It is observed that the system is in static equilibrium. What is the angle of tilt θ of the incline?

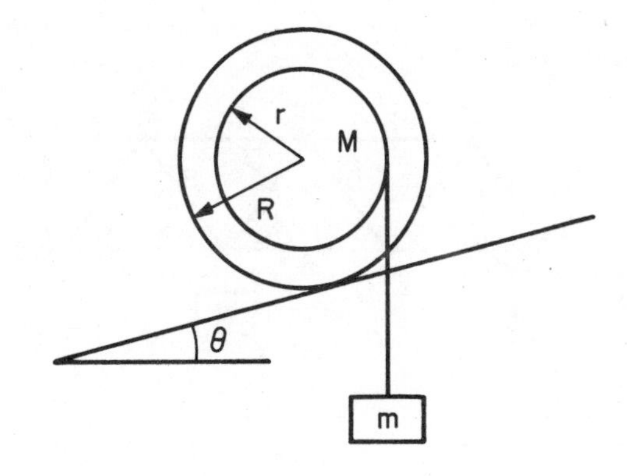

B-11.

A loop of flexible chain, of total weight W, rests on a smooth right circular cone of base radius r and height h. The chain rests in a horizontal circle on the cone, whose axis is vertical. Find the tension in the chain. Neglect friction.

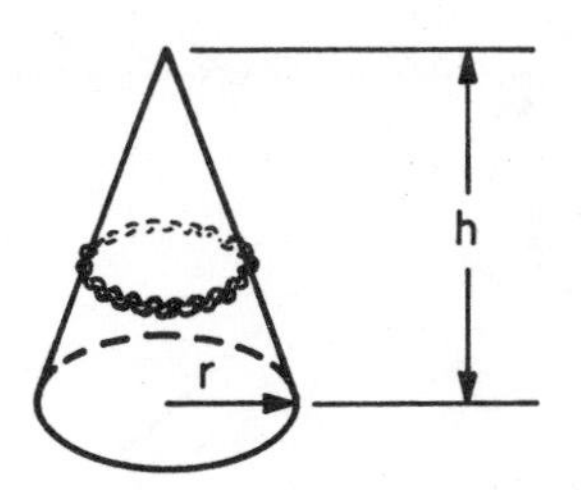

B-12.

A cart on an inclined plane is balanced by the weight w. All parts have negligible frcition. Find the weight W of the cart.

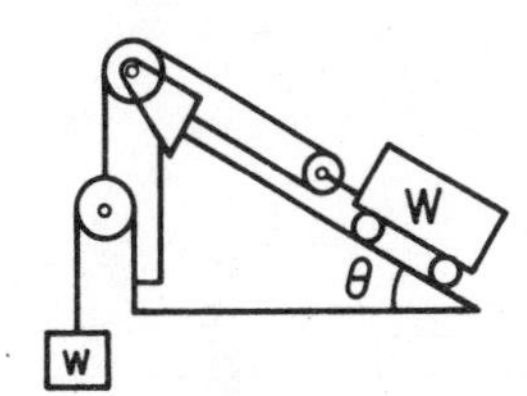

B-13.

A bridge truss is constructed as shown. All joints may be considered frictionless pivots and all members rigid, weightless, and of equal length. Find the reaction forces F_1 and F_2 and the force in the member DF.

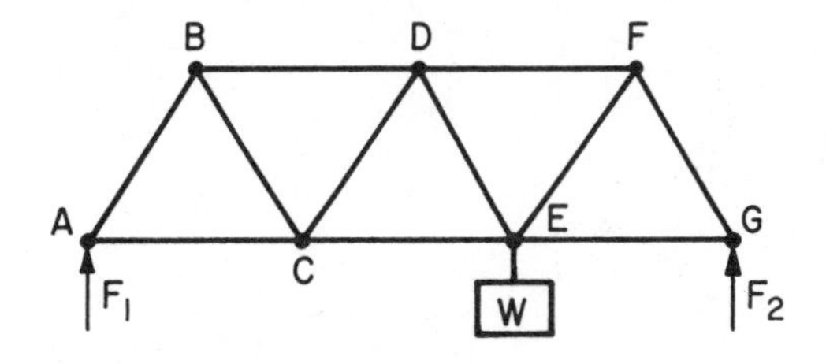

B-14.

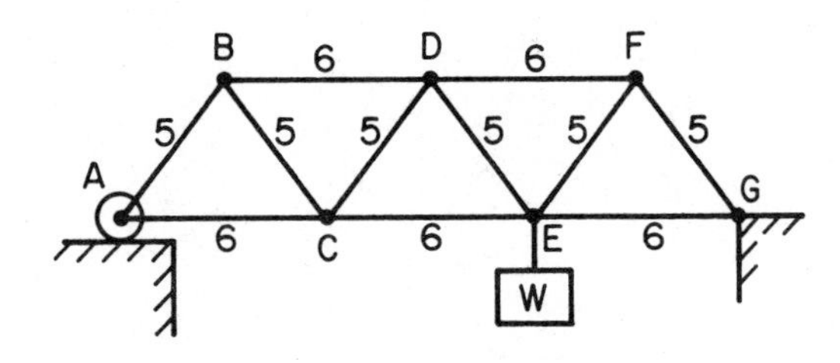

In the truss shown, all diagonal struts are of length 5 units and all horizontal ones are of length 6 units. All joints are freely hinged, and the weight of the truss is negligible.

a) Which of the members could be replaced with flexible cables, for the load position shown?

b) Find the forces in struts BD, and DE.

B-15.

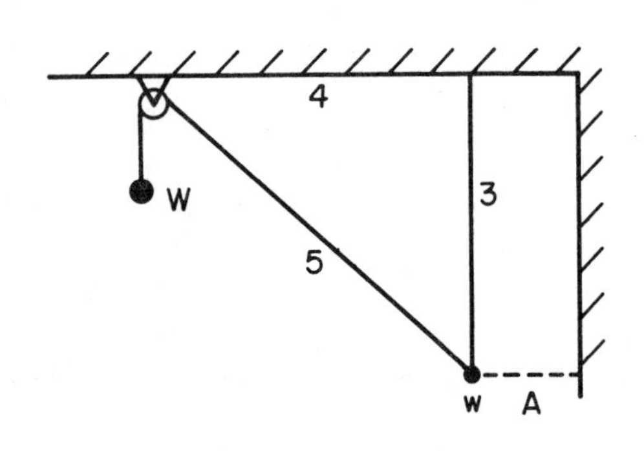

In the system shown, a pendulum bob of weight w is initially held in the vertical position by a thread A. When this thread is burned, releasing the pendulum, it swings to the left and barely reaches the ceiling at its maximum swing. Find the weight W. (Neglect friction, the radius of the pulley, and the finite sizes of the weights.)

B-16.

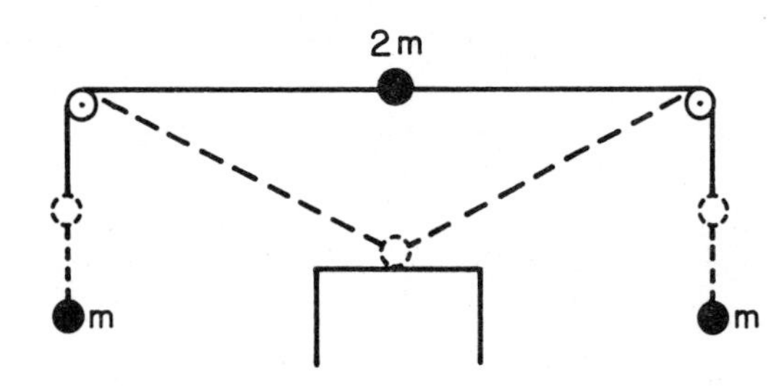

Two equal masses m are attached to a third mass 2m by equal lengths of fine thread and the thread is passed over two small pulleys with negligible friction situated 100 cm apart. The mass 2m is initially held level with the pulleys midway between them, and is then released from rest. When it has descended a distance of 50 cm it strikes a table top. How fast is it then moving?

B-17.

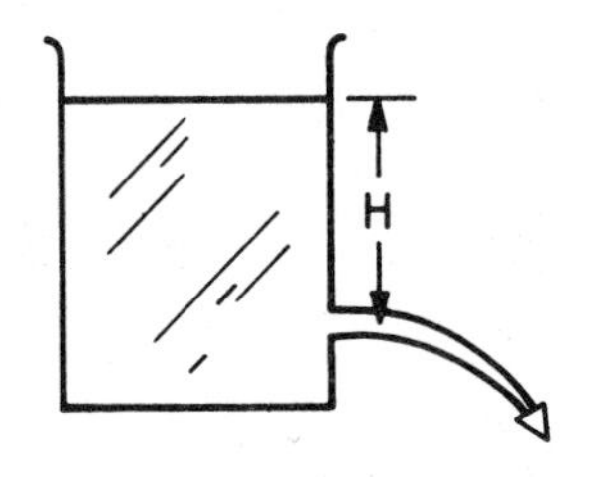

A tank of cross-sectional area A contains a liquid having density ρ. The liquid squirts freely from a small hole of area A a distance H below the free surface of the liquid. If the liquid has no internal friction (viscosity), with what speed does it emerge?

C-1.

Smooth, identical logs are piled in a stake truck. The truck is forced off the highway and comes to rest on an even keel lengthwise but with the bed at an angle θ with the horizontal. As the truck is unloaded, the removal of the log shown dotted leaves the remaining three in a condition where they are just ready to slide, that is, if θ were any smaller, the logs would fall down. Find θ.

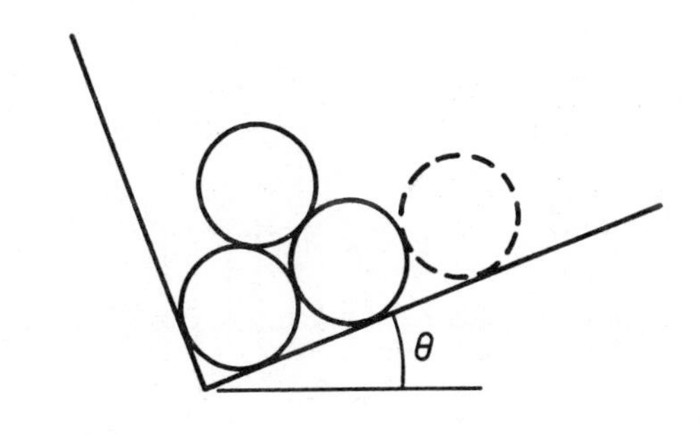

C-2.

A spool of weight w has radii r and R. It is wound with cord, and suspended from a fixed support by two cords wound on the smaller radius. A weight W is then suspended from two cords wound on the larger radius, as shown. W is chosen so that the spool is just balanced. Find W.

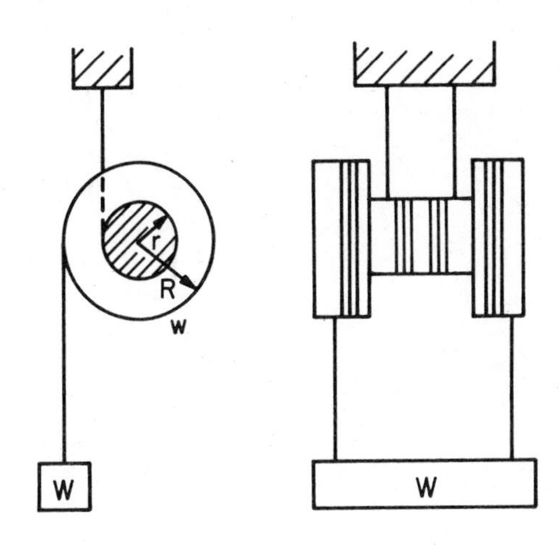

C-3.

A suspension bridge is to span a deep gorge 54 m wide. The roadway will consist of a steel truss supported by six pairs of vertical cables spaced 9.0 m apart, each cable to carry an equal share of the 48.0×10^3 kg weight. The two pairs of cables nearest the center are to be 2.00 m long. Find the proper lengths for the remaining vertical cables, and the maximum tension in the two longitudinal cables, if the latter are to be at a 45° angle with the horizontal at their ends.

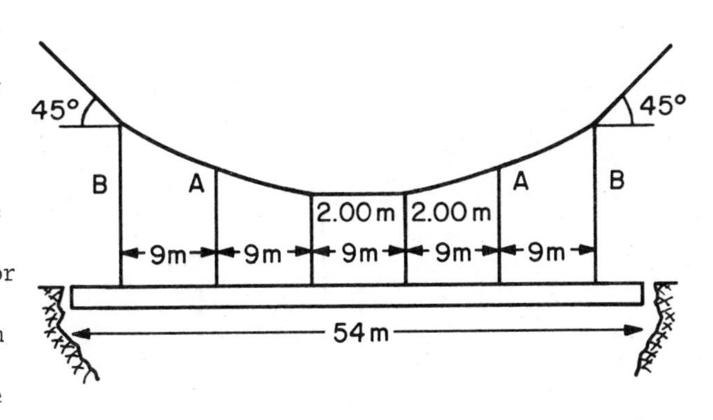

C-4.

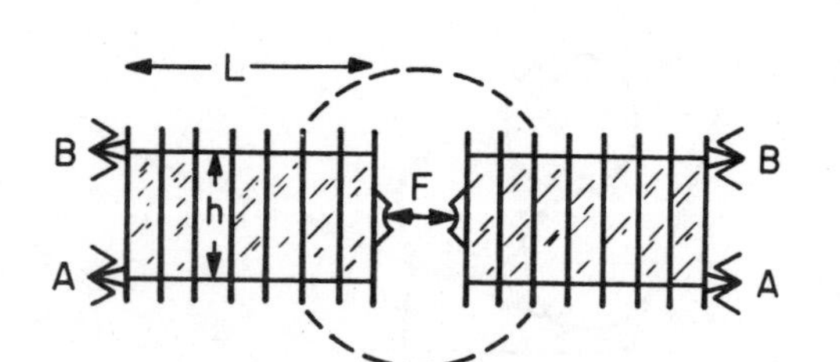

The insulating support structure of a Tandem Van de Graaff may be represented as two blocks of about uniform density, length L, height h and weight W, supported from vertical bulkheads by pivot joints (A and B) and forced apart by a screw jack (F) at the center. Since the material of the blocks cannot support tension, the jack must be adjusted to give zero force on the upper pivot.

a) What force F is required?

b) What is the total force on one of the lower pivots A?

CHAPTER 3

Kepler's Laws and Gravitation

Refer to The Feynman Lectures on Physics, Vol. I, Ch. 7.

1. Some properties of the ellipse.

   The size and shape of an ellipse are determined by specifying the values of any two of the following quantities:

   a : the semi major axis

   b : the semi minor axis

   c : the distance from the center to one focus

   e : the eccentricity

   r_p: the perihelion (or perigee) distance (the closest distance from a focus to the ellipse)

   r_a: the aphelion (or apogee) distance (the farthest distance from a focus to the ellipse.

   The relationships of these various quantities are as follows:

   $a^2 = b^2 + c^2$

   $e = c/a$ (definition of e)

   $r_p = a - c = a(1 - e)$

   $r_a = a + c = a(1 + e)$

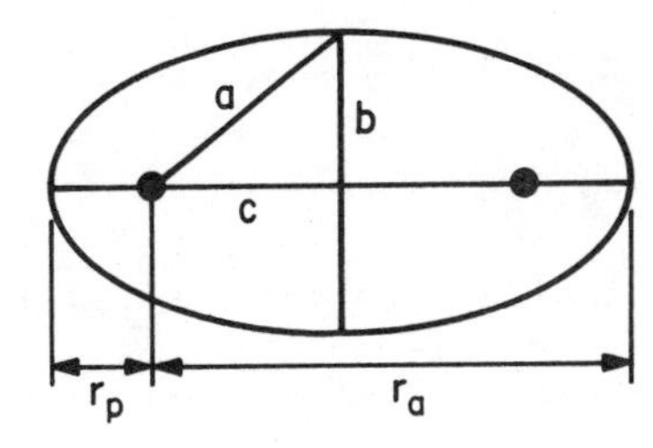

   Show that the area of an ellipse is given by $A = \pi ab$.

A-1.

The distance of the moon from the center of the earth varies from 363,300 km at perigee to 405,500 km at apogee, and its period is $27^d.322$. A certain artificial earth satellite is orbiting so that its perigee height from the surface of the Earth is 225 km, and its apogee height is 710 km. The mean diameter of the Earth is 12,756 km. What is the sidereal period of this satellite?

A-2.

The eccentricity of the Earth's orbit is 0.0167. Find the ratio of its maximum speed in its orbit to its minimum speed.

A-3.

The radii of the Earth and the moon are 6378 km and 1738 km, respectively, and their masses are in the ratio 81.3 to 1.000. Calculate the acceleration of gravity at the surface of the moon. $g_{\oplus} = 9.80 \text{ m s}^{-2}$.

A-4.

In 1986, Halley's comet is expected to return on its seventh trip around the sun since the days in 1456 when people were so frightened that they offered prayers in the churches "to be saved from the Devil, the Turk, and the comet". In its most recent perihelion on April 19, 1910, it was observed to pass near the sun at a distance 0.60 A.U.

a) How far does it go from the sun at the outer extreme of its orbit?

b) What is the ratio of its maximum orbital speed to its minimum speed?

A-5.

A satellite in a circular orbit near the earth's surface has a typical period of about 100 minutes. What should be the radius of its orbit (in earth radii) for a period of 24 hours.

A-6.

Consider two earth satellites of equal orbital radius, one of them in a polar orbit, the other in an orbit in the equatorial plane. Which satellite needed the larger booster rocket and why?

B-1.

A true "Syncom" satellite rotates synchronously with the earth. It always remains in a fixed position with respect to a point P on the earth's surface.

a) Consider the straight line connecting the center of the earth with the satellite. If P lies on the intersection of this line with the earth's surface, can P have any geographic latitude or what restrictions do exist? Explain.

b) What is the distance r_s from the earth's center of a Syncom satellite of mass m? Express r_s in units of the earth-moon distance $r_{\oplus☽}$

Note: Consider the earth a uniform sphere. You may use $T_{☽} = 27$ days for the moon's period.

B-2.

a) Comparing data describing the Earth's orbital motion about the sun with data for the moon's orbital motion about the Earth, determine the mass of the sun relative to the mass of the Earth.

b) Io, a moon of Jupiter, has an orbital period of revolution of $1^{d}.769$ and an orbital radius of 421,800 km. Determine the mass of Jupiter in terms of the mass of the Earth.

B-3.

Two stars, a and b, move around one another under the influence of their mutual gravitational attraction. If the semi major axis of their relative orbit is observed to be R, measured in astronomical units (AU) and their period of revolution is T years, find an expression for the sum of the mass, $m_a + m_b$, in terms of the mass of the sun.

B-4.

If the attractive gravitational force between a very large central sphere M and a satellite m in orbit about it were actually $\vec{F} = - \frac{GMm}{R^{(3 + a)}} \vec{R}$, (where $\vec{R}$ is the vector between them) how would Kepler's second and third law be modified? (In discussing the third law, you should assume a circular orbit.)

C-1.

In making laboratory measurements of g, how precise does one have to be to detect diurnal variations in g due to the moon's gravitation? For simplicity, assume that your laboratory is so located that the moon passes through zenith and nadir. Also, neglect earth-tide effects.

C-2.

An eclipsing binary star system is one whose orbital plane nearly contains the line of sight, so that one star eclipses the other periodically. The relative orbital velocity of the two components can be measured from the Doppler shift of their spectral lines. Let T and V be the observed period in days and orbital velocity in km s^{-1}. Find the total mass of the binary system in solar masses. Note: The mean distance from the earth to the sun is 1.50×10^{8} km.

C-3.

A comet rounds the sun at a perihelion distance of $R_p = 1.00 \times 10^6$ km. At this point its velocity is 500.0 km s^{-1}.

a) What is the radius of curvature of the orbit at perihelion (in km)?

b) For an ellipse with semi-major axis a and semi-minor axis b, the radius of curvature at perihelion is $R_c = b^2/a$. If you know R_c and R_p you should be able to write a relation involving a and only these quantities. Do so, and find a.

c) If you were able to solve for a from the above information, you should be able to calculate the period of the comet. Write the relation, defining all symbols.

C-4.

Using the idea that two mutually gravitating bodies each "fall" toward the other, and thus move about some fixed common point (their center of mass), show that their period in an orbit in which they remain a given, fixed distance apart, depends only upon the sum of their masses and not at all upon the ratio of their masses. This is also true for elliptical orbits. Prove it.

C-5.

How can one find the mass of the moon?

C-6.

The trigonometric parallax of Sirius (i.e., the angle subtended at Sirius by the radius of the Earth's orbit) is 0".378 arc. Using this and the data contained in the figure, deduce as best you can the mass of the Sirius system in terms of that of the sun, a) assuming that the orbital plane is perpendicular to the line of sight, and b) allowing for the actual tilt of the orbit. Is your value in part b) an upper or lower limit (or either)?

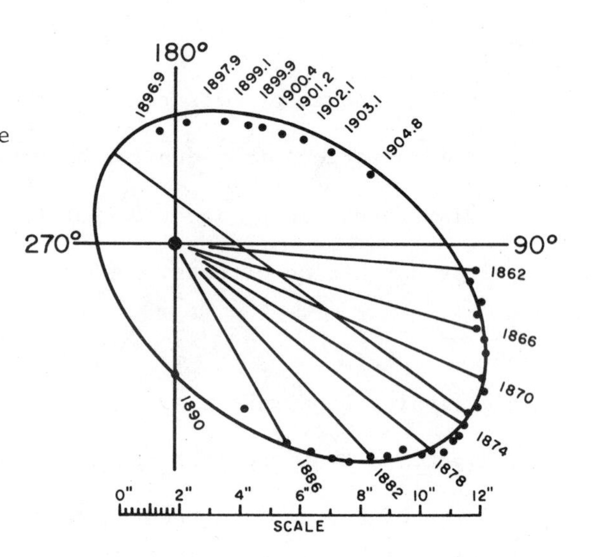

CHAPTER 4

Kinematics

Refer to The Feynman Lectures on Physics, Vol. I, Ch. 8.

1.

a) A body travels in a straight line with a constant acceleration. At $t = 0$, it is located at $x = x_0$ and has a velocity $v_x = v_{x0}$. Show that its position and velocity at time t are

$$x(t) = x_0 + v_{x0}t + \frac{1}{2}at^2$$

$$v_x(t) = v_{x0} + at.$$

b) Eliminate t from the preceding equations, and thus show that, at any time,

$$v_x^2 = v_{x0}^2 + 2a(x - x_0).$$

2. Generalize the preceding problem to the case of three dimensional motion with constant acceleration components, a_x, a_y, a_z, along the three coordinate axis. Show that

a) $x(t) = x_0 + v_{x0}t + \frac{1}{2}a_xt^2$

$y(t) = y_0 + v_{y0}t + \frac{1}{2}a_yt^2$

$z(t) = z_0 + v_{z0}t + \frac{1}{2}a_zt^2$

$v_x(t) = v_{x0} + a_xt$

$v_y(t) + v_{y0} + a_yt$

$v_z(t) = v_{z0} + a_zt$.

b) $v^2 = v_x^2 + v_y^2 + v_z^2 =$

$v_0^2 + 2[a_x(x - x_0) + a_y(y - y_0) + a_z(z - z_0)]$

where $v_0^2 = v_{x0}^2 + v_{y0}^2 + v_{z0}^2$.

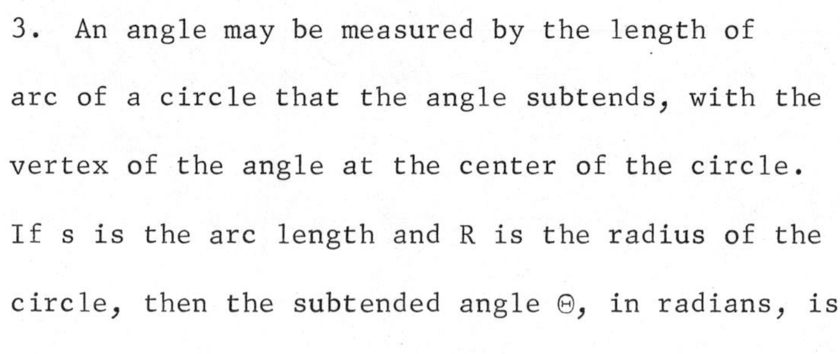

3. An angle may be measured by the length of arc of a circle that the angle subtends, with the vertex of the angle at the center of the circle. If s is the arc length and R is the radius of the circle, then the subtended angle Θ, in radians, is

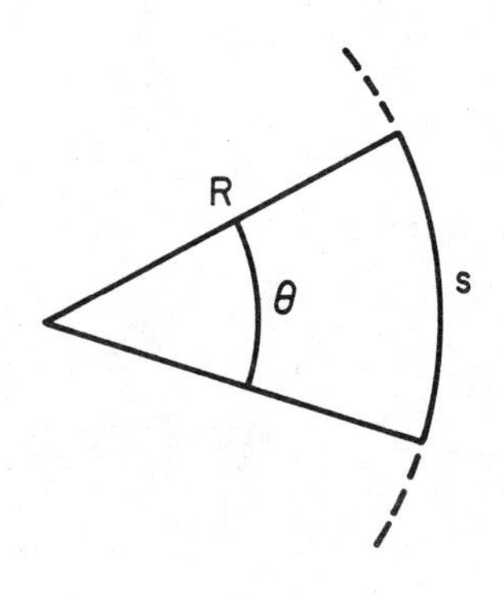

$$\Theta = s/R$$

a) Show that, if $\Theta << 1$ radian, $\sin \Theta \approx \Theta$, and $\cos \Theta \approx 1$.

b) With the above result, and the formulas for the sine and cosine of the sum of two angles, find the derivatives of sin x and cos x, using the fundamental formula

$$\frac{dy}{dx} = \lim_{\Delta x \to 0} \frac{y(x + \Delta x) - y(x)}{\Delta x} .$$

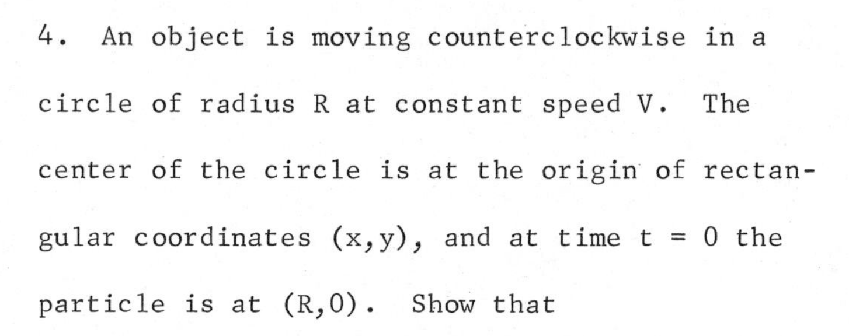

4. An object is moving counterclockwise in a circle of radius R at constant speed V. The center of the circle is at the origin of rectangular coordinates (x,y), and at time t = 0 the particle is at (R,0). Show that

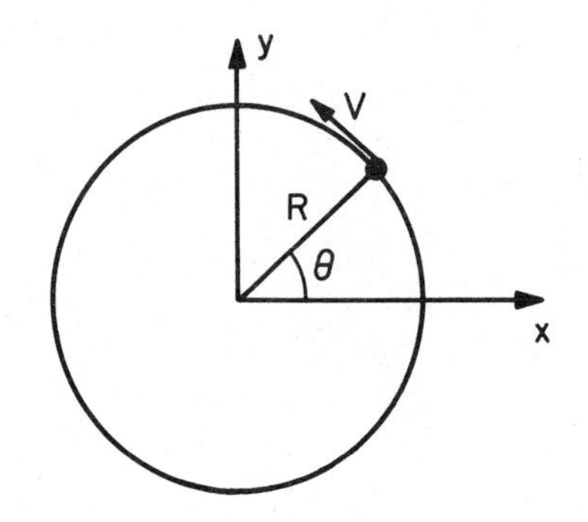

a) $x = R \cos \omega t$
$y = R \sin \omega t$ where $\omega = \frac{V}{R}$ = angular frequency

$v_x = - V \sin \omega t$

$v_y = V \cos \omega t$

$a_x = - \frac{V^2}{R} \cos \omega t$ b) $\ddot{x} + \omega^2 x = 0$

$a_y = - \frac{V^2}{R} \sin \omega t$ $\ddot{y} + \omega^2 y = 0$.

$a = \frac{V^2}{R}$

A-1.

A Skyhook balloon with a scientific payload rises at a rate of 1000 feet per minute. At an altitude of 30,000 feet the balloon bursts and the payload freefalls. (Such disasters do occur!)

a) For what length of time was the payload off the ground?

b) What was the payload's speed at impact?

Neglect air-drag.

A-2.

Consider a train which can accelerate with an acceleration of 20 cm s^{-2} and slow down with a deceleration of 100 cm s^{-2}. Find the minimum time for the train to travel between two stations 2 km apart.

A-3.

If you throw a small ball vertically upward in real air with drag, does it take longer to go up or come down?

A-4.

At the equator, what is the speed of a point at the surface of the earth relative to the center of the earth? What is its angular frequency? What is the ratio of its radial acceleration due to its angular motion and its gravitational acceleration?

B-1.

A Corporal rocket fired vertically was observed to have a constant upward acceleration of 2 g during the burning of the rocket motor, which lasted for 50 seconds. Neglecting air resistance and variation of g with altitude,

a) Draw a v-t diagram for entire flight of rocket.

b) Calculate the maximum height attained.

c) Calculate the total elapsed time from the firing of the rocket to its return to Earth.

B-2.

In a lecture demonstration a small steel ball bounces on a steel place. On each bounce the downward speed of the ball arriving at the plate is reduced by a factor e in the rebound, i.e., $v_{upward} = e\, v_{downward}$.

If the ball was initially dropped from a height of 50 cm above the plate at time t = 0, and if 30 seconds later the silencing of a microphone sound indicated all bouncing had ceased, what was the value of e?

B-3.

A projectile is fired over level terrain at an initial speed v_0, at an angle θ with the horizontal. (Neglect air resistance.)

a) Find the maximum height attained and the range.

b) At what angle should the above projectile be fired in order to attain the maximum range?

B-4.

A champion archer hits a bullseye in a target mounted on a wall a distance L away and situated at a height h above his bow. Deduce the equation between the speed (at which the arrow left his bow), the arrow's initial angle θ with the horizontal, the height, and the distance of the target, whose solution the archer evidently knew.

P.S. The archer did not neglect air resistance, but you may have to.

B-5.

A boy throws a ball upward at an angle of 70° with the horizontal, and it passes neatly through an open window, 32 feet above his shoulder, moving horizontally.

a) How fast was the ball moving as it left his hand?

b) What was the radius of curvature of its path as it passed over the windowsill?

Can you find the radius of curvature of its path at any given time?

B-6.

A small pebble is lodged in the tread of a tire of radius R. If this tire is rolling at speed V without slipping on a horizontal road, find the equations for the x and y coordinates of the pebble as a function of time. Let the pebble touch the road at $t = 0$. Find also the velocity and acceleration components as a function of the time.

B-7.

The driver of a car is following a truck when he suddenly notices that a stone is caught between two of the rear tires of the truck. Being a safe driver (and a physicist too), he immediately increases his distance to the truck to 22.5 meters, so as not to be hit by the stone in case it comes loose. At what speed was the truck traveling? (Assume the stone does not bounce after hitting the ground.)

C-1.

A circus performer was devising a new act. He wanted to combine the human Cannon Ball with a trapeze stunt. He had a cannon out of which he came with a muzzle velocity V. He wanted to get high enough so that he could grab the trapeze ($r = 2$ m) and then continue on up to the platform located at $h = 20$ m above the floor as shown. (Note: the trapeze should not go slack, i.e., his vertical velocity must be zero at both r and h).

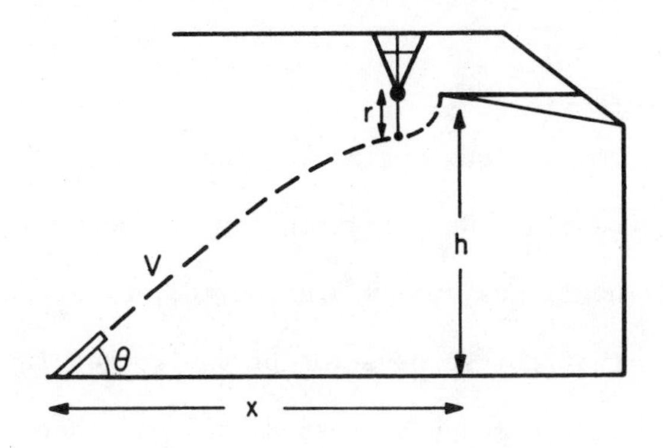

a) At what angle θ must the cannon be set?

b) How far down the tent from the platform (x) should be put the cannon?

c) What value of V must he choose?

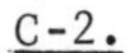

C-2.

A mortar emplacement is set 27,000 ft horizontally from the edge of a bluff that drops 350 ft down from the level of the mortar. It is desired to shell objects concealed on the ground behind the bluff. How close to the bottom edge of the cliff can shells reach if fired at a muzzle speed of 1000 ft/s^{-1}?

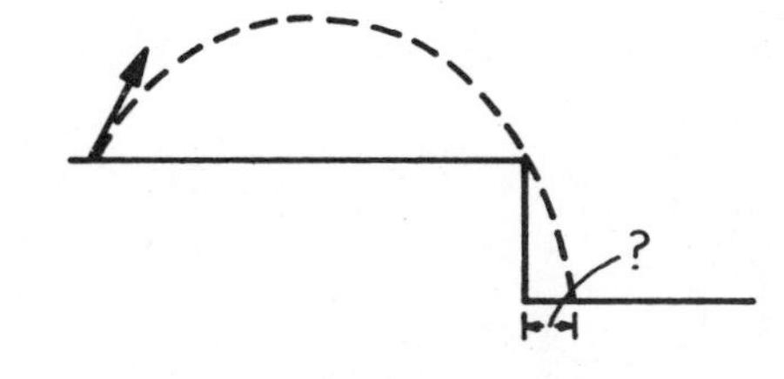

C-3.

A Caltech freshman, inexperienced with suburban traffic officiers, has just received a ticket for speeding. Thereafter, when he comes upon one of the "Speedometer Test" sections on a level stretch of highway, he decides to check his speedometer reading. As he passes the "0" start of the marked section, he presses on his accelerator and for the entire period of the test he holds his car at constant acceleration. He notices that he passes the 0.10 mile post 16 s. after starting the test, and 8.0 s. later he passes the 0.20 mile post.

a) What should his speedomter have read at the 0.20 mile post?

b) What was his acceleration?

C-4.

On the long horizontal test track at Edwards AFB, both rocket and jet motors can be tested. On a certain day, a rocket motor, started from rest, accelerated constantly until its fuel was exhausted, after which it ran at constant speed. It was observed that this exhaustion of the rocket fuel took place as the rocket passed the midpoint of the measured test distance. Then a jet motor was started from rest down the track, with a constant acceleration for the entire distance. It was observed that both rocket and jet motors covered the test distance in exactly the same time. What was the ratio of the acceleration of the jet motor to that of the rocket motor?

CHAPTER 5

Newton's Laws

Refer to The Feynman Lectures on Physics, Vol. I, Ch. 9.

a) Analytical Methods of Solution

A-1.

Two blocks of mass $m_1 = 1$ kg, $m_2 = 2$ kg on a horizontal surface, connected by a string, are being pulled by another string which is attached to a mass $m_3 = 2$ kg hanging over a pulley. Negiect friction and the masses of the pulley and strings.

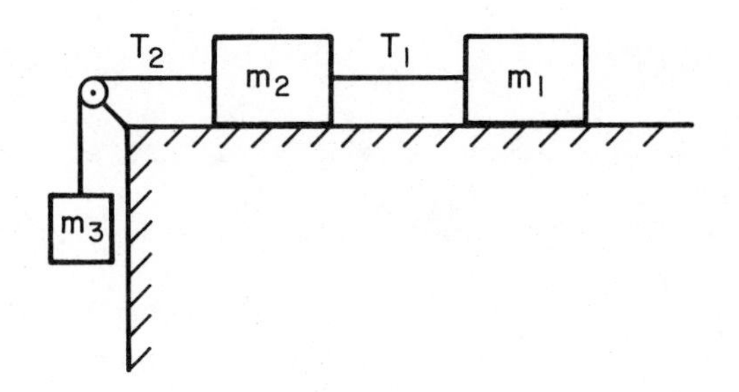

a) Sketch free-body diagrams for all masses, showing the forces acting.

b) Find the acceleration of the masses and the tension in the strings.

A-2.

A mass m (kg) hangs on a cord suspended from an elevator which is descending with an acceleration of 0.1 g. What is the tension in the cord in newtons?

A-3.

Two objects of mass m = 1 kg each, connected by a taut string of length L = 2 m, move in a circular orbit with constant speed $V = 5 \text{ m s}^{-1}$ about their common center C in a zero-g environment. What is the tension in the string in newtons?

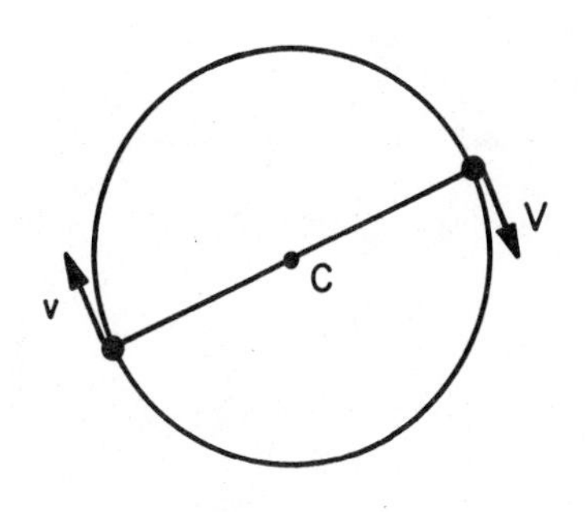

B-1.

What horizontal force F must be constantly applied to M so that M_1 and M_2 do not move relative to M? Neglect friction.

B-2.

What horizontal force F must be constantly applied to M = 21 kg so that m_1 = 5 kg does not move relative to m_2 = 4 kg. Neglect friction.

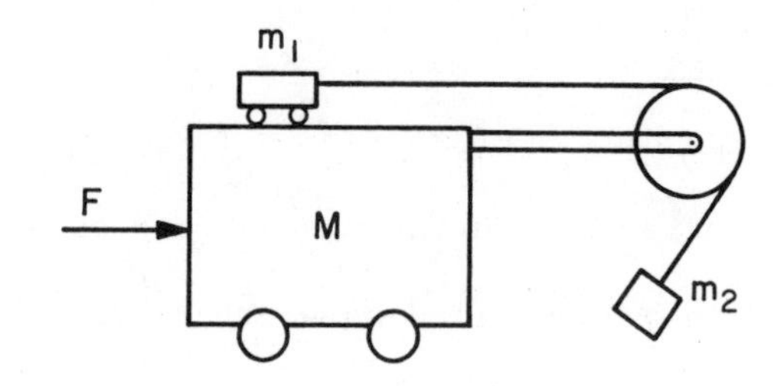

B-3.

In the system shown, M_1 slides without friction on the inclined plane. $\theta = 30^o$, M_1 = 400 g, M_2 = 200 g. Find the acceleration of M_2 and the tension in the cords.

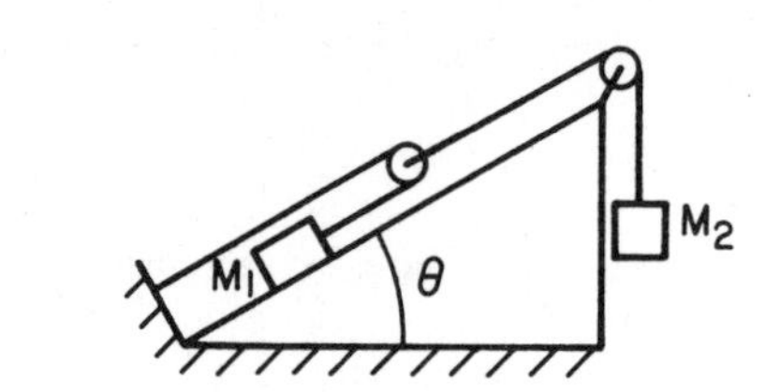

B-4.

A simple crane is made of two parts, "A" with mass M_a, length D, height H, and distance D/2 between wheels of radius r; and part "B", a uniform rod or boom of length L and mass M_b. The crane is shown assembled in the figure, with the pivot point P at midpoint of top of A. The center of gravity of A is midway between the wheels.

a) With the rod or boom B set at angle θ with the horizontal, what is the maximum mass M that the crane can lift without tipping over?

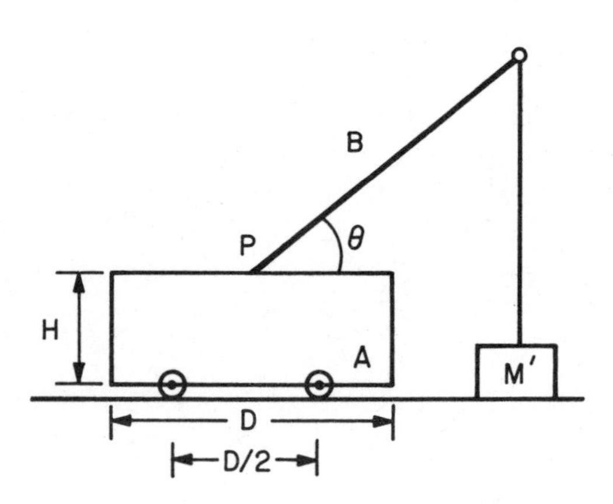

b) If there is a mass M' = 4/5 M at the end of the rope, what is the minimum time necessary to raise this load M' a distance (L sin θ) from the ground? (The angle θ remains fixed, and the mass of the rope may be neglected.)

B-5.

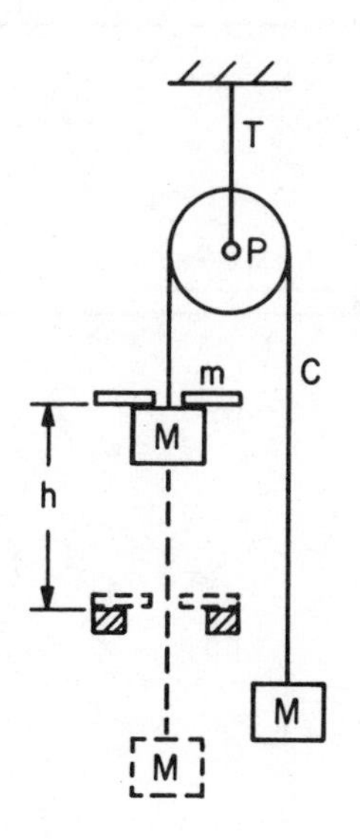

An early arrangement for measuring the acceleration of gravity, called Atwood's Machine, is shown in the figure. The pulley P and cord C have negligible mass and friction. The system is balanced with equal masses M on each side as shown (solid line), and then a small rider m is added to one side. The combined masses accelerate through a certain distance h, the rider is caught on a ring and the two equal masses then move on with constant speed, v. Find the value of g that corresponds to the measured values of m, M, h, and v.

B-6.

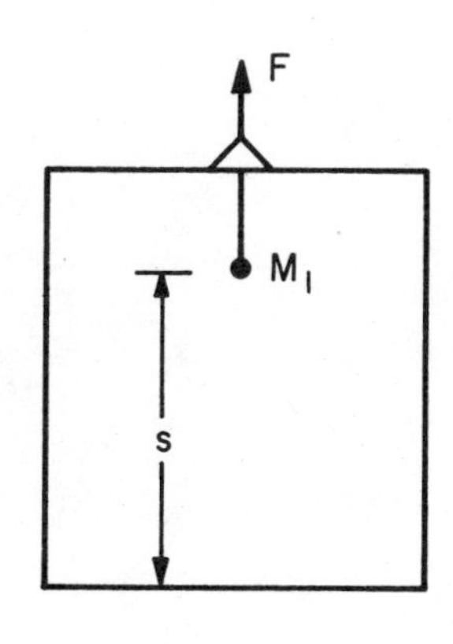

An elevator of mass M_2 has hanging from its ceiling a mass M_1. The elevator is being accelerated upward by a constant force F (F greater than $(M_1 + M_2)g$). The mass M_1 is initially a distance <u>s</u> above the elevator floor.

a) Find the acceleration of the elevator.

b) What is the tension in the string connecting the mass M_1 to the elevator?

c) If the string suddenly breaks, what is the acceleration of the elevator immediately after? What is the acceleration of mass M_1?

d) How long does it take for M_1 to hit the bottom of the elevator?

C-1.

Given the system shown, consider all surfaces frictionless. If m = 150 g is released when it is d = 1 m above the base of M = 1650 g, how long after release will m strike the base of M?

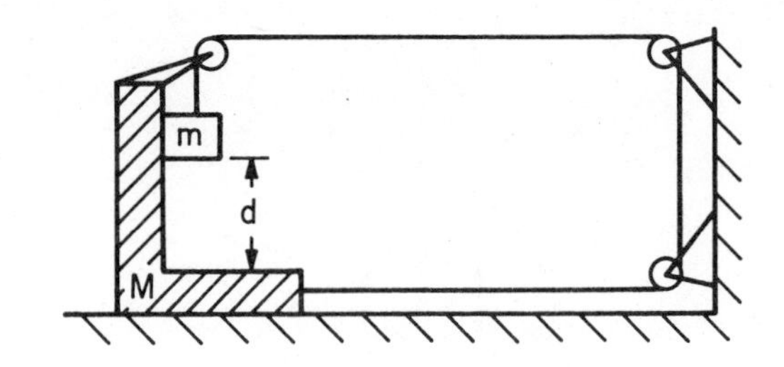

C-2.

None of the identical gondolas on the Martian canal Rimini is quite able to support the load of both Paolo and Francesca, two affectionate marsupials who refuse to go in separate boats. The enterprising gondolier, Giuseppe, collects their fare by rigging them up from the mast as in the figure, using the massless ropes and massless, frictionless pulleys characteristic of Martian construction. Giuseppi ferries them across before they hit either the mast or the deck. How much load does he save? Hint: Remember that the tension in a massless cord that passes over a massless, frictionless pulley is the same on both sides of the pulley.

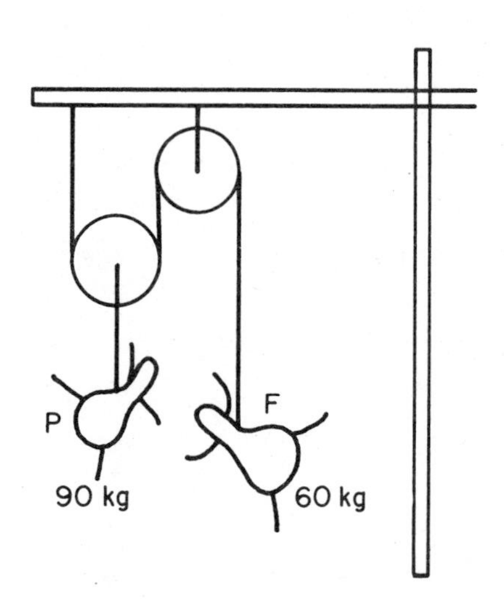

C-3.

A painter weighing 180 lb working from a "bosun's" chair hung down the side of a tall building, desires to move in a hurry. He pulls down on the fall rope with such a force that he presses against the chair with only a force of 100 lb. The chair itself weighs 30.0 lb.

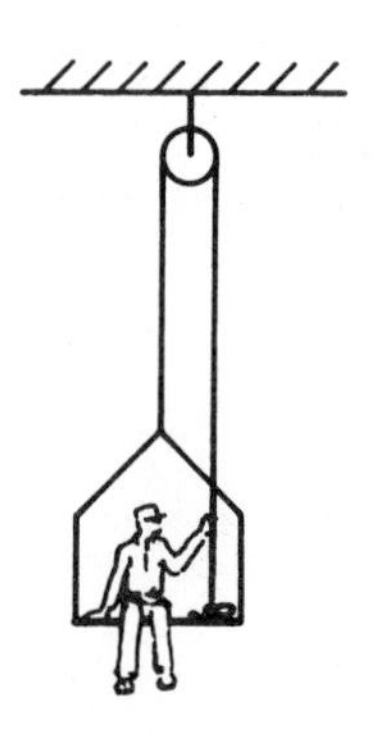

a) What is the acceleration of the painter and the chair?

b) What is the total force supported by the pulley?

C-4.

A space traveler about to leave for the moon has a spring balance and a 1.0 kg mass A, which when hung on the balance on the Earth gives the reading of 9.8 newtons. Arriving at the moon at a place where the acceleration of gravity is not known exactly but has a value of about 1/6 the acceleration of gravity at the Earth's surface, he picks up a stone B which gives a reading of 9.8 newtons when weighed on the spring balance. He then hangs A and B over a pulley as shown in the figure and observed that B falls with an acceleration of 1.2 m/s^2. What is the mass of stone B?

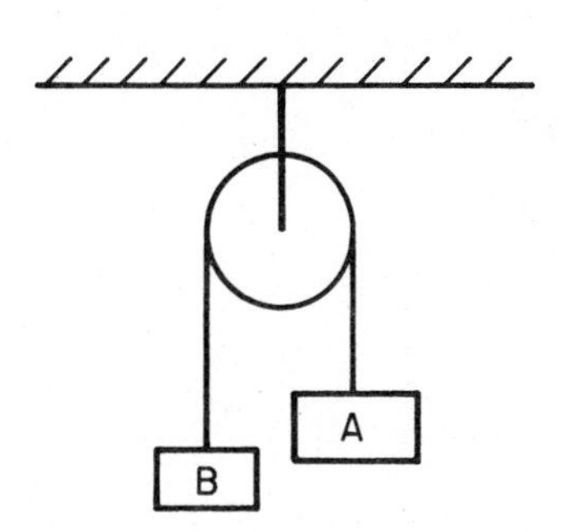

b) Numerical Methods of Solution

C-1.

A mass suspended from a spring hangs motionless, and is then given an upward blow such that it moves initially at unit speed. If the mass and spring constant are such that the equation of motion is $\ddot{x} = - x$, find the maximum height attained by numerical integration of the equation of motion.

C-2.

A particle of mass m moves along a straight line. Its motion is resisted by a force proportional to its velocity, $F = - kv$. If it starts with speed $v = v_0$ at $x = 0$ and $t = 0$, find x as a function of t by numerical integration. Find the time $t_{1/2}$ required to lose half its speed, and the maximum distance x_m attained.

Note:

a) Adjust the scales of x and t so that the equation of motion has simple numerical coefficients.

b) Invent a scheme to attain good accuracy with a relatively coarse interval for Δt.

c) Use dimensional analysis to deduce how $t_{1/2}$ and x_m should depend upon v_0, k, and m, and solve for the actual motion only for a single convenient value of v_0, say $v_0 = 1.00$ (in the modified x and t units).

C-3.

A certain charged particle moves in an electric and a magnetic field according to the equations

$$\frac{dv_x}{dt} = -2v_y$$

$$\frac{dv_y}{dt} = 1 + 2v_x$$

At t = 0 the particle starts at (0,0) with velocity $v_x = 1.00$, $v_y = 0$. Determine the nature of the motion by numerical integration.

C-4.

A shell is fired with a muzzle velocity of 1000 ft s^{-1} at an angle of 45° with the horizontal. Its motion is resisted by a force proportional to the cube of its velocity ($F = -kv^3$). The coefficient k is such that the resisting force is equal to twice the weight of the shell when v = 1000 ft s^{-1}. Find the approximate maximum height attained and the horizontal range by numerical integration, and compare these with the values expected in the absence of resistance.

CHAPTER 6

Conservation of Momentum

Refer to The Feynman Lectures on Physics, Vol. I, Ch. 10.

1.

When two bodies move along a line, there is a special system of coordinates in which the momentum of one body is equal and opposite to that of the other. That is, the total momentum of the two bodies is zero. This frame of reference is called the center-of-mass system (abbreviated CM). If the bodies have masses m_1 and m_2 are are moving at velocities v_1 and v_2, show that the CM system is moving at velocity

$$V_{CM} = \frac{m_1 v_1 + m_2 v_2}{m_1 + m_2}$$

2.

Generalize Ex. 6-1 to any number of masses moving along a line, i.e., show that the velocity of the coordinate system, in which the total momentum is zero, is given by

$$V_{CM} = \frac{\sum m_i v_i}{\sum m_i} .$$

3.

If T is the total kinetic energy of the two masses in Ex. 6-1, and T_{CM} is their total kinetic energy in the CM system, show that

$$T = T_{CM} + \frac{1}{2}(m_1 + m_2)V_{CM}^2 .$$

4.

Generalize the result of Ex. 6-3 to any number of masses. Show that

$$T = T_{CM} + \frac{\sum m_i}{2} V_{CM}^2 .$$

A-1.

Two gliders are free to move on a horizontal air track. One is stationary and the other collides with it perfectly elastically. They rebound with equal and opposite velocities. What is the ratio of their masses?

A-2.

A neutron having a kinetic energy E collides head-on with a stationary nucleus of C^{12} and rebounds perfectly elastically in the direction from which it came. What is its final kinetic energy?

A-3.

A projectile of mass m_p = 10 kg is shot vertically upward from the earth with an initial velocity v_p = 500 m s^{-1}.

a) Calculate the recoil velocity of the earth.

b) Calculate the ratio of the kinetic energy of the earth and the projectile at the moment of their separation.

c) Sketch qualitatively the velocity and kinetic energy of the projectile and of the earth versus time.

Neglect air resistance and the orbital motion of the earth.

B-1.

A particle of mass m = 1.0 kg, traveling at a speed V_0 = 10 m s^{-1}, strikes a particle at rest of mass M = 4.0 kg and rebounds in the direction from which it came, with a speed V_F. If an amount of heat h = 20 joules is produced in the collision, what is V_F? (Define all introduced quantities and state clearly from what physical laws your initial equations are derived.)

B-2.

A machine gun mounted on the north end of a 10,000 kg, 5 m long platform, free to move on a horizontal air-bearing, fires bullets into a thick target mounted on the south end of the platform. The gun fires 10 bullets of mass 100 g each every second at a muzzle velocity of 500 m s^{-1}.

a) Does the platform move?

b) In which direction?

c) How fast?

B-3.

A mass m_1 is connected by a cable over a pulley to a container of water, which initially has a mass $m_2(t = 0) = m_0$. At $t = 0$, the system is released and m_2 (with help of an internal pump) ejects water in the downward direction at a constant rate $\frac{dm}{dt} = r_0$ kg/s with a velocity v_0 relative to the container. Find the acceleration of m_1 as a function of time.

Neglect the masses of cable and pulley.

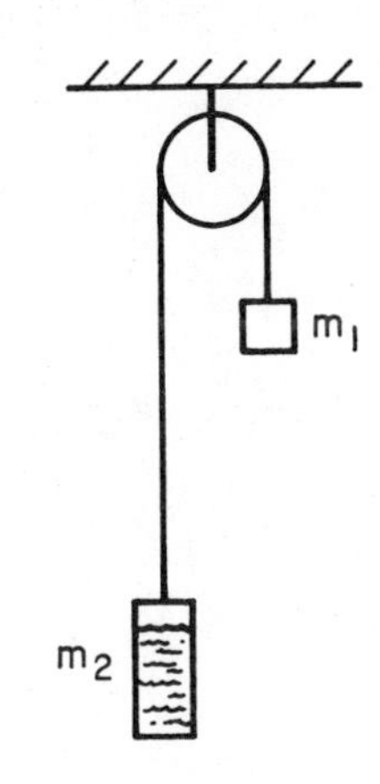

B-4.

A toboggan slides down an essentially frictionless, snow covered slope, scooping up snow along the path. If the slope is 30° and the toboggan picks up 0.50 kg of snow per meter of travel, calculate its acceleration at an instant when its speed is 4.0 m s^{-1} and its mass (including content) is 9.0 kg.

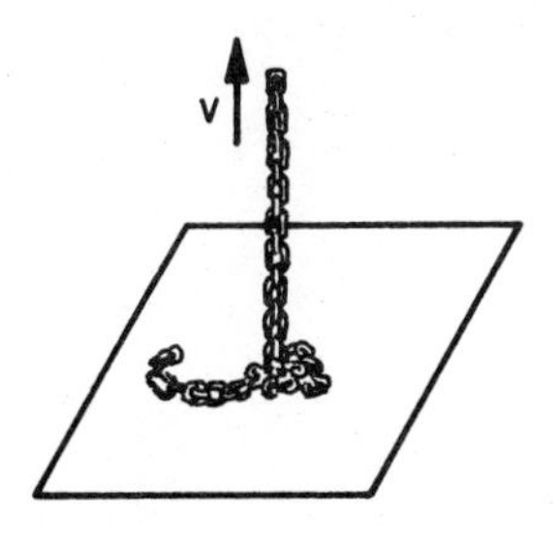

B-5.

The end of a chain, of mass per unit length μ, at rest on a table top at $t = 0$, is lifted vertically at a constant speed v. Evaluate the upward lifting force as a function of time.

C-1.

The speed of a rifle bullet may be measured by means of a ballistic pendulum: The bullet, of known mass m and unknown speed V, embeds itself in a stationary wooden block of mass M, suspended as a pendulum of length L. This sets the block to swinging. The amplitude x of swing may be measured and, using conservation of energy, the velocity of the block immediately after impact may be found. Derive an expression for the speed of the bullet in terms of m, M, L , and x.

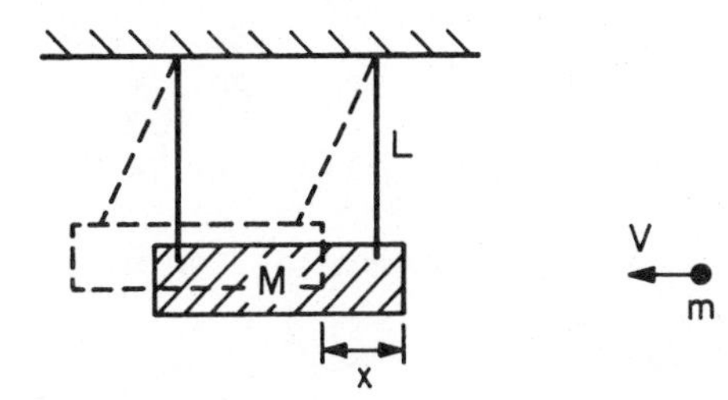

C-2.

Two gliders A and A' are connected rigidly together and have a combined mass M and are separated by a distance 2L. Another glider B of mass m, length L, is constrained to move between A and A'. All gliders move on a very long linear air track without friction. All collisions between (A,A') and B are perfectly elastic.

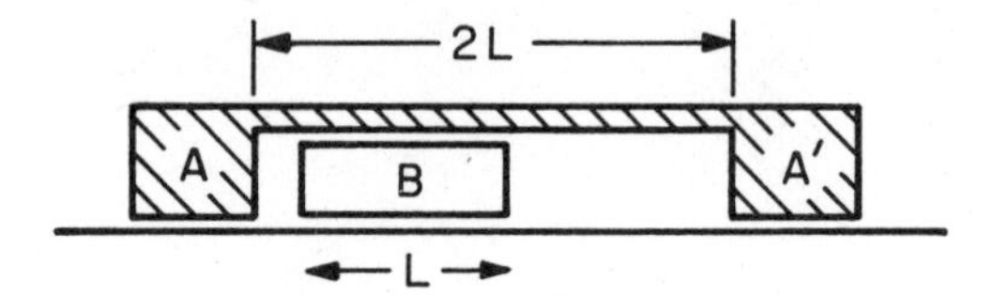

Originally the whole system is at rest and glider B is in contact with glider A. A cap between A and B then is exploded, giving a total kinetic energy T to the system.

a) Show the qualitative features of B's motion, i.e., position x on the track, velocity v with respect to the track, by sketching x and v as functions of time. Use the same time scale for both sketches.

b) Calculate the period τ_0 in terms of T, L, m, M. (Hint: The relative velocity of B with respect to (A,A'):

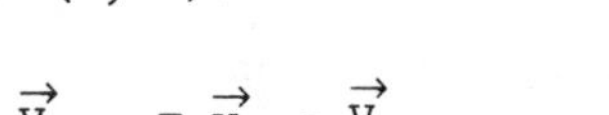

$$\vec{V}_{rel} = \vec{v}_B - \vec{V}_{(A,A')} \quad .$$

C-3.

Two equally massive gliders, moving on a level air track at equal and opposite velocities, v and -v, collide almost elastically, and rebound with slightly smaller speeds. They lose a fraction $f \ll 1$ of their kinetic energy in the collision. If these same gliders collide with one of them initially at rest, with what speed will the second glider move after the collision? (This small residual speed Δv may easily be measured in terms of the final speed v of the originally stationary glider, and thus the elasticity of the spring bumpers may be determined.)

Note: If $x \ll 1$, $\sqrt{1 - x} \approx 1 - \frac{1}{2}x$.

C-4.

A rocket of initial mass M_0 kg ejects its burnt fuel at a constant rate dm/dt = $-r_0$ kg s^{-1} and at a velocity V_0 (relative to the rocket)

a) Calculate the initial acceleration of the rocket (neglect gravity).

b) If V_0 = 2.0 km s^{-1}, how many kilograms of fuel must be ejected per second to develop 10^5 kgwt of thrust?

c) Write a differential equation which connects the speed of the rocket with its residual mass, and solve the equation, if you can.

C-5.

An earth satellite of mass 10 kg and average cross-sectional area 0.50 m^2 is moving in a circular orbit at 200 km altitude where the molecular mean free paths are many meters and the air density is about 1.6 x 10^{-10} kg m^{-3}. Under the crude assumption that the molecular impacts with the satellite are effectively inelastic (but that the molecules do not literally stick to the satellite but drop away from it at low relative velocity), calculate the retarding force that the satellite would experience due to air friction. How should such a frictional force vary with velocity? Would the satellite's speed decrease as a result of the net force on it? (Check the speed of a circular satellite orbit vs. height.)

CHAPTER 7

Vectors

Refer to The Feynman Lectures on Physics, Vol. I, Ch. 11.

Generalize Ex. 6-1 to 6-4 to three dimensional motion using vector notation, e.g.,

1. If two bodies have masses m_1 and m_2 and are moving at velocities $\vec{v}_1$ and $\vec{v}_2$, show that the CM system is moving at velocity

$$\vec{V}_{CM} = \frac{m_1\vec{v}_1 + m_2\vec{v}_2}{m_1 + m_2} .$$

2. Show that for N bodies of masses m_i and velocities $\vec{v}_i$, the velocity of the coordinate system, in which the total momentum is zero, is given by

$$\vec{V}_{CM} = \frac{\sum_{i=1}^{N} m_i\vec{v}_i}{\sum_{i=1}^{N} m_i} .$$

3. If T is the total kinetic energy of the two masses in Ex. 7-1, and T_{CM} their total kinetic energy in the CM system, show that

$$T = T_{CM} + \frac{1}{2}(m_1 + m_2)|\vec{V}_{CM}|^2$$

4. Generalize the result of Ex. 7-3 to N masses, show that

$$T = T_{CM} + \frac{\sum m_i}{2}|\vec{V}_{CM}|^2 .$$

A-1.

A particle is initially at a point $\vec{r}_0$, and is moving under gravity with an initial velocity $\vec{v}_0$. Find the subsequent motion.

A-2.

You are given three vectors

$$\vec{a} = 3\vec{i} + 2\vec{j} - \vec{k}$$

$$\vec{b} = 2\vec{i} - \vec{j} + \vec{k}$$

$$\vec{c} = \vec{i} + 3\vec{j}$$

Find

a) $\vec{a} + \vec{b}$

b) $\vec{a} - \vec{b}$

c) a_x

d) $\vec{a} \cdot \vec{i}$

e) $\vec{a} \cdot \vec{b}$

f) $(\vec{a} \cdot \vec{c})\vec{b} - (\vec{a} \cdot \vec{b})\vec{c}$.

A-3.

A particle of mass 1 kg is moving in such a way that its position is described by the vector

$$\vec{r} = t\,\vec{i} + (t + t^2/2)\vec{j} - (4/\pi^2)\sin \pi t/2\,\vec{k}$$

a) Find the position, velocity, acceleration, and kinetic energy of the particle at $t = 0$ and $t = 1$ second.

b) Find the force which will produce this motion.

c) Find the radius of curvature of the particle's path at $t = 1$ second.

A-4.

A pilot flying at an air speed of 100 knots wishes to travel due north. He knows, from talking to the airport meteorologist, that there is a 25 knot wind from west to east at his flight altitude.

a) In what direction should he head his plane?

b) What will be the duration of his flight, if his destination is 100 land miles away? (Neglect the time for landing and take-off, and note that 1 knot = 1.15 miles per hour.)

B-1.

A cyclist rides at 10 mi hr^{-1} due north and the wind (which is blowing at 6 mi hr^{-1} from a point between N and E) appears to the cyclist to come from a point 15°E of N.

a) Find the true direction of the wind.

b) The direction in which the wind will appear to meet him on his return if he rides at the same speed.

B-2.

A man standing on the bank of a river 1.0 mi wide wishes to get to a point directly opposite him on the other bank. He can do this in two ways: (1) head somewhat upstream so that his resultant motion is straight across, (2) head toward the opposite bank and then walk up along the bank from the point downstream to which the current has carried him. If he can swim 2.5 mi hr^{-1} and walk 4.0 mi hr^{-1}, and if the current is 2.0 mi hr^{-1}, which is the faster way to cross, and by how much?

B-3.

A motorboat that runs at a constant speed V relative to the water is operated in a straight river channel where the water is flowing smoothly with a constant speed R. The boat is first sent on a round trip from its anchor point to a point a distance d directly upstream. It is then sent on a round trip from its anchor point to a point a distance d away directly across the stream. For simplicity assume that the boat runs the entire distance in each case at full speed and that no time is lost in reversing course at the end of the outward lap. If t_V is the time the boat took to make the round trip in line with the stream flow, t_A the time the boat took to make the round trip across the stream, and t_L the time the boat would take to go a distance 2d on a lake.

a) What is the ratio t_V/t_A?

b) What is the ratio t_A/t_L?

B-4.

Use vectors to find the great circle distance between two points on the earth whose latitudes and longitudes are (λ_1, Φ_1) and (λ_2, Φ_2).

Note: Use a system of rectangular coordinates with origin at the center of the earth, one axis along the earth's axis, another pointed toward $\lambda = 0$, $\Phi = 0$, and the third axis pointed toward $\lambda = 0$, $\Phi = 90^\circ W$. (Let longitudes vary from 0° westward to 360°.)

B-5.

What is the magnitude and direction of the acceleration of the moon at

a) New moon

b) Quarter moon,

c) Full moon

Note: $R_{\oplus\odot} = 1.50 \times 10^8$ km,

$R_{\oplus\rightmoon} = 3.85 \times 10^5$ km,

$M_{\odot} = 3.33 \times 10^5 \ M_0$.

B-6.

Two identical 45° wedges M_1 and M_2, with smooth faces and $M_1 = M_2 = 8$ kg, are used to move a smooth-faced mass M = 384 kg. Both wedges rest upon a smooth horizontal plane; one wedge is butted against a vertical wall, and to the other wedge a force F = 592 kgwt is applied horizontally.

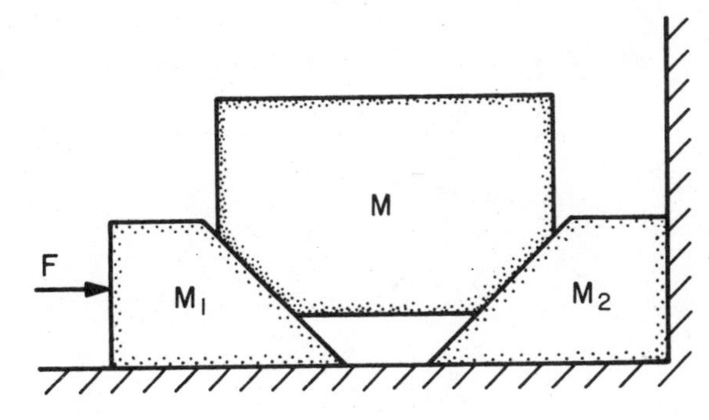

a) What is the magnitude and direction of the acceleration of the movable wedge M_1?

b) What is the magnitude and direction of the acceleration of the larger wedge M?

c) What force does the stationary wedge M_2 exert on the heavy mass M?

Neglect friction.

B-7.

A mass m is suspended from a frictionless pivot at the end of a string of arbitrary length, and is set to whirling in a horizontal circular path whose plane is a distance H below the pivot point. Find the period of revolution of the mass in its orbit.

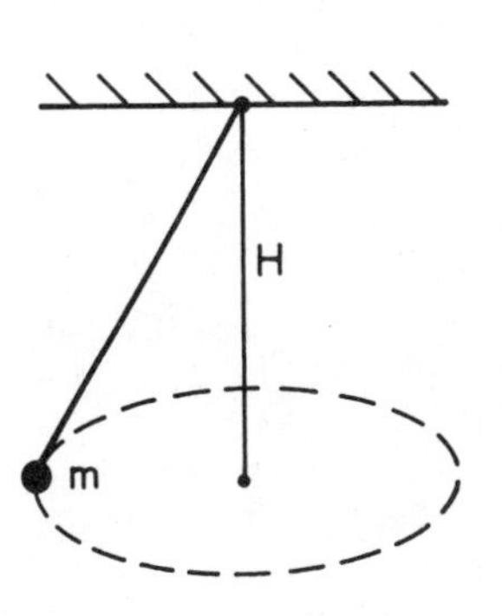

C-1.

Two small, sticky, putty balls, A and B, each of mass 1 gram, travel under the influence of gravity with acceleration $-9.8\,\vec{k}(\text{m s}^{-2})$. Given the initial conditions:

at $t = 0$, $\vec{r}_a(0) = 7i + 4.9\vec{k}$ (meters);

$\vec{V}_a(0) = 7\vec{i} + 3\vec{j}$ (m s^{-1})

$\vec{r}_b(0) = 49\vec{i} + 4.9\vec{k}$ (meters);

$\vec{V}_b(0) = -\,7\vec{i} + 3\vec{j}$ (m s^{-1})

Find $\vec{r}_a(t)$ and $\vec{r}_b(t)$ for all times $t > 0$.

C-2.

You are on a ship traveling steadily east at 15 knots. A ship on a steady course whose speed is known to be 26 knots is observed 6.0 mi due south of you, it is later observed to pass behind you, its distance of closest approach being 3.0 mi.

a) What was the course of the other ship?

b) What was the time between its position south of you and its position of closest approach?

CHAPTER 8

Non-Relativistic Two-Body Collisions in Three Dimensions

Refer to The Feynman Lectures on Physics, Vol. I, Chs. 10 and 11.

The analysis of two-body collisions can often be simplified by the use of the CM-system.

Consider the general case of a non-relativistic two-body collision in the laboratory system. Two masses m_1 and m_2 with velocities $\vec{v}_1$ and $\vec{v}_2$ collide, they may exchange mass during the collision, resulting in two masses m_3 and m_4 with velocities $\vec{v}_3$ and $\vec{v}_4$ after the collision. The conservation laws for energy and momentum give the following relations:

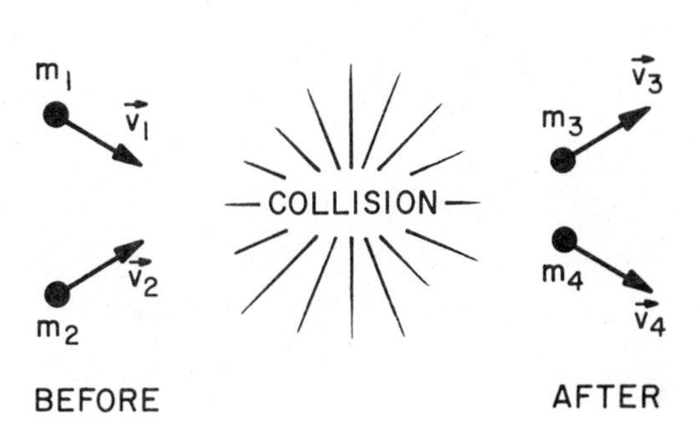

$$\frac{1}{2} m_1 v_1^2 + \frac{1}{2} m_2 v_2^2 + Q = \frac{1}{2} m_3 v_3^2 + \frac{1}{2} m_4 v_4^2$$

$$m_1\vec{v}_1 + m_2\vec{v}_2 = m_3\vec{v}_3 + m_4\vec{v}_4$$

The value of Q determines the inelasticity of the collision process. This method of analysis in the laboratory system is often quite cumbersome and does not easily reveal possible systematics or simple relationships. In most cases, it is preferable to use the CM-system, in which the collision is a linear one.

i) Determine the CM velocity:

Before the collision:

$$\vec{V}_{CM} = \frac{m_1\vec{v}_1 + m_2\vec{v}_2}{m_1 + m_2}$$

After the collision

$$\vec{V}_{CM}' = \frac{m_3\vec{v}_3 + m_4\vec{v}_4}{m_3 + m_4}$$

Note: In all non-relativistic collisions

$$m_1 + m_2 = m_3 + m_4$$

so that

$$\vec{V}_{CM}' = \vec{V}_{CM} \; .$$

In the following discussion we shall consider the particular case of

$$m_1 = m_3$$

$$m_2 = m_4$$

ii) Find the velocities of m_1 and m_2 in the CM system:

$$\vec{U}_1 = \vec{v}_1 - \vec{V}_{CM}$$

$$\vec{U}_2 = \vec{v}_2 - \vec{V}_{CM}$$

In the CM-system, the momenta of the two masses are equal and opposite

$$m_1\vec{U}_1 = - m_2\vec{U}_2$$

that is, $\vec{U}_1$ and $\vec{U}_2$ are collinear if the colliding bodies can be considered point-masses. Also

$$\left| \frac{\vec{U}_1}{\vec{U}_2} \right| = \frac{m_2}{m_1}$$

iii) After the collision, the momenta in the CM-system again must be equal and opposite, i.e.,

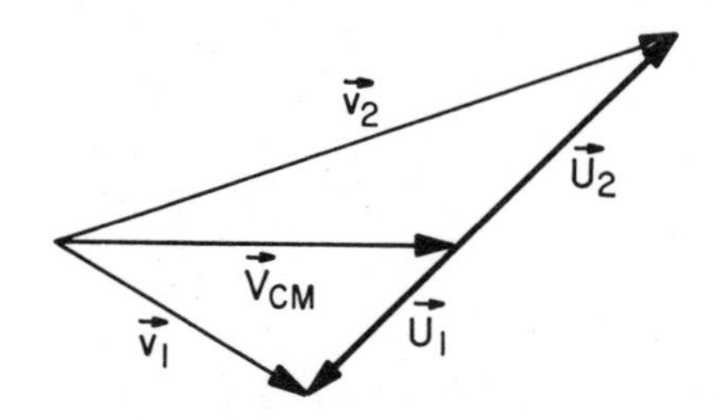

$$m_3\vec{U}_3 = - m_4\vec{U}_4$$

$$\left| \frac{\vec{U}_3}{\vec{U}_4} \right| = \frac{m_4}{m_3}$$

Note that in the CM system, the line of relative motion of the two masses may be rotated to a new direction by the collision. The new direction is not defined by the laws of conservation of energy and momentum, but follows from the geometry of the interaction

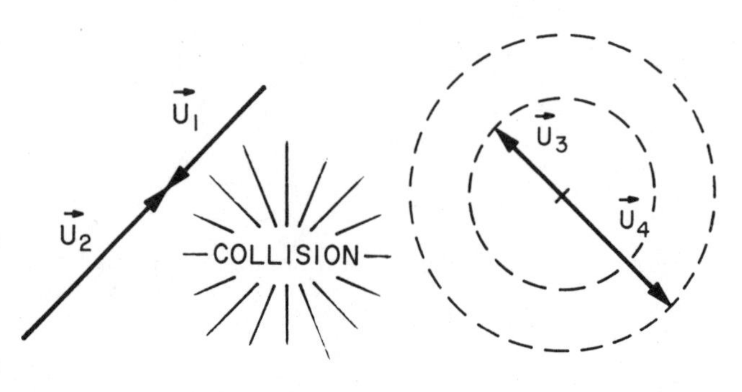

force and the initial relative motion. After the collision, the magnitudes of the velocities $\vec{U}_3$ and $\vec{U}_4$ may be larger, smaller, or equal to those of $\vec{U}_1$ and $\vec{U}_2$, according to whether energy was released, absorbed, or unchanged in the collision. In the geometrical representation, the velocity vectors $\vec{U}_3$ and $\vec{U}_4$ must be collinear and their endpoints must fall on concentric spherical shells (circles in 2-D collisions) of radii

$$\left|\frac{\vec{U}_3}{\vec{U}_4}\right| = \frac{m_4}{m_3}$$

The magnitudes of $\vec{U}_3$ and $\vec{U}_4$ follow from the conservation of energy. In Ex. 7-3 it was shown that the total kinetic energy of two masses can be expressed as

$$T = T_{CM} + \frac{1}{2}(m_1 + m_2)|\vec{V}_{CM}|^2$$

where

$$T_{CM} = \frac{1}{2} m_1|\vec{U}_1|^2 + \frac{1}{2} m_2|\vec{U}_2|^2$$

We know from conservation of momentum:

$$m_1|\vec{U}_1| = m_2|\vec{U}_2| = P$$

therefore

$$T_{CM} = \left(\frac{1}{m_1} + \frac{1}{m_2}\right)\frac{P^2}{2}$$

Note: $\left(\frac{1}{m_1} + \frac{1}{m_2}\right) = \frac{1}{m_r}$ (definition of the "reduced mass" m_r of two masses).

In this notation

$$T_{CM} = \frac{P^2}{2m_r}$$

Before the collision:

$$T = T_{CM} + \frac{1}{2}(m_1 + m_2)|\vec{V}_{CM}|^2$$

After the collision:

$$T' = T + Q = T'_{CM} + \frac{1}{2}(m_3 + m_4)|\vec{V}'_{CM}|^2$$

In non-relativistic collisions:

$$m_1 + m_2 = m_3 + m_4$$

$$\vec{V}_{CM} = \vec{V}'_{CM}$$

therefore

$$T'_{CM} = T_{CM} + Q = T_{CM}\left(1 + \frac{Q}{T_{CM}}\right)$$

Also,

$$T'_{CM} = \frac{1}{2} m_3 |\vec{U}_3|^2 + \frac{1}{2} m_4 |\vec{U}_4|^2$$

and since

$$m_3 |\vec{U}_3| = m_4 |\vec{U}_4| = P'$$

it follows

$$T'_{CM} = \left(\frac{1}{m_3} + \frac{1}{m_4}\right) \frac{P'^2}{2} = \frac{P'^2}{2m_r'}$$

In the particular case under discussion ($m_1 = m_3$, $m_2 = m_4$):

$$m_r = m_r'$$

consequently, from $T'_{CM} = T_{CM} \left(1 + \frac{Q}{T_{CM}}\right)$ follows:

$$P'^2 = \left(1 + \frac{Q}{T_{CM}}\right) P^2$$

This expression gives the magnitude of the velocities in the CM system after the collision.

a) Elastic Collision

$Q = 0$ kinetic energy unchanged in the collision

$$P'^2 = P^2$$

Therefore

$$|\vec{U}_3| = |\vec{U}_1|$$
$$|\vec{U}_4| = |\vec{U}_2|$$

b) Inelastic Collision

$Q > 0$ kinetic energy released in the collision

$Q < 0$ kinetic energy absorbed in the collision

$$P'^2 = \left(1 + \frac{Q}{T_{CM}}\right) P^2$$

Therefore

$$|\vec{U}_3| = \left(1 + \frac{Q}{T_{CM}}\right)^{1/2} |\vec{U}_1|$$

$$|\vec{U}_4| = \left(1 + \frac{Q}{T_{CM}}\right)^{1/2} |\vec{U}_2|$$

iv) The velocities in the laboratory system after the collision are obtained simply by adding the CM velocity $\vec{V}'_{CM}$ to $\vec{U}_3$ and $\vec{U}_4$.

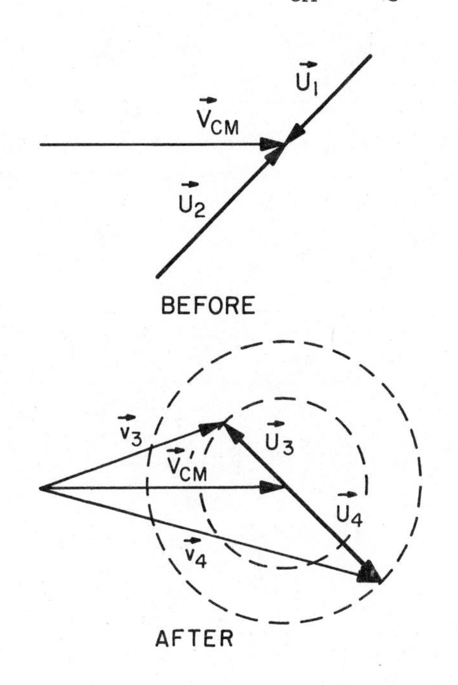

$$\vec{v}_3 = \vec{V}'_{CM} + \vec{U}_3$$

$$\vec{v}_4 = \vec{V}'_{CM} + \vec{U}_4$$

Significant general and specific information on two-body collisions often can be directly deduced from the above geometrical representation of the scattering kinematics.

1.

Analogous to the above discussion, derive the results for a three-dimensional non-relativistic collision ($m_1 + m_2 = m_3 + m_4$) for the case $m_1, m_2 \neq m_3, m_4$.

e.g., Show that in the collision of two bodies with initial momenta $\vec{p}_1$ and $\vec{p}_2$, the final momenta are given by

$$\vec{p}_3 = \vec{P}_3 + m_3 \vec{V}_{CM}$$

$$\vec{p}_4 = \vec{P}_4 + m_4 \vec{V}_{CM}$$

where $\vec{p}_i = m_i \vec{v}_i$ momentum of mass m_i in laboratory system

$\vec{P}_i = \vec{p}_i - m_i \vec{V}_{CM}$ momentum of mass m_i in CM system

$$|\vec{P}_1| = |\vec{P}_2| = \sqrt{2m_r T_{CM}}$$

$$|\vec{P}_3| = |\vec{P}_4| = \sqrt{2m_r' T'_{CM}} .$$

B-1.

A moving particle collides perfectly elastically with an equally massive particle initially at rest. Show that the two particles move at right angles to one another after the collision.

B-2.

A moving particle of mass M collides perfectly elastically with a stationary particle of mass $m < M$. Find the maximum possible angle through which the incident particle can be deflected.

B-3.

A particle of mass m_1 and velocity $\vec{v}_1$ collides perfectly elastically with another particle of mass $m_2 = 3m_1$ which is at rest ($\vec{v}_2 = 0$). After the collision, m_2 moves at angle $\theta_2 = 45^\circ$ with respect to the original direction of m_1. Find θ_1, the final angle of motion of m_1, and $\vec{v}_1{}'$, $\vec{v}_2{}'$ the final velocities.

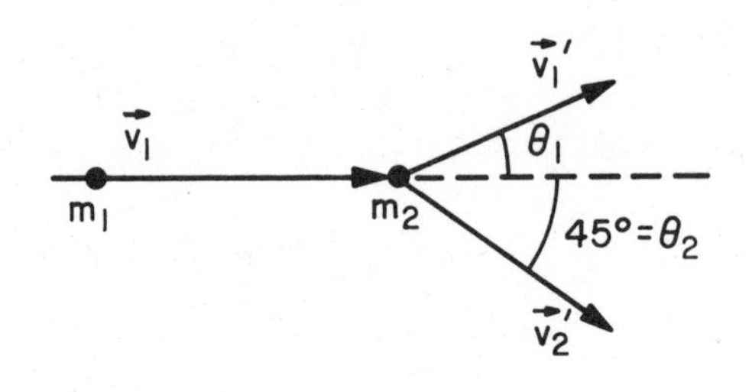

B-4.

Two particles of equal mass m are shot at one-another from perpendicular directions with equal speeds. After they collide, it is found that one particle was deflected 60° from its initial direction, towards the initial direction of the other particle (see figure). Determine the angle α by which the second particle gets deflected towards the initial direction of the first if the collision is elastic.

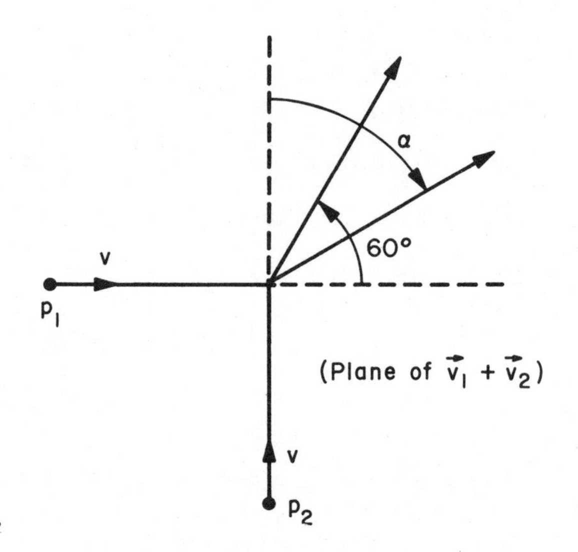

B-5.

Two particles of equal mass are traveling on courses at right angles to each other with speeds of $v_1 = 8$ m s^{-1} and $v_2 = 6$ m s^{-1}, respectively. They collide elastically. After the collision m_1 is observed to be traveling in a path which makes an angle $\theta = \tan^{-1} 1/2$ with respect to the direction of its path before the collision.

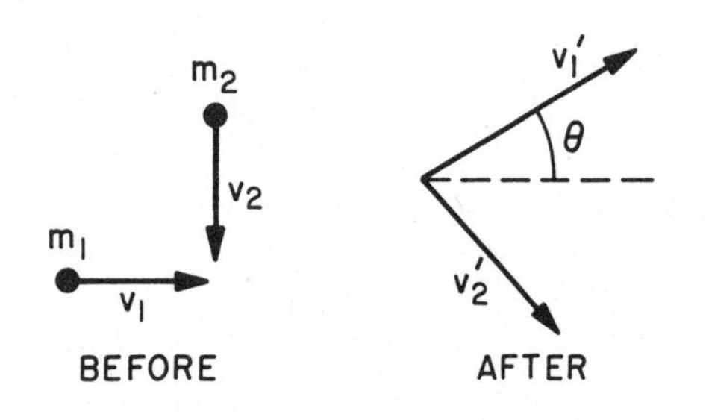

a) What is the vector velocity of the center of mass (give Cartesian components)?

b) What are the magnitudes U_1, U_2 of the final velocities in the CM system?

c) What is the final velocity of particle 1 in the lab. system?

B-6.

A proton moving along the x-axis with a speed of $v_0 = 1.00 \times 10^7$ m s^{-1} collides elastically with a stationary proton. After the collision, one proton moves in the x-y plane at an angle of 30° with the x-axis. Find the velocities (speed and direction!) of both protons after the collision.

B-7.

A proton moving along the x-axis with a speed of 1.00×10^7 m s^{-1} collides elastically with a stationary beryllium nucleus. After the collision the Be nucleus is observed to move in the x-y plane at an angle of 30° with the x-axis. Find:

a) The speed of the Be nucleus in the lab system.

b) The final velocity of the proton in the lab system.

c) The final velocity of the proton in the CM system.

Note: Assume the relative masses of the Be nucleus and proton to be 9:1.

B-8.

A circular air puck of mass 100 g and radius 2.00 is initially moving at a speed of 150 cm s^{-1} on a horizontal table, when it collides elastically with a stationary air puck of mass 200 g and radius 3.00 cm. At the instant of collision, the line joining the centers of the two pucks makes an angle of 60° with the original line of motion of the 100 g puck. If there is no friction, either with the table or between the pucks, find the speed and direction of motion of each puck after the collision.

B-9.

An object of mass m_1, moving with a linear speed v in a laboratory system, collides with an object of mass m_2 which is at rest in the laboratory. After the collision, it is observed that $(1 - \alpha^2)$ of the kinetic energy in the CM system was lost in the collision. What was the percentage loss of energy in the laboratory system?

B-10.

a) A particle of mass m collides perfectly elastically with a stationary particle of mass $M > m$. The incident particle is deflected through a 90° angle. At what angle Θ with the original direction of m does the more massive particle recoil?

b) If in the collision a fraction $1 - \alpha^2$ of the CM energy is lost, what is the recoil angle of the originally stationary particle?

B-11.

A proton with kinetic energy 1 MeV collides elastically with a stationary nucleus and is deflected through 90°. If the proton's energy is now 0.80 MeV, what was the mass of the target nucleus in units of the proton mass?

B-12.

A puck of mass 1 kg, moving at a speed of 6 m s^{-1} due N collides with a stationary puck of mass 2 kg. After the collision, the 1 kg puck is moving at 45° NE of its original direction, at a speed of $2\sqrt{2}$ m s^{-1}.

a) What is the velocity of the 2 kg puck after impact?

b) What fraction of the kinetic energy was lost in the CM system?

c) Through what angle was the 1 kg puck deflected in the CM system?

B-13.

A "particle" of mass $m_1 = 2$ kg, moving with a velocity $\vec{v}_1 = 3\vec{i} + 2\vec{j} - \vec{k}$ m s^{-1} collides inelastically with a second particle of mass $m_2 = 3$ kg, moving with a velocity $\vec{v}_2 = -2\vec{i} + 2\vec{j} + 4\vec{k}$ m s^{-1}.

a) Find the velocity of the composite particle.

b) Find the kinetic energy in the CM system of the above particles before impact.

CHAPTER 9

Forces

Refer to The Feynman Lectures on Physics, Vol. I, Ch. 12

1.

The pressure inside a soap bubble ($P + \Delta P$) is greater than the outside pressure (P) because of the surface tension. Show that in terms of the pressure differential ΔP the surface tension of a spherical soap bubble of radius R is given by the expression

$$\sigma = \frac{R}{4}\,\Delta P.$$

A-1.

A 3 kg object has a motion given by $x = 6t^2 - 2t^3$ (x in meters, t in seconds). What is the force (in newtons) acting on the object at $t = 4$ seconds.

A-2.

Two masses, $m_1 = 4$ kg and $m_3 = 2$ kg, are connected with cords of negligible weight over essentially frictionless pulleys to a third mass, $m_2 = 2$ kg. The mass m_2 moves on a long table with a coefficient of friction: $\mu = 1/2$.

a) What is the acceleration of mass m_1 after the system is released from rest?

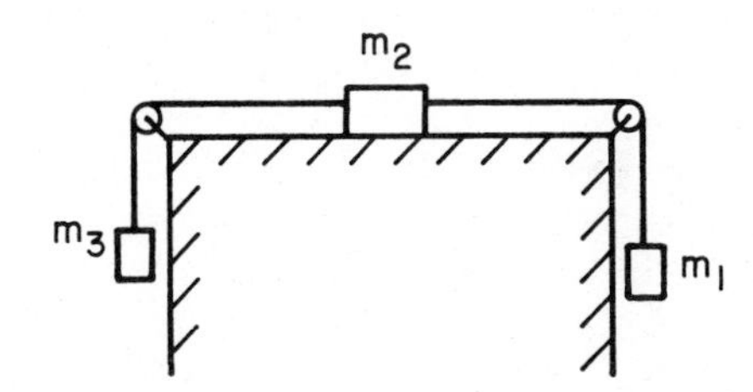

A-3.

The interiors of two soap bubbles of equal radii are connected by a thin tube. Describe what will happen in a realistic case.

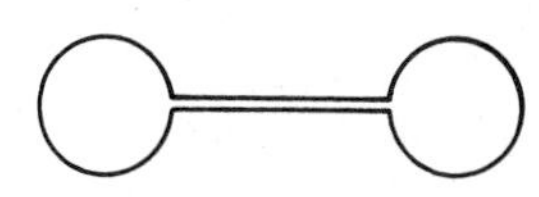

B-1.

A rocket powered high speed sled running on rails employs pivot shoes between the sled and the rails, as shown in the diagram. Each shoe has replaceable rubbing pads at the heel and toe. The coefficient of friction between the rubbing pads and the rail is μ. The rate at which the rubbing pad material is worn off during the operation of the rocket sled is proportional to the friction force acting on the rubbing pad.

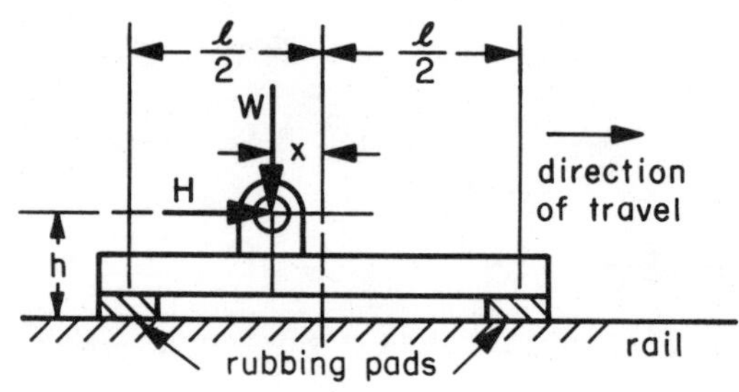

If the shoe pivot point is at a given height h above the rail surface, at what horizontal distance, x, from the vertical centerline between the two rubbing pads should the pivot point P be placed so that the two rubbing pads will wear away at the same rate?

W = that portion of the weight of the rocket sled carried by the shoe in the diagram.

H = horizontal component of force at the shoe pivot point.

ℓ = total length between centers of the two rubbing pads.

B-2.

Adjustable supports that can be slid up and down vertical posts are very useful in many applications. Such a support is shown, with pertinent dimensions. If the coefficient of static friction between post and support is 0.30, and if a load 50 times the weight of the hanger is to be placed on the hanger at X, what is the minimum value of X for no slipping of the hanger?

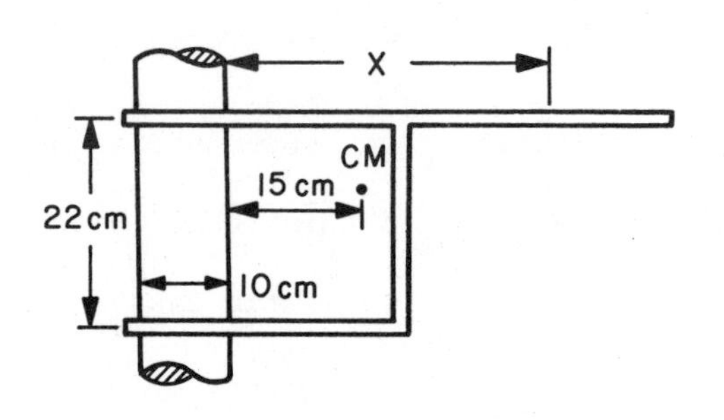

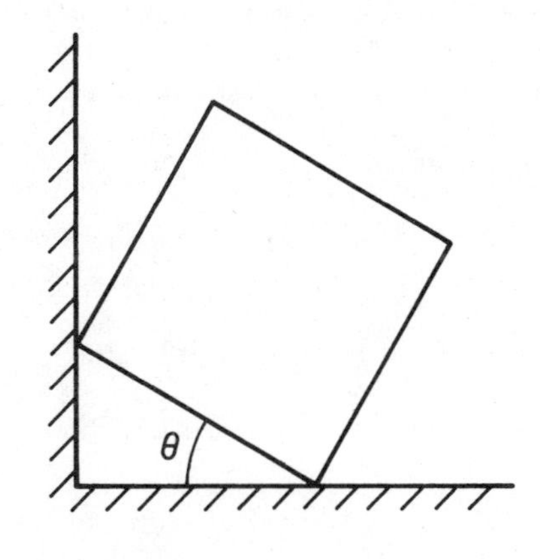

B-3.

A cube of mass M rests tilted against the wall as shown in the diagram. There is no friction between the wall and the cube, but the friction between the cube and floor is just sufficient to keep the cube from slipping. When $0 < \theta < 45^{\circ}$, find the minimum coefficient of friction as a function of θ. Check whether your answer is reasonable by noting values of μ for $\theta \to 0$ and $\theta \to 45^{\circ}$ and by calculating θ for which $\mu = 1$.

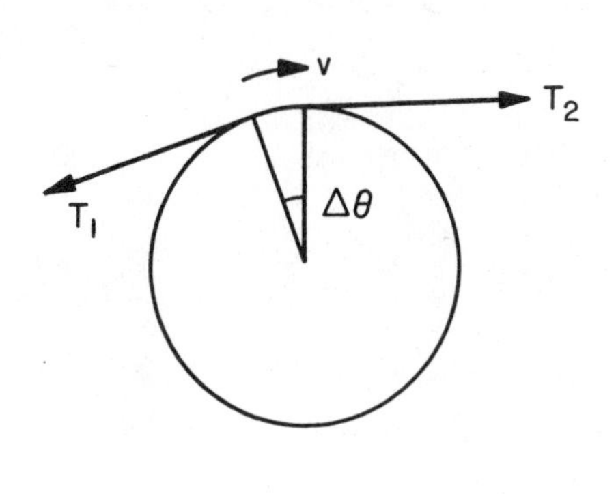

B-4.

a) A cord moving at a low speed v rubs against a round post and deviates from a straight line by a small angle $\Delta\theta \ll 1$ radian. If the tension on one side of the post is $T + \Delta T$ and on the other side is T, what is the difference ΔT introduced by the friction?

b) Integrate the preceding equation to find the ratio of tensions at the two ends of a cord wrapped around a circular post a finite angle α and pulled so as to slip.

B-5.

A 5 g bullet is fired horizontally into a 3 kg wooden block resting on a horizontal surface. The coefficient of sliding friction between the block and surface is 0.2. The bullet remains embedded in the block, which is observed to slide 25 cm along the surface. What was the velocity of the bullet?

B-6.

In their investigation at the scene of an automobile accident the police found, by measurement, that car A left skid marks 150 feet long before it collided with car B.

It was also known that the coefficient of friction between rubber and the pavement at the scene of the accident was not less than 0.6 . Show that car A must have been exceeding the posted speed limit of 45 mph just prior to the accident. (Note that 60 mph = 88 feet/sec. and acceleration due to gravity = 32 feet/sec^2.)

B-7.

An object rests at the base of a frictionless 20° incline 1.00 m long (slant). If the incline is accelerated along the table with an acceleration $a = 4.00\ \text{m s}^{-2}$, how long does it take the object to slide to the top of the slope?

B-8.

A block of mass m slides on an inclined plane tilted at an angle θ with the horicontal. The coefficient of sliding friction is $\mu < \tan\theta$. Let $m = 1.00$ kg, $\mu = 0.20$ and $\theta = 30^\circ$. If the block is projected up the plane at an initial speed $3.00\ \text{m s}^{-1}$,

a) How far up the plane does it go?

b) How long does it take to go up and back to its starting point?

c) How much energy is lost to heat in the process?

B-9.

In the arrangement shown, the inclined plane is 130 cm long and its upper end is 50 cm above the level of the lower end. The block m_2 rests on the plane, and has a mass of 60 g. The block m_1 has a mass 200 g. The coefficient of static friction between the two blocks is 0.50; the coefficient of sliding friction between the lower block and the plane is 0.33. A force F upward and parallel to the plane is applied to the lower block.

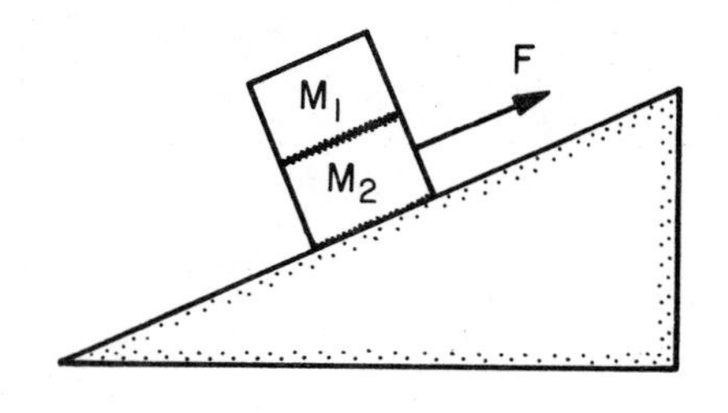

a) What is the acceleration of the lower block when the upper block just starts to slip on it?

b) What is the maximum value of F before this slipping takes place?

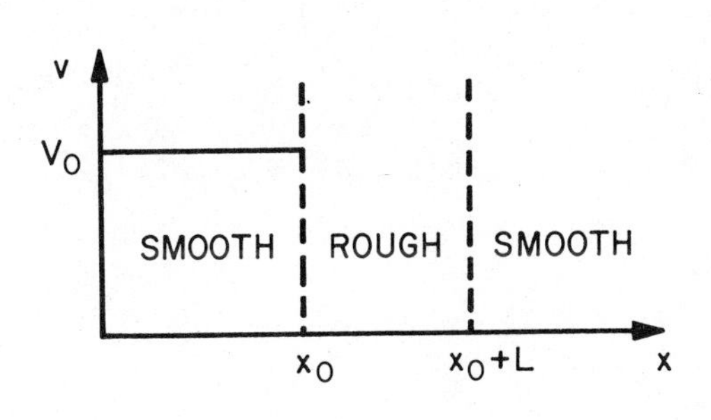

B-10.

An ice puck of mass m is sliding without friction at velocity v_0 cm s^{-1} when it meets a short strip of ice L cm wide, where there is a frictional force proportional to velocity. Find an expression for the velocity as a function of position x and complete the graph.

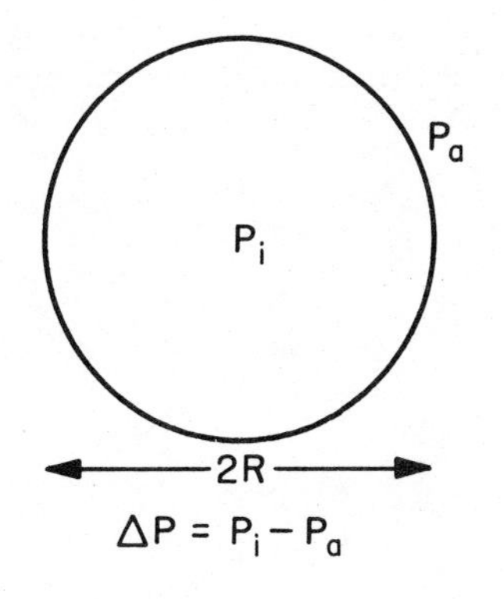

B-11.

In a small increase ΔR of a soap bubble's radius work must be done against the surface tension, which leads to an increase ΔE in surface energy. $\epsilon = \frac{\Delta E}{\Delta A}$, the change in surface energy per change in surface area is called the specific surface energy. From the PVW find how the specific surface energy depends upon the radius R, over-pressure ΔP, etc., of the bubble. What is the numerical value of the ratio σ/ϵ = ?

B-12.

An air-conditioned school bus is approaching a railway crossing. One of the children has tied a hydrogen filled balloon to a seat. You observe that the anchor line of the balloon makes an angle of 30° with the vertical in the direction of motion. Is the driver decelerating or accelerating the bus, and by how much? (Would a highway patrol officer commend the driver for his skill?)

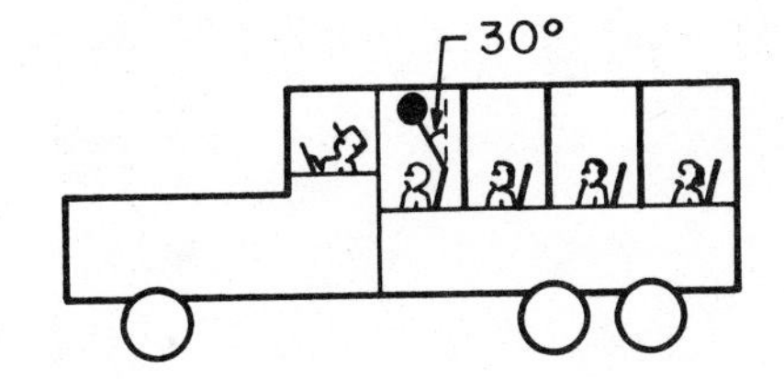

B-13.

A charged particle moves in a plane at right angles to a magnetic field $\vec{B}$. Show that the particle moves in a circular path, and find the radius of the circle.

Find the time required for the particle to go around the orbit. This result is of importance in the operation of a cyclotron. Why?

C-1.

A mass of 1000 g is supported by a cord 5.0 feet long fastened to a ring free to move on a horizontal rod. The coefficient of static friction between the ring and the rod is 0.75. A second cord is fastened to the weight and passes over a pulley fastened to the rod 8-1/3 ft to the left of the ring as shown. Weights W are attached to the other end of this cord until the ring just begins to slip. Find:

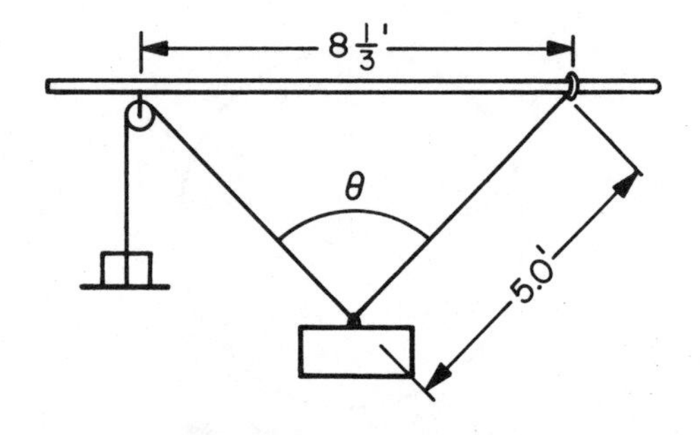

a) The value of W when slipping just begins.

b) The tension in the five foot length of cord,

c) The angle Θ.

C-2.

A side view of a simplified form of vertical latch is as shown. The lower member A can be pushed forward in its horizontal channel. The smooth sides of the channels have negligible friction, but at the interfaces of A and B, which are at 45° with the horizontal, there exists a static coefficient of friction μ. What is the minimum force F that must be applied horizontally to A to start motion of the latch, if B has a mass m?

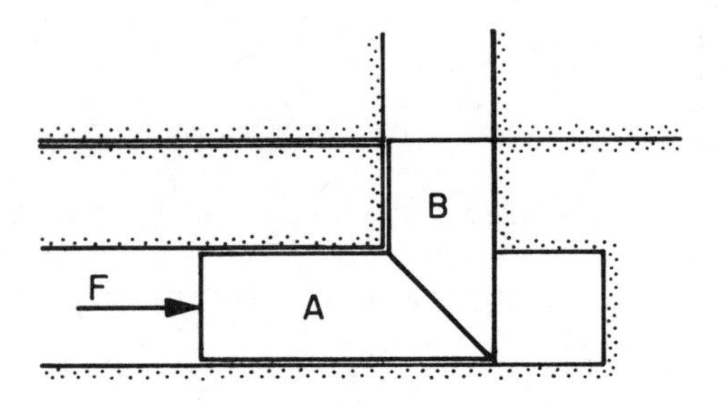

C-3.

A particle of weight W rests on a rough inclined plane which makes an angle α with the horizontal.

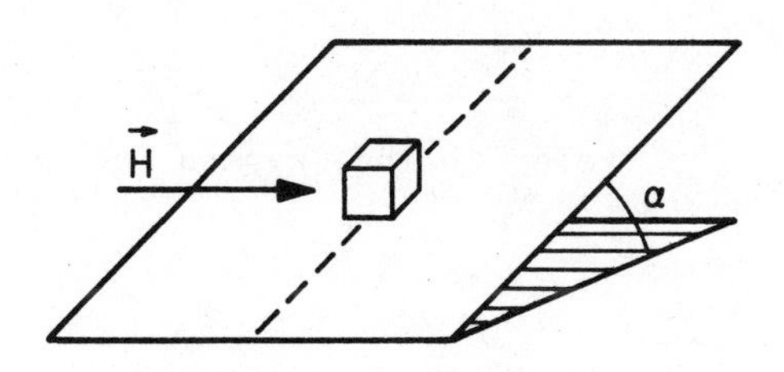

a) If the coefficient of static friction $\mu = 2 \tan \alpha$, find the least horizontal force H_{min}, acting transverse to the slope of the plane

C-4.

The gauge pressure inside a certain closed bottle of carbonated water is 3.00×10^6 dynes cm^{-2}. The surface tension of water is 73 dynes cm^{-1}. (Assume this is also the value for water in contact with CO_2 gas.) When the bottle is gently opened, a bubble will grow inside the liquid if it is initially "born" larger than a certain critical size at a local nucleating center. Calculate this critical size for the conditions stated.

C-5.

A particle of charge q and mass m moves in a combined electric and magnetic field E_y and B_z. (All other field components are zero.)

a) Write the equations of motion of the particle.

b) Apply a Galilean transformation to the coordinate system:

$$x' = x - (E_y/B_z)t$$

$$y' = y$$

$$z' = z$$

c) What do you conclude concerning the motion of a particle in crossed electric and magnetic fields?

CHAPTER 10

Potentials and Fields

Refer to The Feynman Lectures on Physics, Vol. I, Chs. 13 and 14.

A-1.

A mass m collides with a spring of spring constant k. At what point does it first come to rest? Neglect the mass of the spring.

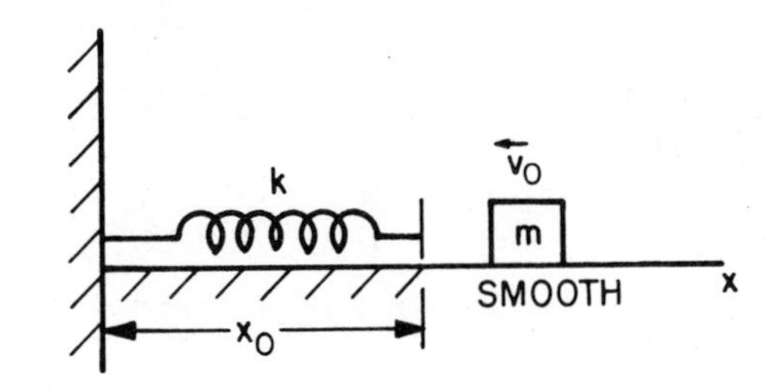

A-2.

A certain spring has a force constant k. If it is stretched to a new equilibrium length within its linear range by a constant force F, show that it has the same force constant for displacement from the new equilibrium position.

A-3.

A hollow spherical asteroid travels freely through space. There is a small particle of mass m in its interior. At what point in the interior will the particle be in equilibrium position.

A-4.

The speed needed for a body to leave the Earth's gravitational field is (approximately) 7.0 mi s^{-1}. If an interplanetary probe is given an initial speed of 8.0 mi s^{-1} just above the Earth's atmosphere, with what speed relative to the Earth will it be traveling when it is at a distance of 10^6 mi from the Earth?

A-5.

If the Earth carried a net charge of 1.00 C, what would its potential be?

A-6.

A spherical shell of radius 0.50 m is (uniformly) charged to a potential of 10^6V. Find the charge on the shell.

A-7.

The maximum electric field strength that can be supported by dry air at atmospheric pressure without sparking (or corona discharge) is about 31 kV cm^{-1}. Calculate the maximum potential to which an isolated, smooth sphere of diameter 20 cm can be raised (in air) without breakdown.

B-1.

An object of mass 6.0 kg is free to move along the x-axis on a frictionless track. In each of the cases given it starts from rest at $x = 0$, $t = 0$.

a) It moves 3.00 m under the action of a force $F = (3 + 4x)$ N in the x-direction where x is in m,

(1) What velocity does it acquire?

(2) What is its acceleration at that point?

(3) What power is being expended on it at that point?

b) It moves for 3.00 seconds under the action of a force $F = (3 + 4t)$ N in the x-direction where t is in seconds.

(1) What velocity does it acquire?

(2) What is then its acceleration?

(3) What power is being expended on it at that time?

B-2,3,4.

A force $\vec{F} = 1.5\, y\, \vec{i} + 3x^2 \vec{j} - 0.2(x^2 + y^2)\vec{k}$ (Newtons) acts upon a particle of mass 1.00 kg. At $t = 0$ the particle is located at $\vec{r} = 2\vec{i} + 3\vec{j}$ (meters) and is moving with a velocity $\vec{v} = 2\vec{j} + \vec{k}$($m\ s^{-1}$).

B-2.

Find, at $t = 0$

a) The force on the particle.

b) The acceleration of the particle.

c) The kinetic energy, and

d) The rate of change of kinetic energy.

B-3.

Approximately what will be the location, the velocity, and the kinetic energy of the above particle at t = 0.01 s?

B-4.

The particle moves from point (0,-1,0) to the point (0,+1,0) on a frictionless track under the action of the force $\vec{F}$ (plus a certain force of constraint). Find the work done by the force $\vec{F}$ if the track is

a) A straight track along the y-axis.

b) A circular track in the z-y plane. Is this a conservative force?

B-5.

A small, frictionless car coasts on an inclined track with a circular loop-the-loop of radius R at its lower end. From what height H above the top of the loop must the car start in order to traverse the loop without leaving the track?

B-6.

The lowest portion of a frictionless slide is part of a cylindrical surface of radius R subtending an angle θ on each side of the vertical as shown. The slide begins at a vertical height H above its lowest point. A small object of mass m starts from rest at the upper end and slides down.

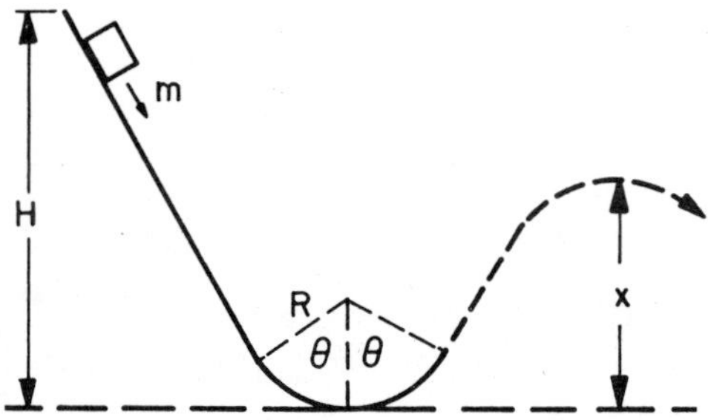

a) What is the maximum height x of its trajectory above the lowest point after m leaves the slide?

B-7.

A small glider of mass $\underline{m}$ kg is connected to point P by means of a spring of negligible free (unstretched) length and of force constant k Nm^{-1}. The point P is adjustable in position but once adjusted it does not move. The glider is free to move without friction on the outside surface of a circular hoop of radius $\underline{R}$ which stands in a vertical plane. Let OP = d. If the mass starts from rest at the top of the hoop at A and barely loses contact with the hoop as it passes the lowest point B, find $\underline{d}$.

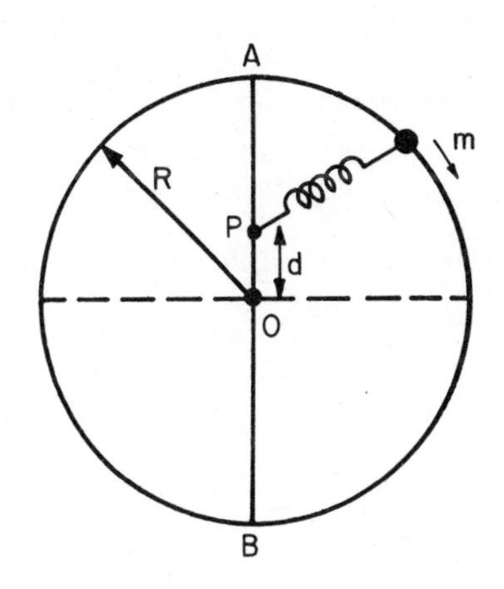

B-8.

A flexible cable of length L which weighs M kg m^{-1} hangs over a pulley of negligible mass, radius, and friction. Initially, the cable is just balanced. It is given a slight push to unbalance it, and it proceeds to accelerate. Find its speed as the end flies off the pulley.

B-9.

A particle starts from rest at the top of a frictionless sphere of radius R and slides on the sphere under the force of gravity. How far below its starting point does it get before flying off the sphere?

B-10.

A car with a mass of 3000 lb has a motor of 85 horsepower. To travel at a constant speed of 30 mph on the level the car must use 20 hp. Assuming that the frictional forces are the same, what is the steepest hill the car can climb at this same speed? (Specify the angle or some function of the angle that the slope of the hill makes with the horizontal.)

B-11.

An automobile weighing 1000 kg is powered by an engine whose rated power is 120 kW. If the engine develops this power at a speed of 60 km h^{-1}, what is the maximum acceleration the car can have at this speed?

B-12.

World records (1960) for the shot-put, the discus and the javelin were respectively 19.30 m, 59.87 m, and 86.09 m. The masses of the missiles involved are respectively 7.25 kg, 2 kg, and 0.8 kg. Compare the work done by each champion in making his record toss, assuming that each trajectory starts at an elevation of 1.80 m above level ground and has an initial elevation of 45°. Neglect air resistance.

B-13.

A certain spherical body of radius R and mass M has a uniform mass density throughout its volume. Find the gravitational potential and the gravitational field strength as a function of the distance from the center. Sketch your results graphically.

B-14.

Find the gravitational acceleration $\vec{a}$ at a point P at distance x from the surface of a spherical mass of radius R and density ρ, which has a spherical cavity of radius R/4 whose center is situated at a distance R/4 beyond the center of the large sphere C, on the line PC produced.

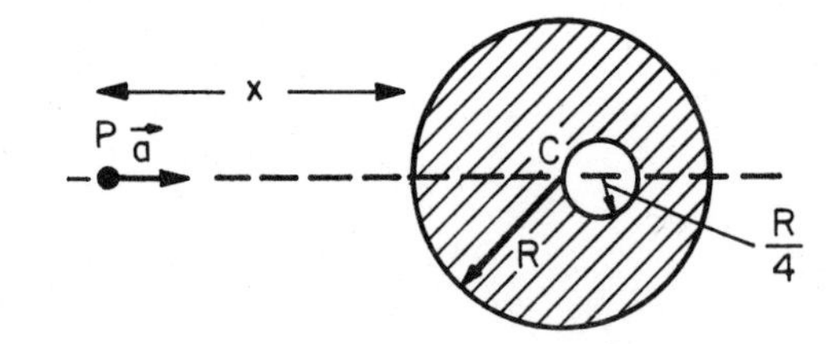

B-15.

Consider a material of density ρ in the form of an extended (infinite) plate of thickness d. A spherical cavity of radius r (less than d/2) is cut at the origin of coordinates.

a) What gravitational force will act on a small mass m if located at any point Y along y-axis?

b) Sketch the force → as a function of Y.

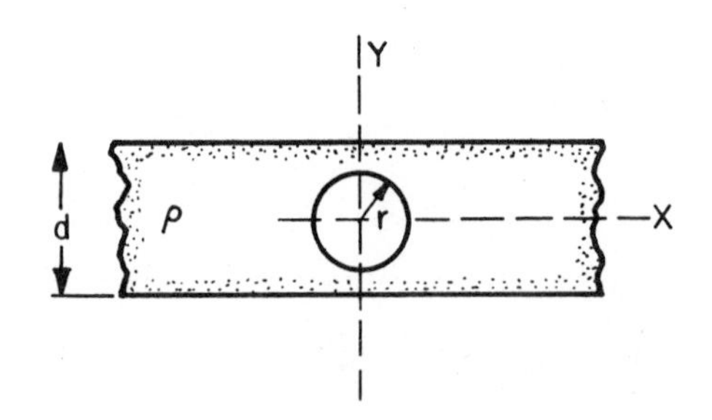

B-16.

A small body of mass m moves under gravity in an elliptical orbit of eccentricity e and semi major axis a about a large mass M. (Assume that M remains stationary.) Evaluate the total energy of m (kinetic plus potential). (Note that E does not depend upon e.)

B-17.

a) Deduce Kepler's third law for elliptical orbits.

b) Show that all orbits having a given total energy per unit mass will have the same period. (Assume $m \ll M$ for simplicity.)

B-18.

Often, a capacitor consists of two (metallic) bodies, equally and oppositely charged. The capacitance C is then defined as the ratio of the charge on one body divided by the potential difference between them:

$$C = Q/(\Phi_2 - \Phi_1) \text{ (Farad)}$$

Find the capacitance of a pair of concentric spherical shells, of radii A and B.

C-1.

A 25 g weight hanger is attached to a spring of negligible mass whose force constant is $k = 15.3\ Nm^{-1}$. A mass m = 50 g is dropped from a height h = 9.0 cm onto the stationary weight hanger, with which it collides inelastically. What is the minimum height attained by the mass m below its starting point?

C-2.

Water (density 62.5 lb ft^{-3}) is pumped through a smooth hose whose nozzle has a cross-sectional area of 5.5 sq. in. When the nozzle is aimed at an angle of 30° above the horizontal, the water stream is observed to have the apex of its trajectory 16 ft above the level of the nozzle. The pump inlet is connected to a large reservoir, and the water in the reservoir stands at an elevation 8.0 ft below the nozzle. If the over-all efficiency of the pump and the driving motor is 60 percent, what power in kilowatts is being drawn from the electric line feeding the motor?

C-3.

Estimate the pressure at the center of the moon in atmospheres. (1 atm = 1.02×10^6 dynes cm^{-2}). Use the following data for the moon:

Mass = 7.0×10^{22} kg

Radius = 1740 km

Surface gravity = 160 cm s^{-2}

Mean density = 3.34 g cm^{-3}.

C-4.

What is the minimum work necessary to move a rock of mass m_1 from the earth's surface to the moon's surface?

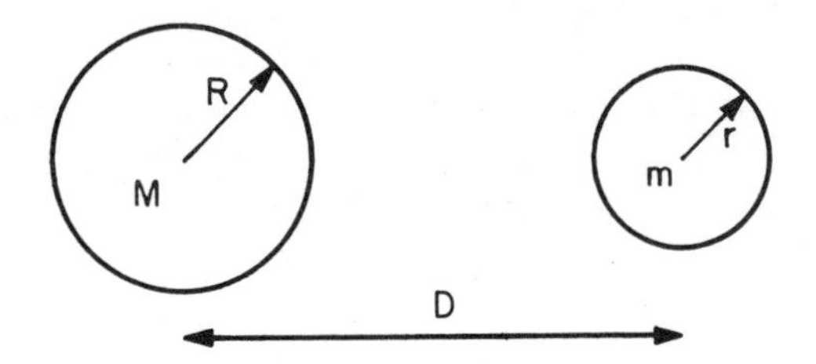

C-5.

A satellite of mass m moves in a circular orbit around an asteroid of mass M (M >> m). If the asteroid's mass was suddenly* reduced to one-half its former value, what would happen to the satellite? Describe its new orbit.

* How it could happen: The satellite is placed in orbit at a large distance from the asteroid to monitor the test of a nuclear device on the asteroid. The explosion expells half the asteroid's mass without directly affecting the distant satellite.

C-6.

With what minimum speed must an interstellar probe be launched from near the Earth's surface in order to escape from the solar system with a residual speed of 10 mi s^{-1} relative to the sun? The speed of the Earth in its orbit is 18.5 mi s^{-1}. If it is desired to have the probe moving in a prescribed direction when it has escaped from the sun, what then is the maximum launching speed that could be required?

C-7.

It is desired to send a solar probe into an orbit with a perihelion distance of 0.010 AU and having the same period as the Earth, so that data recorded during the flight may be transmitted to Earth one year after the launching date. With what speed, and in what direction relative to the Earth-sun line, should the probe be launched from the Earth? The orbital speed of the Earth is 30 km s^{-1}.

CHAPTER 11

Units and Dimensions

A-1.

What are the dimensions of

a) The force constant of a spring

b) Work

c) Torque

d) Surface Tension

e) Coefficient of friction

f) Coefficient of viscosity

g) Gravitational field

h) Electric field

i) Magnetic induction

j) E/B?

A-2.

Show that the quantity $(\epsilon_0 c)^{-1}$ has the dimensions of resistance, and evaluate it numerically.

A-3.

Moe and Joe, two cosmic physicists who grew up on different planets, meet at an interplanetary symposium on weights and measures to discuss the establishment of a universal system of units. Moe proudly describes the merits of the MKSA system, used in every civilized region of the Earth. Joe equally proudly describes the beauties of the M'K'S'A' system, used everywhere else in the solar system. If the constant factors relating the basic mass, length, and time standards of the two systems are μ, λ, and τ, such that

$$m' = \mu m, \quad l' = \lambda l, \text{ and } t' = \tau t$$

what factors are needed to convert the units of velocity, acceleration, force, and energy between the two systems?

A-4.

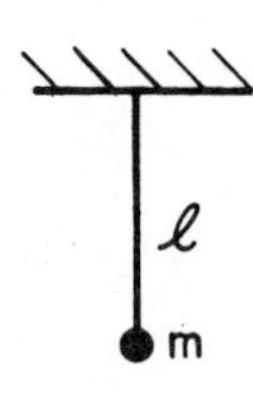

Use dimensional analysis to derive the dependence of the period of a simple pendulum on its physical parameters.

B-1.

What is the numerical magnitude of $G M_{\odot}$ if lengths are measured in AU and times in years?

B-2.

If a scale model of the solar system is made, using materials of the same respective average densities as the sun and planets, but reducing all linear dimensions by a scaling factor k, how will the periods of revolution of the planets depend on k?

B-3.

From dimensional analysis find the dependence on m, k, etc., of the period of the mass-spring system shown. (Neglect friction.)

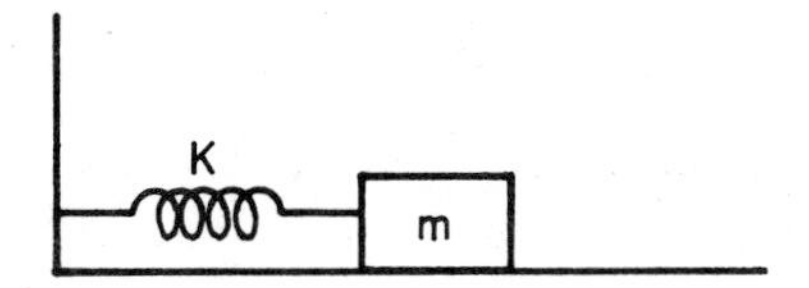

B-4.

A mass m is whirling in a circle with speed v at the end of a string of length ℓ. (Neglect gravity.) Find how the tension in the string and the radial acceleration of the mass varies with these quantities.

B-5.

A projectile of mass m is fired at an angle θ with the horizontal at an initial speed v. Find how the horizontal range and time of flight depend upon the relevant quantities.

B-6.

A liquid drop of radius R, density ρ, may oscillate, with the surface tension σ providing the restoring force. Find how the period of oscillations will depend upon these parameters.

B-7.

A student discovers that he can tune the house piano by changing the tension in the wires. If the frequency is inversely proportional to length of the string, how does it depend on the length ℓ, the tension T, and the linear density σ?

B-8.

It is observed that water waves on a very deep ocean travel with a speed v that depends upon their wavelength λ, but not upon their amplitude. Find how the speed should depend upon the wavelength and the density of the water.

C-1.

A box of volume V contains N particles of mass m, moving in various random directions with speed v. From dimensional analysis find how the pressure of such a gas depends upon N, V, m, and v. Can you draw any conclusions concerning the nature of absolute temperature?

C-2.

Show that Kepler's third law R^3/T^2 = const. follows from the application of Newton's law $F = \frac{GMm}{R^2}$ to circular orbits. Use dimensional considerations.

CHAPTER 12

Relativistic Kinematics and Dynamics. Mass and Energy Equivalence

Refer to The Feynman Lectures on Physics, Vol. I, Chs. 15 and 16.

A-1.

Solve the Lorentz transformation for x,y,z,t in terms of x', y', z', t'.

A-2.

Write the Lorentz transformation in differential form, $dx = \gamma(dx' + \beta c dt')$ etc., and thus evaluate $dx/dt = v_x$ in terms of v_x', V, etc.; do the same for $dy/dt = v_y$.

A-3.

A particle which moves along the x-axis has a velocity v_x and an acceleration a_x. What velocity and acceleration will it have in the S' system which is moving at velocity V with respect to the first system?

A-4.

A stick of length L = 5 m is at rest in a system S and oriented at an angle $\theta = 30^{\circ}$ with respect to the x-axis. What are the apparent length and orientation angle of this stick as measured by an observer in the system S', which moves at a speed of $v_x = c/2$ with respect to the first system?

A-5.

A muon is formed high in the atmosphere and travels at a speed v = 0.990 c for a distance of 5.00 km before it decays.

a) How long does the muon "live", as measured by us and as it would appear in its own frame of reference?

b) What thickness of atmosphere does the muon traverse, as measured in its reference frame?

A-6.

Show that an electron has a rest energy $m_e c^2 = 0.511$ MeV.

B-1.

A particle of rest mass m_0 is caused to move along a line in such a way that its position is

$$x = \sqrt{b^2 + c^2t^2} - b$$

What force must be applied to the particle to produce this motion?

B-2.

The total electrical energy generated in the USA in 1965 amounted to 1.05×10^{12} kWh.

a) How much mass was converted into energy in this process?

b) If all of the mass change in the conversion of deuterium into helium were available (some is lost in neutrinos), how much heavy water per second would be needed to supply the necessary deuterium?

Note: $M_{H^2} = 2.0147$ amu $M_{He^4} = 4.0039$ amu.

B-3.

The total power incident at the top of the Earth's atmosphere from the sun is about 1.4 kW m^{-2}. If this energy all arises from the conversion of ordinary hydrogen into helium, how much hydrogen, in metric tons per second, does the sun "burn"? (Neglect the loss into neutrinos.)

C-1.

a) Evaluate the acceleration of gravity in l.y. y^{-2}.

b) If an isolated spaceship accelerates at such a rate that its occupants feel a constant acceleration equal to that of gravity at the Earth's surface, and does so for a period of 5.00 y as measured by a stationary (unaccelerated) observer who is at rest with respect to the ship at t = 0, how far has the ship gone, and how fast is it traveling, at the end of this time?

CHAPTER 13

Relativistic Energy and Momentum

Refer to The Feynman Lectures on Physics, Vol. I, Chs. 16 and 17.

A-1.

Show that the speed of a 1 GeV electron differs from c by one part in 8×10^6.

A-2.

a) Express the momentum of a particle in terms of its kinetic energy T and rest energy m_0c^2.

b) What is the speed of a particle whose kinetic energy is equal to its rest energy?

A-3.

The rest mass of a proton is $m_p = 938$ MeV. In the cosmic radiation, protons having an energy of about 10^{10} GeV have been detected by indirect methods. Assume that a proton of this energy travels diametrically across a galaxy whose diameter is about 10^5 l.y. How long does this require, as measured in the proton's reference frame?

B-1.

A particle of charge q, momentum p, is moving in a circle of radius R at right angles to a magnetic field B.

a) If q is measured in units of an electron charge, p is measured in MeV/c, and B is measured in gauss, what is the relation between p, B, and R? (Let $q = Z\,q_e$.)

b) What is the radius of curvature of a proton of K.E. = 60 GeV in a B = 0.3 gauss field?

B-2.

A cyclotron is being designed to accelerate protons to a kinetic energy of 150 MeV. The magnetic field strength is to be 1.00×10^4 G.

a) What must be the minimum radius of the magnet pole pieces?

b) What frequency must be used on the acceleration electrodes?

c) By what percentage must the driving frequency be changed to allow for relativistic effects during the acceleration of a given particle?

B-3.

A body of mass M, at rest in the laboratory, disintegrates into two parts of rest mass m_1 and m_2. Determine relativistically the kinetic energies T_1 and T_2 of the disintegration products.

B-4.

A pion ($m_\pi = 273\ m_e$) at rest decays into a muon ($m_\mu = 207\ m_e$) and a neutrino ($m_\nu = 0$). Find the kinetic energy and momentum of the muon and the neutrino in MeV.

B-5.

An excited atom of total mass m is at rest in a given coordinate system. It emits a photon, thereby losing energy ΔE. Taking into account the recoil of the atom, calculate the energy of the photon.

B-6.

A particle of rest mass m_0, moving at speed $v = 4c/5$, collides inelastically with a similar particle at rest.

a) What is the speed of the composite particle?

b) What is its rest mass?

B-7.

The Berkeley "bevatron" was designed to accelerate protons to sufficiently high energy to produce proton-antiproton pairs by the reaction

$$p + p \rightarrow p + p + (p + \bar{p}).$$

The so-called threshold energy of this reaction corresponds to the situation when the four particles on the right move along together as a single particle of rest mass $M = 4\ m_p$. If the target proton is at rest before collision, what kinetic energy must the bombarding proton have at threshold?

B-8.

Calculate the threshold kinetic energy for the production of a proton-antiproton pair by an electron-electron collision

$$e^- + e^- \rightarrow e^- + e^- + p^- + p^+$$

You may use $m_e \simeq .5$ MeV

$m_p \simeq 1$ GeV.

Compare this energy with the energy required in a p-p collision (Ex. B-7.).

B-9.

A proton-antiproton pair may be created in the absorption of a photon (γ) by a proton at rest.

$$\gamma + P \rightarrow P + (P + \bar{P})$$

What min. energy E_γ must the photon have? (Express E_γ in terms of proton rest energy $m_p c^2$). Compare this energy with the energy required in a p-p collision (Ex. B-7), and in an e-e collision (Ex. B-8).

C-1.

A proton of mass M collides head-on with another proton at rest and produces a π-meson of mass $m \ll M$.

$$p + p \rightarrow p + p + \pi$$

a) What is the minimum kinetic energy of the incident proton?

b) What is the kinetic energy of the meson at threshold?

Note: You may use non-relativistic expressions for kinetic energies and velocity transformations.

c) Approximately what error is made by using non-relativistic expressions?

C-2.

A π^0-meson may decay into two γ-rays* while at rest or in flight: $\pi^0 \rightarrow \gamma + \gamma$

Note: A γ-ray is a photon: $E_\gamma = p_\gamma c = h\nu$.

a) If the decaying π^0 has a velocity $\vec{v}$ and rest mass m_π and the γ-ray is emitted at an angle θ with respect to the original direction of the π^0, find the γ-ray energy as function of m_π, v, and θ.

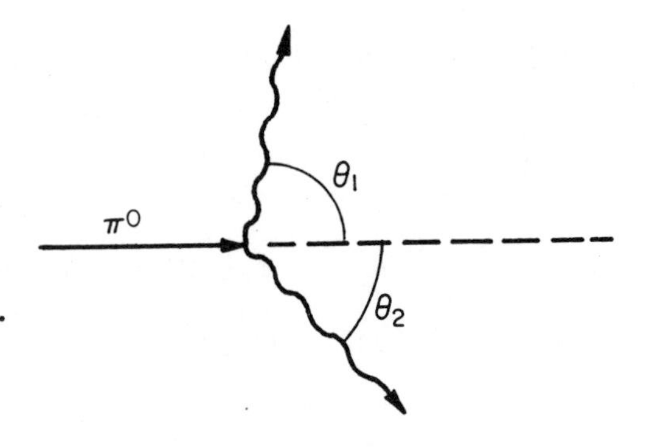

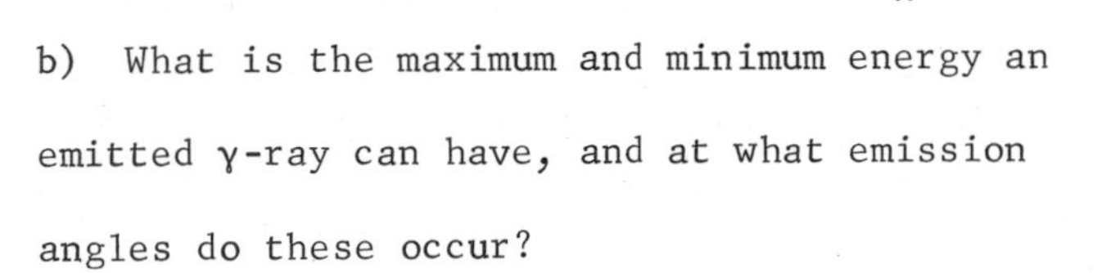

b) What is the maximum and minimum energy an emitted γ-ray can have, and at what emission angles do these occur?

c) Can you find a simple function of E_{max} and E_{min} which is independent of the velocity of the π^0, and what is its physical meaning?

* The existence and the numerical value of the mass of the π^0 were inferred from measurements of this nature.

Reference: A.G. Carlson, J.E. Hooper, and D.T. King, Phil. Mag. 41, p. 701-724, (1950).

PART II

CHAPTER 14

Rotation in Two Dimensions. The Center of Mass

Refer to the Feynman Lectures on Physics, Vol. I, Chs. 18 and 19.

1.

A rigid wheel of radius R is rolling without slipping on a horizontal surface. The plane of the wheel is vertical, and the axis of the wheel is moving horizontally with a speed V relative to the surface. If the axis of the wheel is parallel to the z-axis, V is in the positive x-direction, and θ is the angle through which the wheel has rotated since a certain point P on the rim was in contact with the ground, show that the instantaneous velocity (speed and direction) of the point P is given by

$$\vec{v} = V[(1 - \cos\theta)\vec{i} + \sin\theta\ \vec{j}]$$

2.

The knowledge of the surface area (or volume) swept out by a plane curve (or area) can be used to find the center of mass of a thin, curved uniform wire or a thin uniform plane sheet.

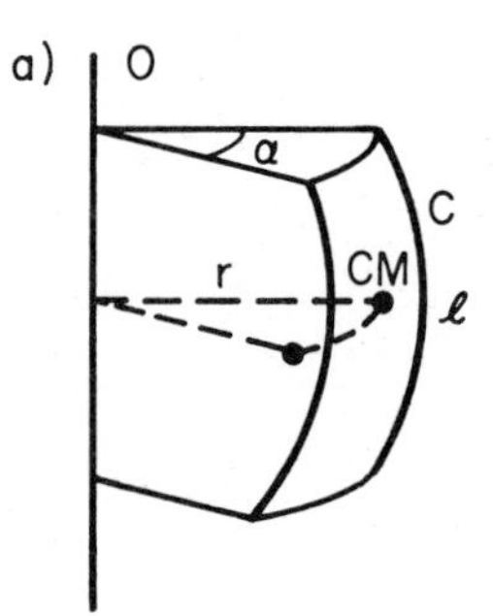

a) Show that the surface area A swept out by the plane curve C in its rotation through an angle α about the axis O which lies in the plane of C is equal to the length of C times the distance through which the CM moves

$$A = \alpha r \ell$$

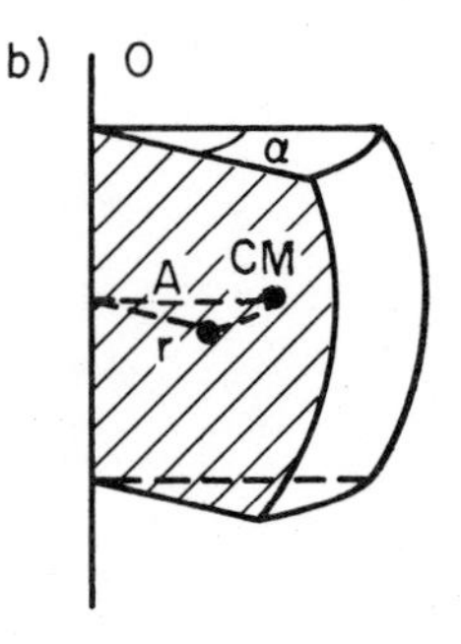

b) Show that the volume swept out by the plane area A in its rotation through an angle α about the axis O is equal to the area A times the distance which the CM moved

$$V = \alpha r A$$

3.

Show that the CM of any collection of particles moves as would a single particle having a mass equal to the sum of the masses of the individual particles, and subject to the vector sum of all forces acting on the separate particles:

$$M\ddot{\vec{R}} = \sum_i \vec{f}_i$$

A-1.

A force $\vec{F} = 30\,\vec{i} + 40\,\vec{j}$ Newtons acts at the point at $\vec{r} = 8\vec{i} + 6\vec{j}$ meters. Find:

a) The torque about the origin.

b) The magnitude of the lever arm of the force.

c) The component of the force perpendicular to $\vec{r}$.

A-2.

A yo-yo on a horizontal table is free to roll without slipping. If a horizontal force F is applied, will it roll in or opposite to the direction of F? Why?

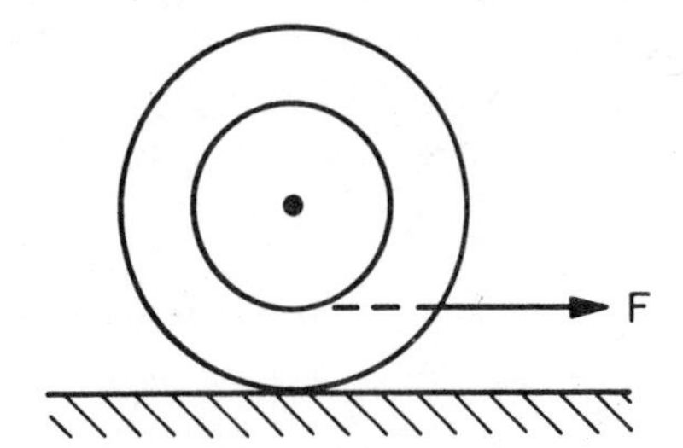

A-3.

At what latitude is the tangential speed of a point due to the earth's rotation 200 m s^{-1} less than it is in Los Angeles (latitude 34°N)?

A-4.

A circle of radius R is revolved around an axis AA' tangent to it to generate a torus. Find the volume of this torus.

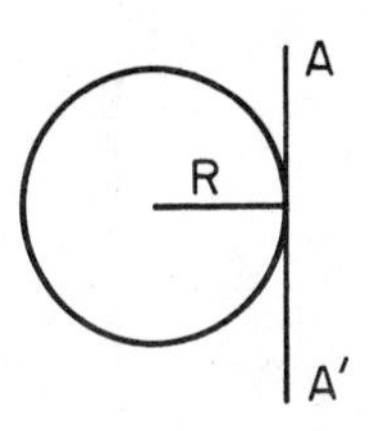

A-5.

A mass M and a mass 2M are rotating about their CM at angular velocity ω at a fixed distance R apart. What is their kinetic energy of rotation?

B-1.

Find the CM of a thin uniform wire of length L, bent into a circular arc of radius $R(R > L/2\pi)$. Use coordinates with origin at the center of the circle and with the x-axis passing through the center of the wire.

Use this result to find the CM of a circular sector made of uniform sheet metal, if the sector has a radius R and subtends an angle α at the center.

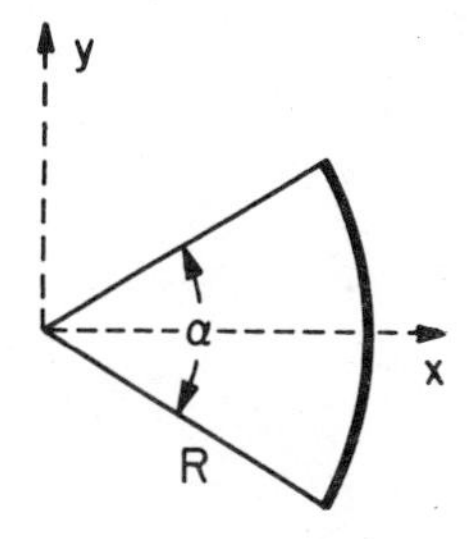

B-2.

A disc of uniform density has a hole cut out of it, as shown. Find the center of mass.

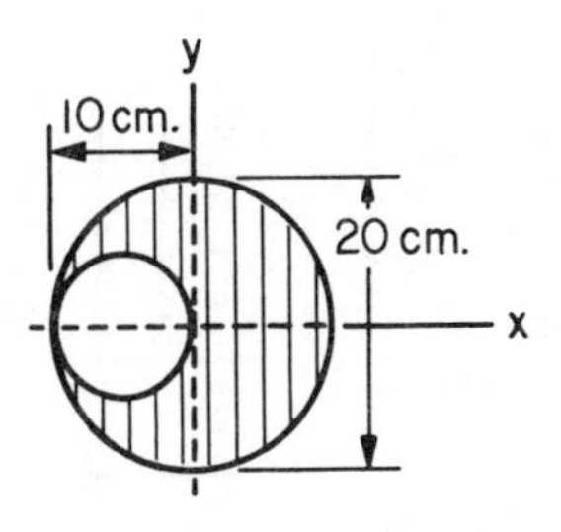

B-3.

A solid cylinder has a density which varies by quadrants as shown, with the numbers indicating relative densities. If the x-y axes are as indicated, what is the equation of the line drawn through the origin and through the center of mass?

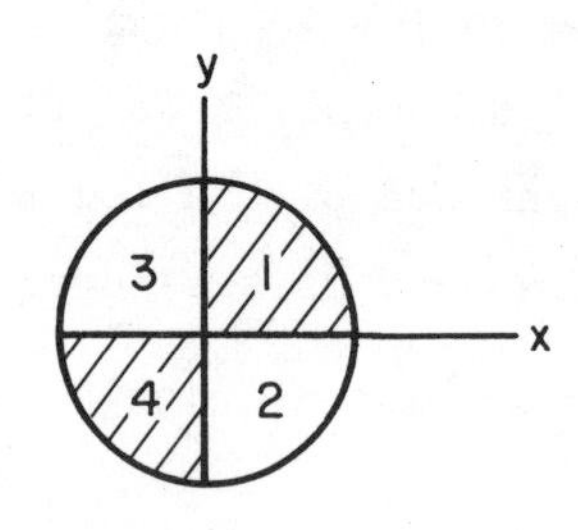

B-4.

A cylinder of radius π cm and mass 3 kg is cut into thirds. The same thing is done to a second cylinder of radius π cm and mass 6 kg. A piece from one cylinder is glued to a piece from the other one giving the arrangement shown, where the radius OA is horizontal. The floor has sufficient friction that slipping cannot occur, and the wall has negligible friction.

a) What is the force of the cylinder on the wall?

b) How far from the center along the radius OA would one have to place a point mass M so that the system would remain in equilibrium if the wall were removed?

Note: For the location of the CM of a sector of a circle, see Ex. B-1.

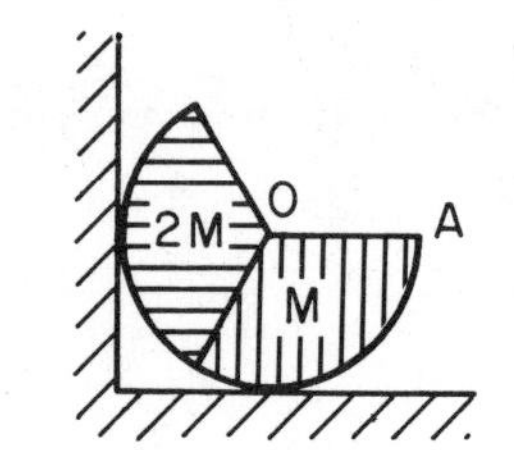

B-5.

A rod of length R is made of two uniform pieces of equal length R/2 each, but one piece weighs twice as much as the other. The rod is suspended by cords of length R attached to each end and to a nail at P. When the system comes to rest, what angle α does the rod make with the horizontal?

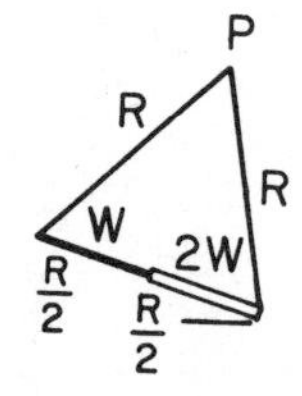

B-6.

The L-shaped body shown in the figure is made of sheet metal of uniform thickness and rests on a frictionless, horizontal table. It is struck with a sudden blow in the direction shown, and is observed to move away without rotating. How far from the vertex 0 was the blow applied?

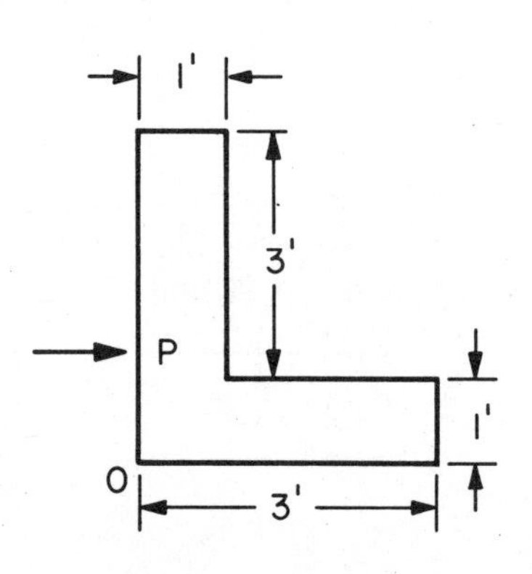

B-7.

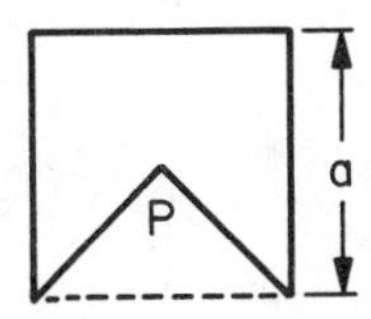

From a square piece of uniform sheet metal an isosceles triangle is to be cut out from one edge, as shown, such that the remaining metal, when suspended from the apex P of the cut, will remain in equilibrium in any position. What is the altitude of the cutout triangle?

B-8.

Masses M_1 and M_2 are placed at the opposite ends of a rigid rod of length L and negligible mass; the dimensions of M_1 and M_2 are negligible compared to L. The rod is to be set rotating about an axis perpendicular to it. Through what point on this rod should this axis pass in order that the work required to set the rod rotating with an angular speed ω_0 shall be a minimum?

B-9.

The essential elements of one form of simple speed governor are as shown: to a vertical shaft a horizontal rod is mounted symmetrically and on the horizontal rod are freely sliding brake shoes. When the shaft turns, the brake shoes press against the inner surface of a stationary cylindrical brake drum. If the brake shoes are each of mass m, and their thickness dimension is negligible compared to the inner radius of the brake drum r, if the coefficient of sliding friction between the shoes and the drum is μ, develop the formula for the power required to turn the governor shaft in terms of m, r, μ, and f, the frequency of rotation of the shaft.

C-1.

A uniform brick of length L is laid on a smooth horizontal surface. Other equal bricks are now piled on as shown, so that the sides form continuous planes, but the ends are offset at each brick from the previous brick by a distance L/a, where a is an integer. How many bricks can be used in this manner before the pile topples over?

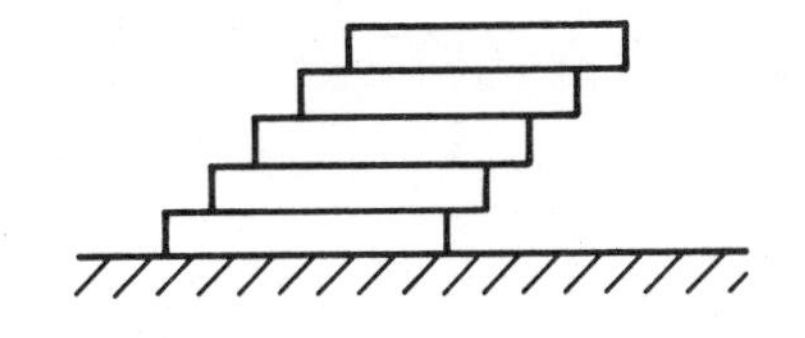

C-2.

A rotating governor, as shown, is to be designed to shut off power when the machine to which the governor is directly connected reaches a speed of 120 rpm. The operating collar C weighs 10.0 lb and slides without friction on the vertical shaft AB. C is so designed to shut off power when the distance AC reduces to 1.41 ft. If the four links of the governor framework are each 1.00 ft long between frictionless pivots and are relatively massless, what value should the masses M have so that the governor will operate as planned?

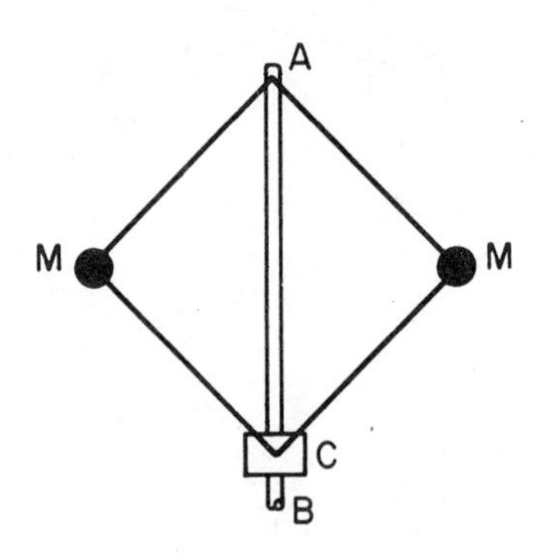

C-3.

Four masses M in the same plane in field-free space connected by very light springs of spring constant k are spinning at angular velocity ω about an axis perpendicular to the plane and through the center of symmetry. The springs have a relaxed length L. Assuming equilibrium, by how much are the springs extended? What condition determines whether stable equilibrium is possible?

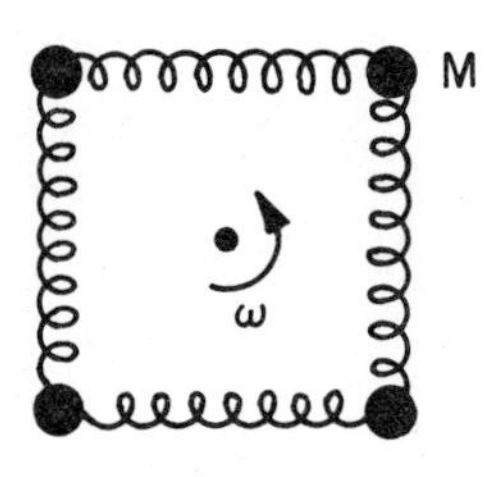

CHAPTER 15

Angular Momentum. The Moment of Inertia

Refer to the Feynman Lectures on Physics, Vol. I, Chs. 18 and 19.

1..

A mass point moves under the influence of a central force - that is, a force whose line of action passes through a fixed point. Show that the angular momentum of the mass remains constant. Show also that this result is equivalent to Kepler's second law of planetary motion.

2.

The statement $\vec{\tau} = \frac{d\vec{L}}{dt}$ is generally true for a rigid body if one considers all forces including inertial (pseudo) forces.

If inertial forces are not included in the analysis, $\vec{\tau} = \frac{d\vec{L}}{dt}$ is still a correct relation for

1. any fixed axis outside the body;
2. any axis of fixed direction through the CM of the body;
3. an axis about which the body is rotating at a given moment (instantaneous axis of rotation).

How many of the above statements can you prove?

A-1.

A straight, uniform wire of length L and mass M is bent at its midpoint to form the angle θ. What is its moment of inertia for an axis passing through the point A, perpendicular to the plane determined by the bent wire?

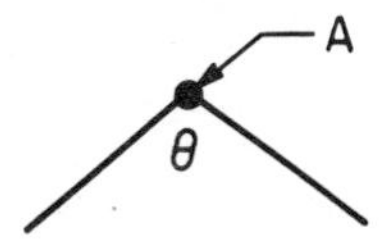

A-2.

A thin uniform trapdoor of mass m and width ℓ is hinged at one edge to a level floor and stands vertically. If allowed to fall, with what angular speed will it strike the floor? Neglect friction in the hinge.

A-3.

A mass m is hung from a string wound around a solid circular cylinder of mass M and radius r, pivoted on bearings of negligible friction as shown. Find the acceleration of m.

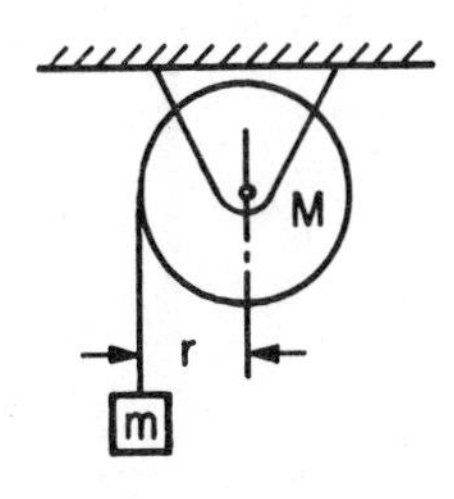

B-1.

Calculate the moments of inertia of the following rigid bodies, each of which has a mass m;

a) a thin, straight uniform rod of length L, about a perpendicular axis through one end;

b) a thin, straight, uniform rod of length L, about a perpendicular axis through its center;

c) a thin-walled hollow circular cylinder of radius r, about its axis, and

d) a solid circular cylinder of radius r, about its axis.

B-2.

Calculate the moment of inertia of the object shown, about the axis A which is perpendicular to the plane of the figure. The object consists of 4 semicircles of radius "a" of uniform thin wire, of total mass M.

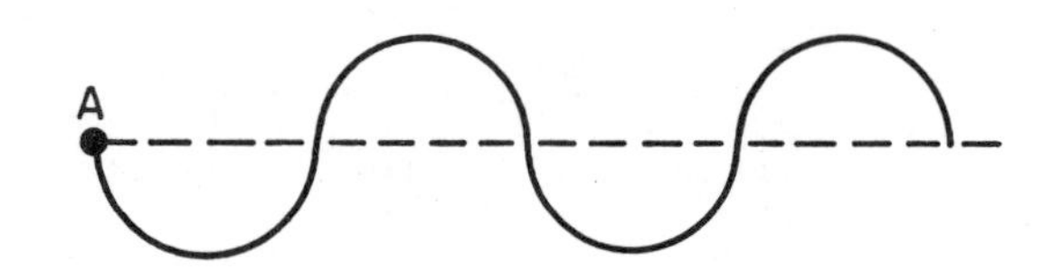

B-3.

A horizontal thin rod of mass M, length L rests at one end on a support and is suspended by a string at the other end. What force is exerted by the rod on the support immediately after the string is burned?

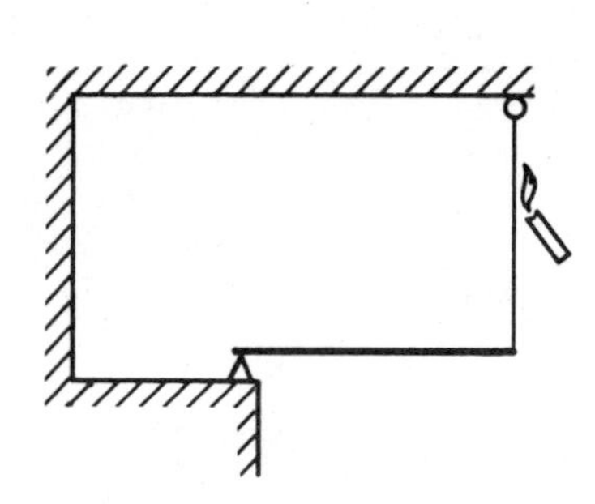

B-4.

Eight thin uniform rods, each of length L and mass m, are held in the form of a plane square by the framework of negligible mass shown dotted in Fig. A. The square is set rotating freely about a frictionless axle through O, perpendicular to the plane of the framework, with an angular speed of ω_0 rad s^{-1}. While thus rotating, an internal mechanism K, attached to the framework and with an unchanging moment of inertia about O of $\frac{40}{3} mL^2$, collapses the square to the cross shown in Fig. B. How much work was done by the mechanism in the collapsing process?

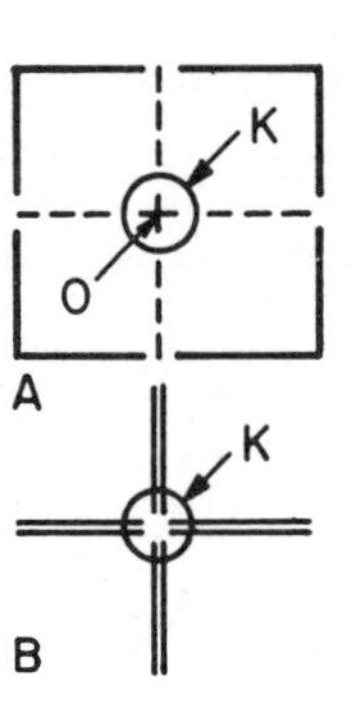

B-5.

a) Starting from rest, a symmetrical object rolls (without slipping) down an incline of height h. The moment of inertia of the object about its center of mass is I, the mass is M, and the radius of the rolling surface in contact with the incline is r. Determine the linear velocity of the center of mass at the bottom of the incline.
b) Apply the general equation of a) to determine the velocity of the center of mass if the object is

i) a sphere

ii) a disc

iii) a disc of mass M_1 and outer radius R_1, with a spindle of mass m_2 and radius r_2 on which the disc rolls.

B-6.

On an endless belt that is inclined at an angle θ with the horizontal, a uniform cylinder is placed, its axis horizontal and perpendicular to the edge of the belt. The surfaces are such that the cylinder can roll without slipping on the belt. How should the belt be caused to move so that, when released, the axis of the cylinder does not move?

B-7.

Two visually indistinguishable cylinders of equal mass and identical outside dimensions roll down an inclined plane. One of the cylinders reaches the bottom sooner than the other. What do you conclude from that? Justify your model of the composition of the two cylinders by calculating the observed effect.

B-8.

A spherical ball of radius R contains an empty spherical concentric hole of radius $r (r < R)$. The mass per unit volume, ρ, is constant between r and R. Express the moment of inertia I of the ball about an axis passing through the center in terms of r, R, and ρ, and also in terms of r, R, and the total mass M.

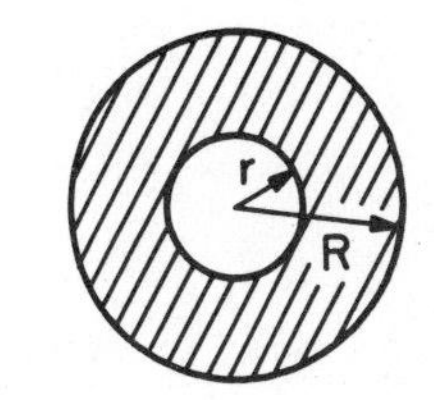

B-9.

A uniform, solid ball is placed at rest on an incline of slope angle θ. What is the minimum value μ_0 of the coefficient of static friction μ between ball and incline so that the ball will roll down the incline without slipping?

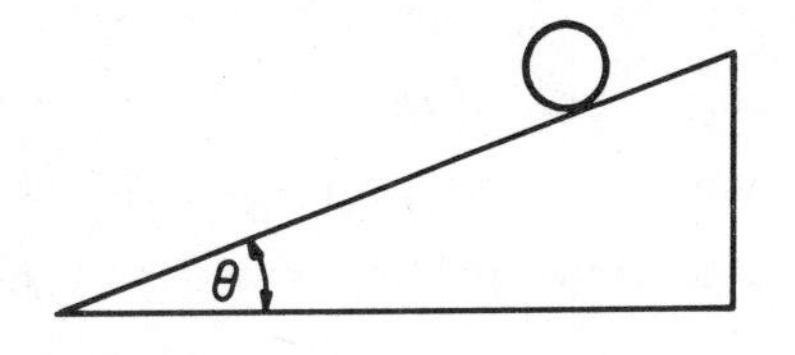

B-10.

A yo-yo like spool consists of two uniform discs, each of mass M and radius R, and an axle of radius r and negligible mass. A thread wound around the axle is attached to the ceiling, and the spool is released from rest a distance D below the ceiling.

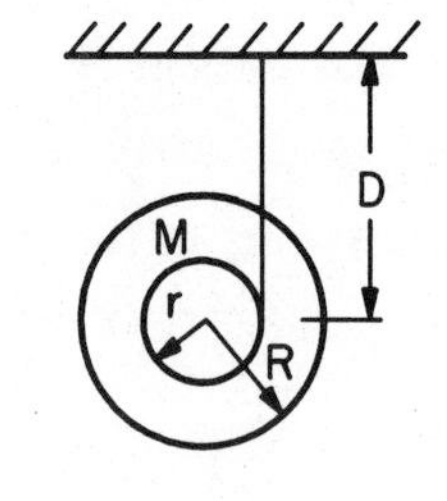

a) If there is to be no pendulum - like swinging motion, what angle should the thread make with the vertical as the spool is released?

b) What is the downward acceleration of the center of the spool?

B-11.

The hoop H of radius r, rolls without slipping down the incline. The starting height h is such that the hoop acquires a velocity just sufficient to "loop the loop"; i.e., the hoop just maintains contact with the circular track at point P. What is the h?

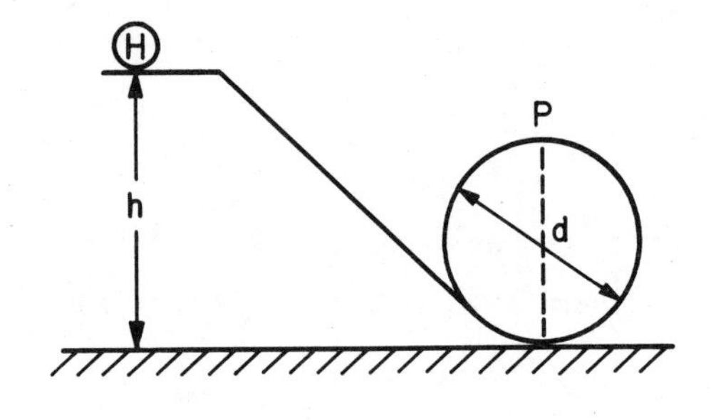

B-12.

An air puck of mass m moves on the surface of a horizontal table, guided by a string attached to m and passing downward through a small hole in the table top. Initially the length of string above the table is r_1, and the mass is set moving at speed v_1 in a circular path of this radius. The string is then pulled downward through the hole until an amount r_2 remains above the table. Find:

a) the final speed of the mass m;

b) the work required to pull the string through the hole from r_1 to r_2, and

c) the magnitude of the force needed to hold the radius constant, using the principle of conservation of energy.

B-13.

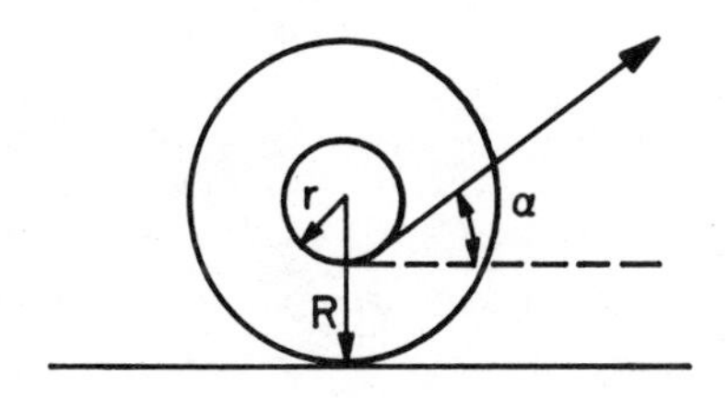

A yo-yo of mass M, outer radius R, and moment of inertia I, on a horizontal table is free to roll without slipping. A force F is applied at the inner radius r at an angle α with the horizontal.

a) Find the acceleration of the yo-yo, if the yo-yo does not rise from the table top.

b) How strong a force F at the angle α is needed in order to lift the yo-yo off the table?

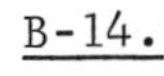

B-14.

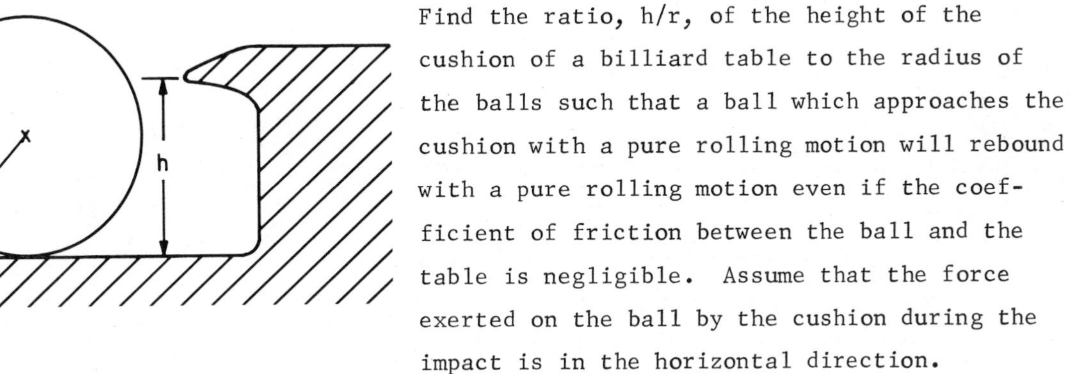

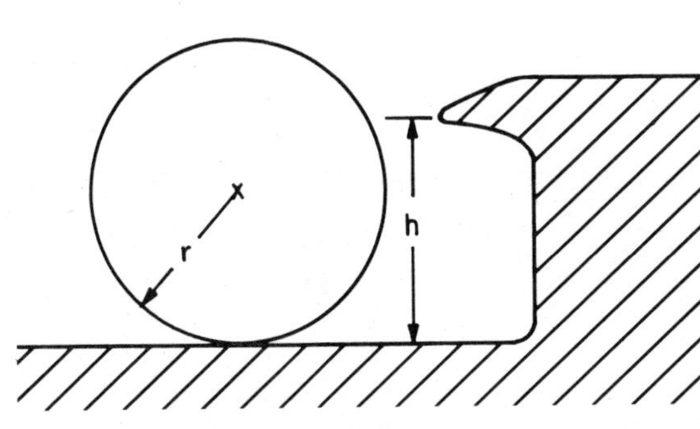

Find the ratio, h/r, of the height of the cushion of a billiard table to the radius of the balls such that a ball which approaches the cushion with a pure rolling motion will rebound with a pure rolling motion even if the coefficient of friction between the ball and the table is negligible. Assume that the force exerted on the ball by the cushion during the impact is in the horizontal direction.

C-1.

An irregular plate of metal of uniform thickness and mass M has its center of mass at C, and the moment of inertia for an axis perpendicular to the sheet is known, I_a. Under what conditions of r_1, r_2, and r_3 can one correctly express the moment of inertia for an axis through B, also perpendicular to the sheet, as

$$I_B = I_A + Mr_3^2 \quad ?$$

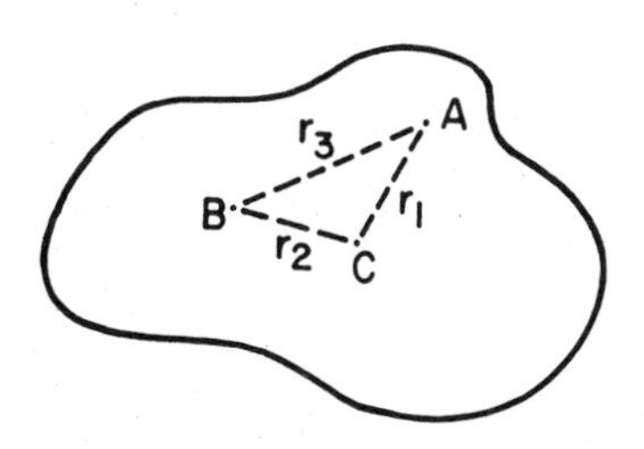

C-2.

An adaptation of an inking arrangement for a printing press is as shown in the figure. K is a firmly supported, but idling, inking roller of negligible moment of inertia; P is a driven press roll firmly supported and T is a transfer roll freely floating between K and P. T is a solid cylinder of radius r and mass M; it always rolls without slipping on both K and P, and the geometry is such that the line of centers TP is θ above the horizontal. What is the maximum angular acceleration A that can be given to P without T losing contact with K?

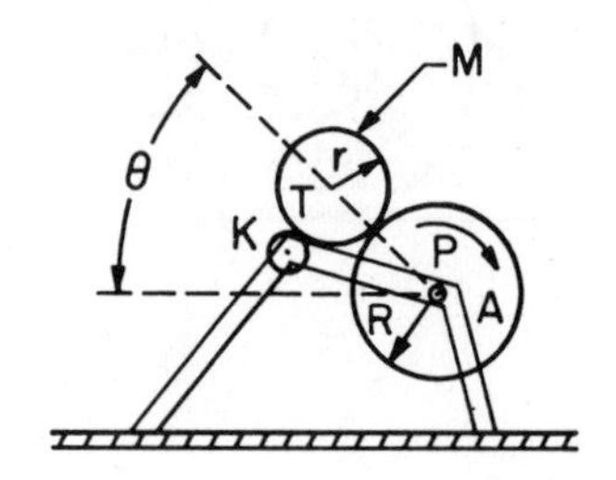

C-3.

A thin uniform rod of length 2ℓ rotating in a horizontal plane with angular velocity ω_0 about a fixed, vertical axis through its center is placed gently on a horizontal table having a coefficient of friction μ. How much time is required for the rod to stop its rotation? Assume that the rod is uniformly supported by the table (each element of length is supported by the table just beneath it).

C-4.

A uniform bowling ball of radius R and mass M is initially launched so that it is sliding with speed V_0 without rolling on an alley with a coefficient of friction μ. How far does the ball go before it starts rolling without slipping, and what is then its speed?

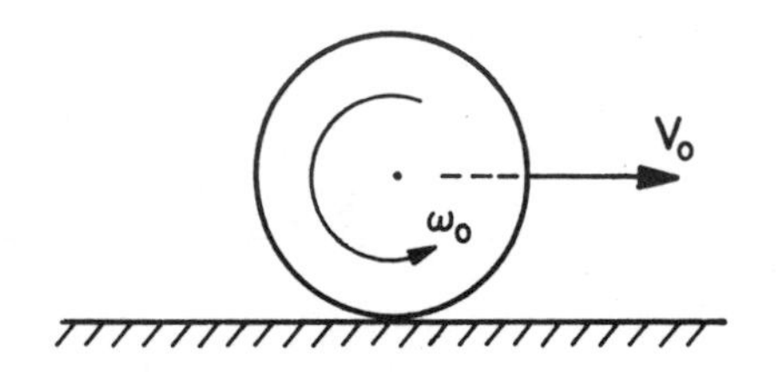

C-5.

An amusing trick is to press a finger down on a marble, on a horizontal table top, in such a way that the marble is projected along the table with an initial linear speed V_0 and an initial backward rotational speed ω_0, ω_0 being about a horizontal axis perpendicular to V_0. The coefficient of sliding friction between marble and top is constant. The marble has radius R.

a) What relationship must hold between V_0, R, and ω_0 for the marble to slide to a complete stop?

b) What relationship must hold between V_0, R, and ω_0 for the marble to skid to a stop and then start returning toward its initial position, with a final constant linear speed of 3/7 V_0?

C-6.

A uniform circular disc of radius R and mass M is arranged to spin freely with angular speed ω on a horizontal plane on a pivot P at its center. Pinned to its edge are two small masses m attached by cords of length ℓ wrapped around its periphery, as shown. While the disc is spinning, these masses are released simultaneously without disturbing the angular momentum of the system. Thereupon, the small masses fly off, their restraining cords being released from hooks H,H' when the cords extend radially outward. Find ℓ, the length of these cords such that the disc will be stopped by the action.

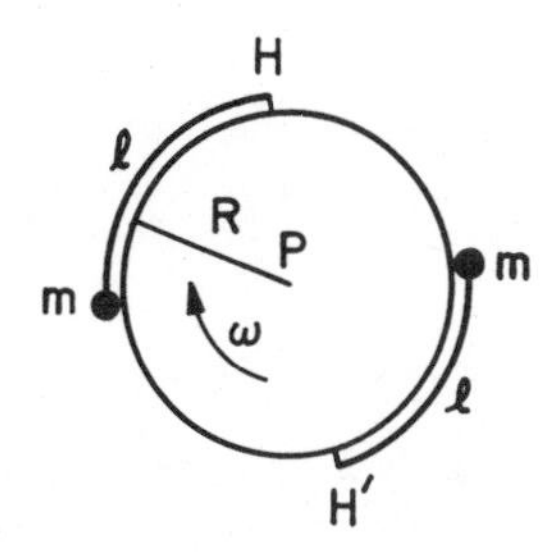

Note: This scheme has been used to reduce the spinning motion of satellite vehicles.

C-7.

If Moe (coordinates x', y') rotates relative to Joe (coordinates x,y), who is at rest, find the equations for the apparent force components that must act on a particle according to Moe and show that these consist of the components of the true force $\vec{F}$ as seen by Joe, plus two pseudo forces: a radial centripetal force and a Coriolis force at right angles to the velocity.

C-8.

Find the angular momentum of a planet of mass m moving in a circular orbit of radius R. Using this result, deduce that the distance of the moon from the earth will increase over a long period of time because of its tidal drag on the earth's rotation. Also, discuss the conservation of energy in the earth-moon system, from the standpoint of the possibility of escape of the moon.

CHAPTER 16

Rotation in Three Dimensions

Refer to the Feynman Lectures on Physics, Vol. I, Ch. 20.

1.

Any three vectors $\vec{A}$, $\vec{B}$, and $\vec{C}$ may be thought of as defining a solid body having six faces, parallel in pairs -- a parallelepiped. Show that the volume enclosed by such a figure is

$$V = |\vec{A}\cdot(\vec{B} \times \vec{C})|$$

2.

By writing the vectors in component form, or otherwise, prove the following vector equalities:

$$\vec{a} \times (\vec{b} + \vec{c}) = \vec{a} \times \vec{b} + \vec{a} \times \vec{c}$$
$$(\alpha\vec{a}) \times \vec{b} = \alpha(\vec{a} \times \vec{b})$$
$$\vec{a}\cdot(\vec{b} \times \vec{c}) = (\vec{a} \times \vec{b})\cdot\vec{c}$$
$$\vec{a} \times (\vec{b} \times \vec{c}) = \vec{b}(\vec{a}\cdot\vec{c}) - \vec{c}(\vec{a}\cdot\vec{b})$$
$$\vec{a} \times \vec{a} = 0$$
$$\vec{a}\cdot(\vec{a} \times \vec{b}) = 0$$

3.

A rigid body is rotating with an angular velocity $\vec{\omega}$ about a fixed axis. Show that the velocity of any point P in the body is $\vec{v} = \vec{\omega} \times \vec{r}$, where $\vec{r}$ is a vector from any point on the axis of rotation to the point P.

4.

A collection of N particles with masses m_i, positions $\vec{r}_i$, and velocities $\vec{v}_i$ have a certain angular momentum

$$\vec{L} = \sum \vec{r}_i \times \vec{p}_i = \sum m_i\vec{r}_i \times \vec{v}_i$$

On the other hand, as viewed in a coordinate system moving with their center of mass, suppose they have an angular momentum $\vec{L}_{CM}$. If $\vec{R}_{CM}$ and $\vec{V}_{CM}$ are the position and velocity of the CM, and $M = \sum m_i$ is the total mass of the particles, show that

$$\vec{L} = \vec{L}_{CM} + M\,\vec{R}_{CM} \times \vec{V}_{CM}$$

5.

A rigid body is rotated through an infinitesimal angle $\Delta\Theta_1$ about a certain axis and is then rotated through an infinitesimal angle $\Delta\Theta_2$ about some other axis intersecting the first axis at some point 0. Show that the net displacement of any point in the body is the same as it would be if it were instead rotated through a single infinitesimal angle about some intermediate axis, and show how to find this axis and angle. Use this to prove that a rigid body subjected simultaneously to angular velocities about various axes moves as it would with a single angular velocity equal to their vector sum, treating each angular velocity as a vector of length ω directed along the axis of rotation.

$$\vec{\omega} = \vec{\omega}_1 + \vec{\omega}_2$$

A-1.

A parallelpiped with one vertex at the origin has three adjacent vertices at the points (10, -5, 3), (3, -4, 7), and (-5, -6, 3) in rectangular coordinates (x,y,z). What is its volume?

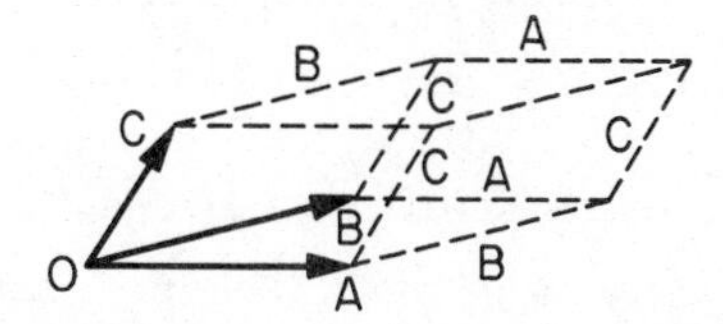

A-2.

If the polar icecaps were to melt, what would happen to the earth's period of rotation? Explain.

A-3.

How would you distinguish a hard-boiled egg from a raw egg (without cracking the shell)?

A-4.

A jet airplane in which all the engines rotate in the direction of a right-handed screw advancing in the flight direction is executing a left turn. Does the gyroscopic effect of the engines tend to cause the airplace to:

a) roll right
b) roll left
c) yaw right
d) yaw left
e) pitch up
f) pitch down

Why?

B-1.

Two equal masses are connected by a flexible string. An experimenter holds one mass in his hand and causes the other mass to whirl in a horizontal circle about the held mass; he then releases the held mass.

a) If the string breaks during the experiment, did it break before, or after he released the masses?

b) If the string does not break, describe the motion of the masses subsequent to their release.

B-2.

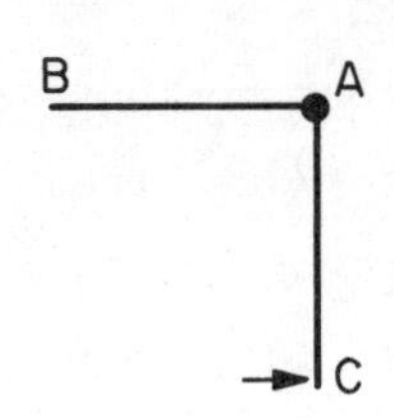

Two uniform, equal stiff rods AB and AC are freely hinged at A and placed on a smooth horizontal table with AC ⊥ AB. A horizontal blow is delivered perpendicular to AC at C. Find the ratio of the resulting linear velocities of the centers of mass of AB and of AC, immediately after this impulse.

B-3.

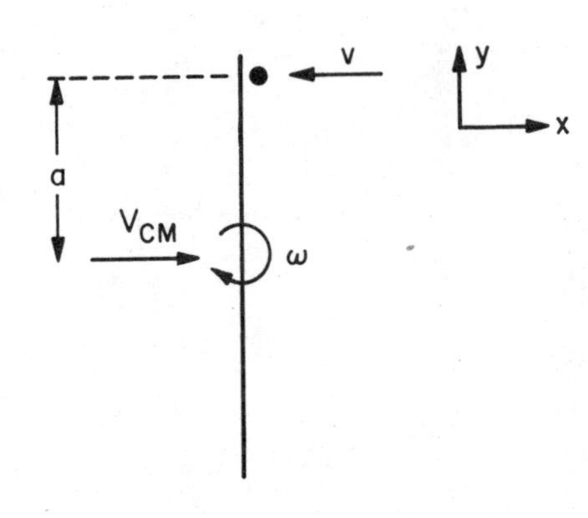

A thin uniform rod of mass M and length L and a puck of mass m slide without friction on a horizontal plane. At a certain instant the rod is perpendicular to the direction of its center of mass velocity, which is $\vec{V}_{cm} = +V\vec{i}$ and has angular velocity around its center of mass $\vec{\omega} = -\omega\vec{k}$. At this instant it is hit by the puck which was originally moving with velocity $\vec{v} = -v\vec{i}$. Find v and the distance a between the center of the rod and the point of contact which will leave the rod motionless after impact. Consider the collision perfectly elastic.

B-4.

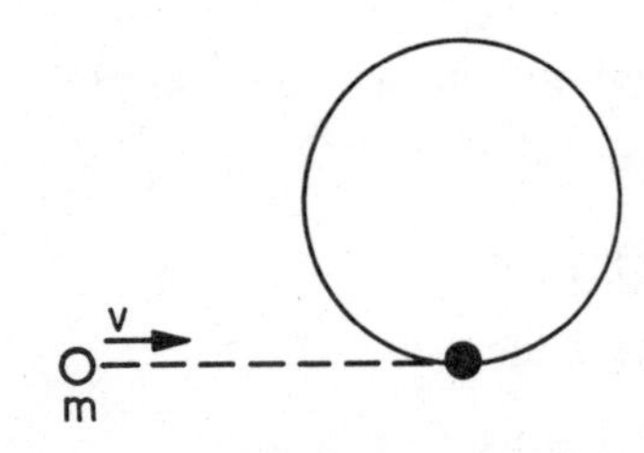

A thin circular wooden hoop of mass m and radius R rests on a horizontal frictionless plane. A bullet, also of mass m, moving with horizontal velocity v, strikes the hoop and becomes embedded in it as shown in the figure.
Calculate the center of mass velocity, the angular momentum of the system about the CM, the angular velocity ω of the hoop, and the kinetic energy of the system, before and after collision.

B-5.

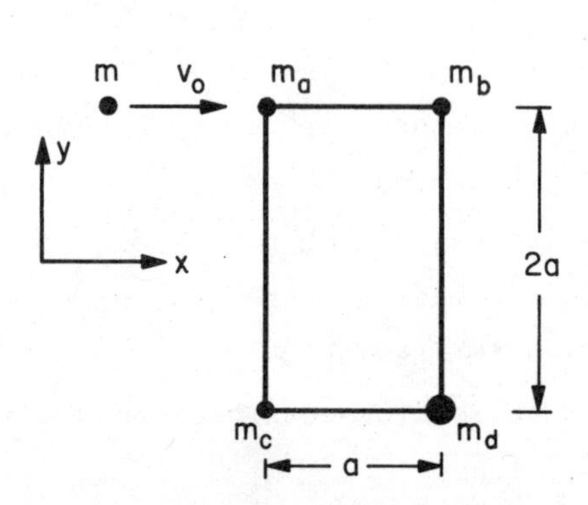

The 4 masses ($m_a = m_b = m_c = \frac{m_d}{2}$) shown lie on the corners of a rectangle on a frictionless horizontal surface. They are rigidly connected by rods of negligible weight. Another mass $m = m_a$ of velocity v_0 in the positive x-direction collides with m_a and sticks to it. Describe the motion of the object after collision.

B-6.

A uniform rod of length L and mass M is at rest on a frictionless horizontal surface. The rod receives an impulse $J = \int Fdt$ of very short duration applied at right angles to the rod at a point P where OP = r.

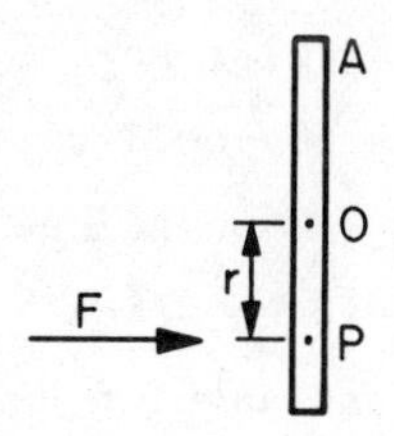

a) Just after the impulse, what is the velocity of the center of mass O? What is the angular velocity about O? What is the instantaneous velocity of the end point A?

b) Determine the distance AP for which the velocity of the point A is zero just after the impact.

c) If the rod is supported vertically from a pivot at A, where should a blow be struck to set the rod in rotation about A without exerting an initial sidewise force on the pivot?

B-7.

A thin rod of mass M and length L rests on a horizontal frictionless surface. A small piece of putty, also of mass M, and with velocity v directed perpendicularly to the rod, strikes one end and sticks, making an inelastic collision of very short duration.

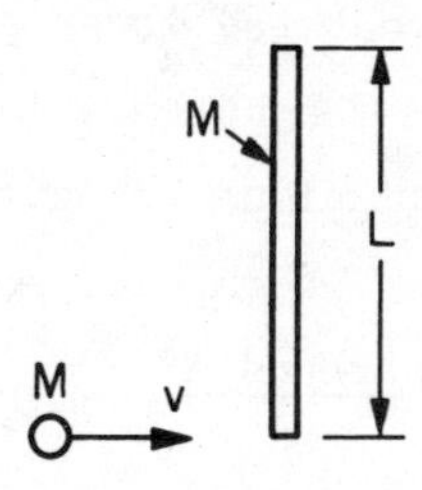

a) What is the velocity of the center of mass of the system before and after the collision?

b) What is the angular momentum of the system about its center of mass just before the collision?

c) What is the angular velocity (about the center of mass) just after the collision?

d) How much kinetic energy is lost in the collision?

B-8.

Two equal, rigid rods of length L and mass M are free to move without friction on a horizontal surface. Initially, one rod is stationary and the other is translating at speed V along a line perpendicular to the two rods. (See figure.) The rods collide in such a way that the center of one meets one end of the other, and they henceforth stick together. Find the linear speed and angular velocity of the composite rod after impact.

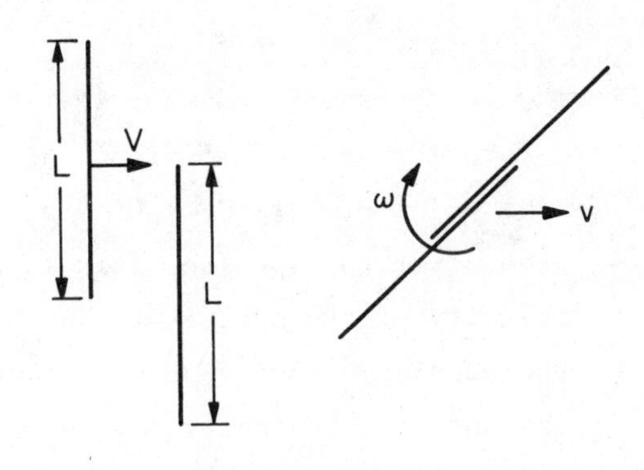

B-9.

A thin uniform rod AB of mass M and length L is free to rotate in a vertical plane about a horizontal axle at end A. A piece of putty, also of mass M, is thrown with velocity V horizontally at the lower end B while the bar is at rest. The putty sticks to the bar. What is the minimum velocity of the putty before impact which will make the bar rotate all the way around A?

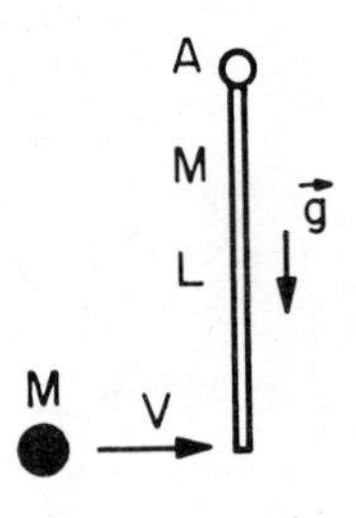

B-10.

A thin rigid board of mass M, width w, and length ℓ is suspended vertically from a frictionless horizontal axis at its top edge. A bullet of mass m, traveling with velocity v perpendicular to the board, lodges in the center of the board.

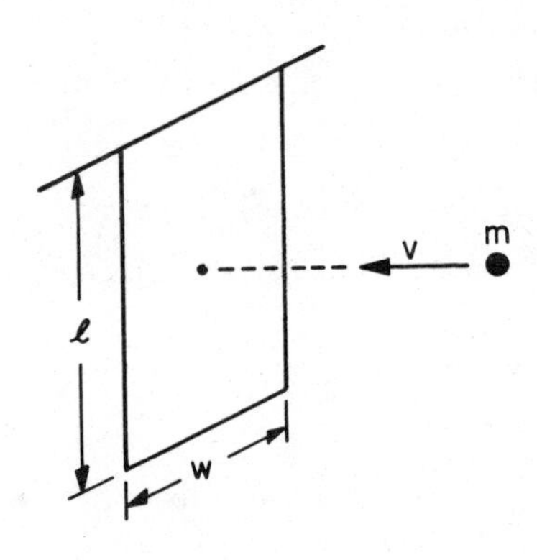

a) Just after impact, what is the speed of the bullet?

b) Through how large an angle θ will the system turn?

c) What impulse is felt by the bearings supporting the axis?

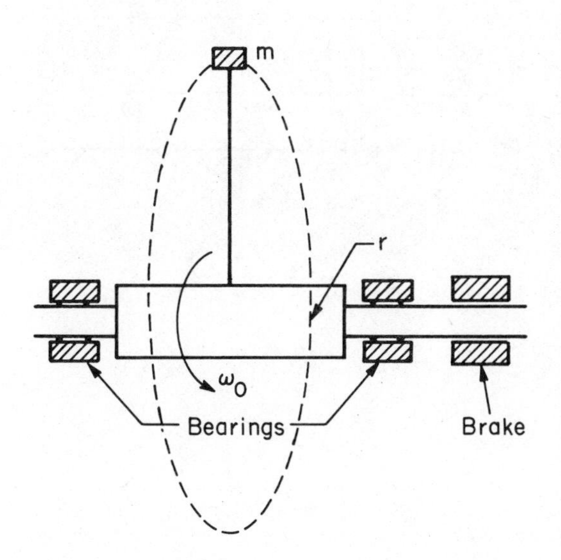

B-11.

A horizontal spindle, of radius r and moment of inertia about its axis of I_0, has attached to it a cord which in turn is attached to a mass m (whose dimensions are small compared to the other dimensions in the problem). Originally the spindle is rotated about its horizontal axis with a constant angular speed ω_0, and the mass m swings with the same angular speed in a vertical circle of radius R. ω_0 is so large that the effect of gravity is negligible. At t = 0, a brake is actuated, stopping the motion of the spindle in a few degrees of rotation.

a) What angular impulse did the brake have to supply?

b) When the cord has wound itself exactly ten times around the spindle, it breaks. What was its breaking strength? (Warning: angular momentum is not conserved after the spindle is stopped: can you see why?)

B-12.

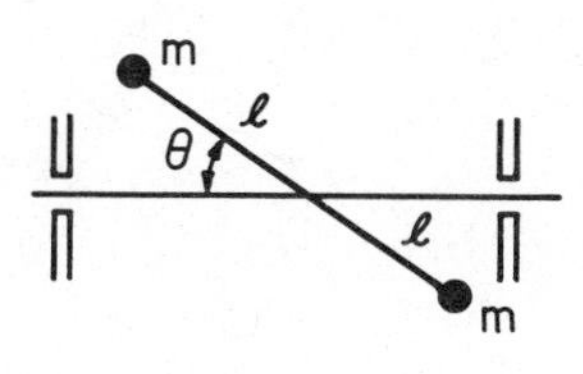

Two rods, each of length ℓ, each with a mass m attached at its end, are clamped at an angle θ to a shaft as shown. (The shaft and rods are in the same plane.) What torque must the bearings be able to withstand, if the clamping angle θ can be set anywhere from zero to 90°, and the maximum angular velocity of the shaft is ω? (Neglect mass of rods and treat the m's as point masses.)

B-13.

A uniform thin rod of mass M and length ℓ is mounted at its center of mass on an axis inclined 45° to its length.

a) What is the direction of the angular momentum vector with respect to the axis of rotation?

b) What is the bearing torque of this rod rotating at angular velocity ω?

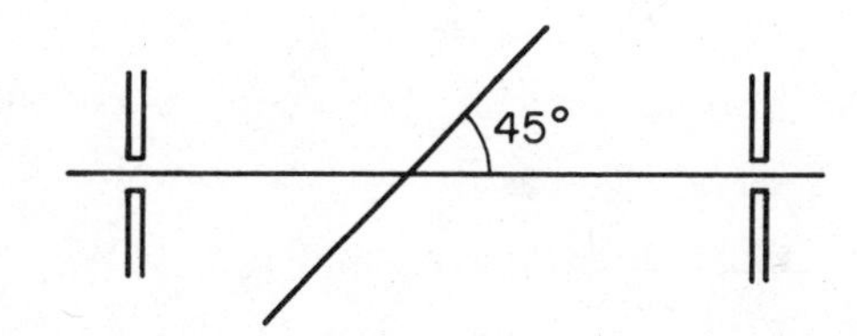

B-14.

A thin solid wheel on a horizontal axle is constrained to travel in a circle of radius R on a horizontal table. The axle pivots freely in all directions about the point A, which is fixed on the vertical driveshaft. If the mass of the wheel is m, its radius r, and its angular velocity about its axis is $\vec{\omega}$, with what force does it press on the table?

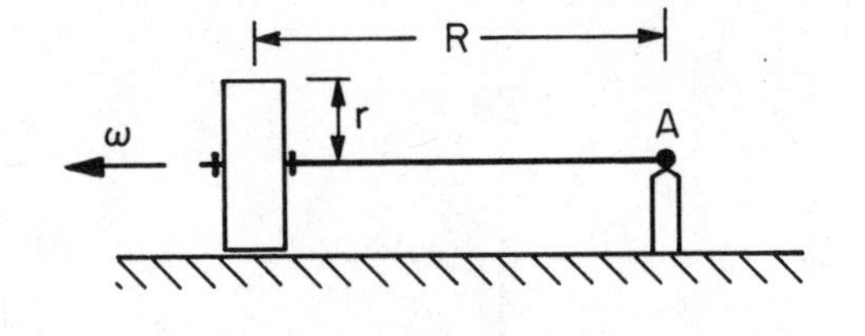

Use:

$m = 1$ kg $\qquad$ $R = 50$ cm

$r = 10$ cm $\qquad$ $\omega = 12000$ rad/min

B-15.

A turntable T_1, at rest, has mounted on it a turntable T_2 rotating with angular velocity ω. At a certain time an internal clutch acts on the axle of T_2 to stop it with respect to T_1, but T_1 is free to revolve. T_1 alone has mass M_1 and moment of inertia I_1 about an axis A_1 through its center perpendicular to its plane; and T_2 has mass M_2 and I_2 about a similarly situated axis A_2; the distance between A_1 and A_2 is r. Find Ω for T_1 after T_2 stops. (Ω is the angular velocity of T_1.)

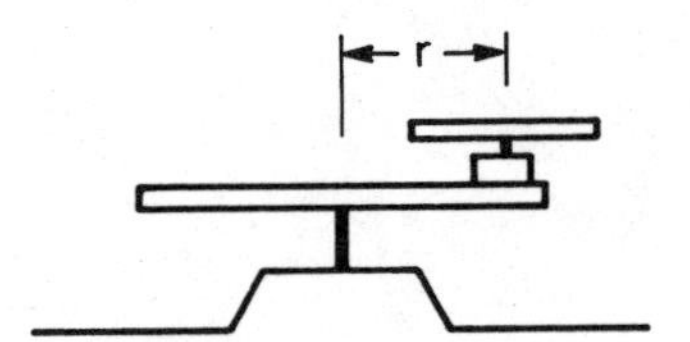

B-16.

A man stands on a rotating platform at a distance R from the center. He throws a a ball at speed V to another man diametrically opposite to him on the platform, also at radius R. If the platform turns with angular velocity ω,

a) What is the radius of curvature of the ball's trajectory, as seen in the rotating system?

b) At what angle with respect to the diameter should the throw be aimed. (Show on a diagram.)

c) What does the trajectory look like to a stationary observer? Note: Assume $V \gg \omega R$ so centrifugal pseudo force may be ignored.)

B-17.

A certain satellite vehicle is approximately a uniform circular cylinder of mass m, radius a, and length L, with $L = 6a$. It is initially spinning at angular velocity ω_0 about its long axis, but because of small internal vibrations (due to a slight precessional motion at the start), energy is gradually transformed into heat. As a result, the satellite "slows down". Describe the only possible final state of rotation, and find the corresponding angular velocity, if as much energy as possible is transformed into heat. Assume that no outside influences are present.

B-18.

If all the ice on earth were to melt, the height of mean sea level would increase by about 200 ft. Taking the mean latitude of the existing ice caps as 80°, and neglecting the irregular distribution of the oceans, by about how many seconds would the length of the day increase? Assume the earth is a sphere of radius 6370 km and moment of inertia 8.11×10^{37} kg m^2.

B-19.

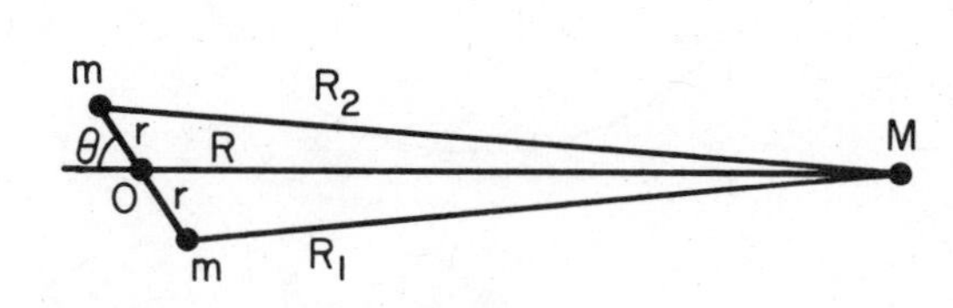

Two equal masses m are fixed on a massless rod a distance 2r apart, and are attracted gravitationally by a mass M, situated at a distance $R \gg r$ from the center O of the rod. The rod makes an angle θ with R. Find the approximate value of the torque on the rod about its center.

C-1.

The elastic restoring torque exerted by a torsion fiber is proportional to the angle of twist: $\tau_{fiber} = -k\Theta$.

a) Show that the potential energy of such a fiber twisted through an angle Θ is $U = 1/2\, k\Theta^2$.

b) The deflecting torque exerted on a galvanometer coil is given by the expression

$$\tau = n\,AB\,i$$

where i = current through the coil

n = number of turns of wire on the coil

B = the magnetic field produced by the permanent galvanometer magnet.

In a laboratory experiment, the charge on a capacitor is measured by discharging the capacitor through a galvanometer coil and noting the resulting maximum deflection. Here $|i| = |dq/dt|$, and the discharge takes place so quickly that the galvanometer coil does not appreciably move away from its initial $\Theta = 0$ position during the time that current flows. Neglecting friction, show that the maximum "throw" of the galvanometer is proportional to the initial charge on the capacitor.

C-2.

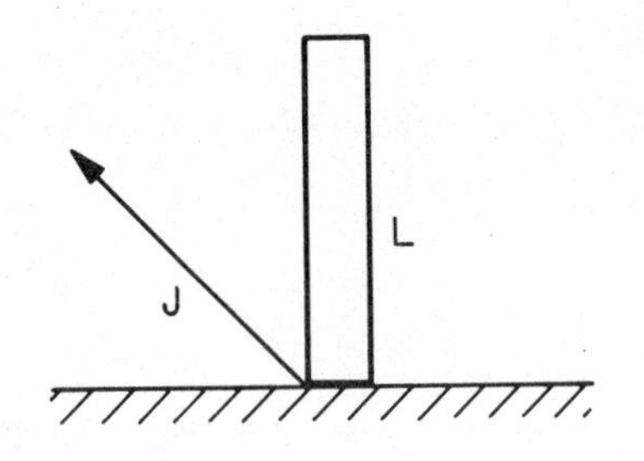

An upright rod of mass M and length L is given an impulse J at its base, directed at 45° upward from the horizontal, which sends the rod flying. What value(s) should J have so that the rod lands vertically again? (i.e., upright on the end at which J was applied).

C-3.

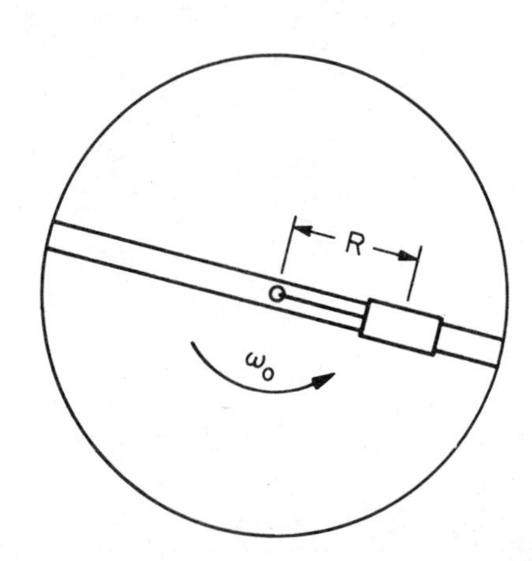

A turntable of moment of inertia I_0 rotates freely on a hollow vertical axis. A cart of mass m runs without friction on a straight radial track on the turntable. A cord attached to the cart passes over a small pulley and then downward through the hollow axis. Initially the entire system is rotating at angular speed ω_0, and the cart is at a fixed radius R from the axis. The cart is then pulled inward by applying an excess force to the cord, and eventually arrives at radius r, where it is allowed to remain.

a) What is the new angular velocity of the system?

b) Show in detail that the difference in the energy of the system between the two conditions is equal to the work done by the centripetal force.

c) If the cord is released, with what radial speed $\dot{r}$ will the cart pass the radius R?

C-4.

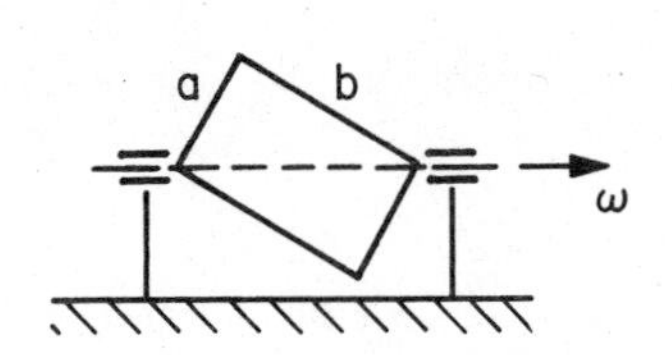

A thin rectangular plate of mass M, sides a,b, rotates about an axis along its diagonal with angular velocity ω.

a) What are the forces on the bearings?

b) What is the kinetic energy of the rotating plate?

C-5.

A flywheel having the shape of a uniform thin circular plate of mass 10.0 kg and radius 1.00 m is mounted on a shaft passing through its CM but making an angle of $1^{\circ}0'$ with its plane. If it rotates about this axis with angular velocity 25.0 radians s^{-1}, what torque must be supplied by the bearings?

C-6.

A uniform thin disc of radius R, mass M is mounted on a universal bearing permitting rotation about any axis. Initially it spins about a vertical axis (z-direction) with angular velocity ω_0. A small mass m with velocity v_0 in the positive z-direction collides elastically with the rim of the wheel and rebounds in the negative z-direction.

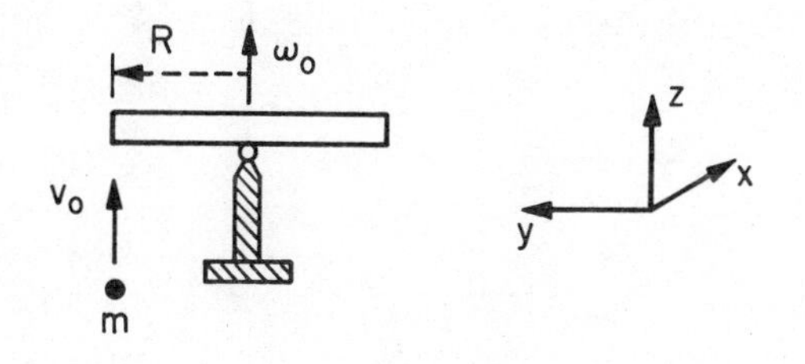

a) What is the direction of the angular momentum of the disc after the collision?

b) Describe the motion of the figure axis. Indicate by a sketch the trajectory of the point of intersection of the figure axis with a unit sphere as seen from the top.

C-7.

A pair of 10 cm radius, 2 kg disc flywheels with "frictionless" bearings are spinning at 1000 rad/s and are supported at a distance d = 15 cm on either side of a universal bearing by a small diameter bar AB of mass M = 1 kg and length 4d, as shown.

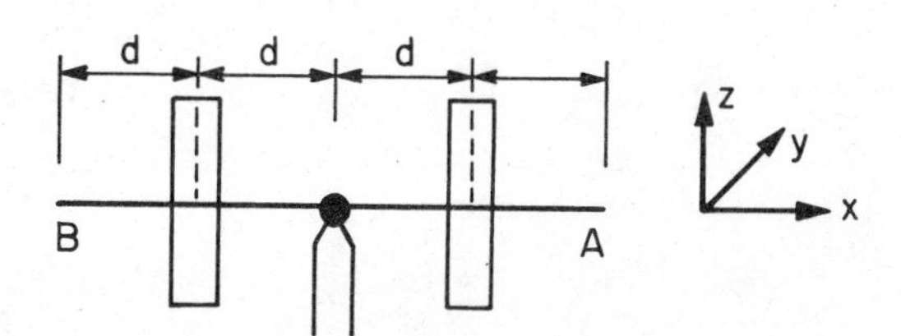

a) If a ball of mass m = 10 g is dropped from a height h = 5 cm onto the tip A of the bar and rebounds upwards, give the components of the resulting angular momentum of the flywheels and sketch the motion of the tip of the bar as seen from the +x direction. Also, give the angular velocity of this motion and the radius of the circle described by the tip once circular motion is attained.

b) If the same ball instead were attached to the tip A, then what would be the angular velocity of precession Ω, neglecting nutation? What would be the angular momentum and the rotational kinetic energy associated with Ω? How much potential energy is lost as the tip sinks below the x-y plane?

C-8.

The moon and the sun both exert a torque upon the earth because of the earth's oblateness. Which body exerts the greater torque and by approximately what factor?
Hint: You may wish to make use of the accidental fact that the two bodies subtend almost equal angles in the sky as seen from earth.
2nd Hint: The mean density of the sun is 1.41 g cm^{-3}, and that of the moon is 3.34 g cm^{-3}.

C-9.

The equatorial and polar radii of the earth are 6378.388 km and 6356.912 km. Its specific gravity ρ at various depths D below the surface are shown in the table below (* denotes a discontinuity).

D(km)	ρ
0	2.60
30*	3.0 / 3.3
100	3.4
200	3.5
400	3.6
1000	4.7
2000	5.2
2900*	5.7 / 9.4
3500	10.2
5000*	11.5 / 16.8
6000	17.1

Using these values, estimate:

a) The moment of inertia of the earth.

b) Its rotational angular momentum.

c) Its rotational kinetic energy, and

d) The time required for the rotational axis to precess about the pole of the ecliptic due to the torques of the moon and the sun.

(The tilt of the earth's axis is $23\ 1/2^{\circ}$.)

CHAPTER 17

The Harmonic Oscillator. Linear Differential Equations

Refer to the Feynman Lectures on Physics, Ch. 21.

1.

Show that the small amplitude oscillations of a rigid body which is suspended a distance D above its center of mass, are described by

$$\frac{d^2\theta}{dt^2} + \frac{MDg}{I}\,\theta = 0$$

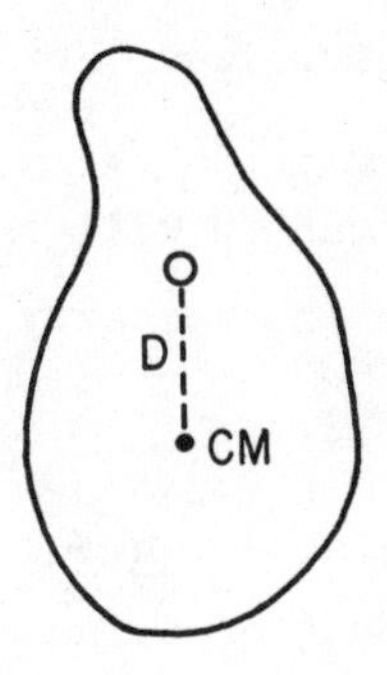

and that the period of oscillation T is given by

$$T = 2\pi\sqrt{\frac{I}{MgD}}$$

where M is the mass of the body and I is the moment of inertia about the suspension axis.

A-1.

Which (if either) of the masses shown moves in SHM (i.e., sinusoidal motion)?

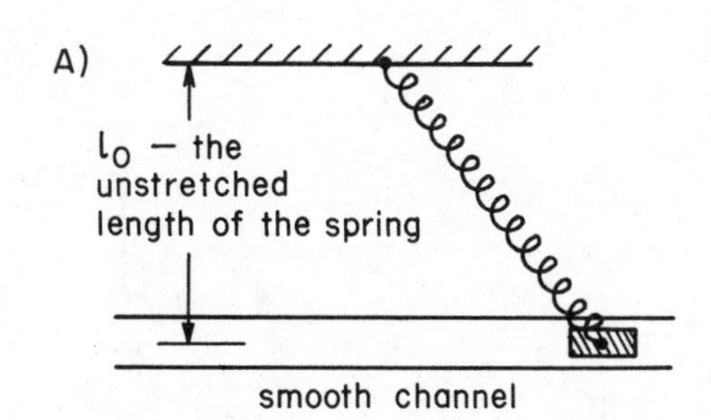

B) $\theta \ll 1$

R

rolls without slipping

A-2.

A uniform rod of mass M, length L swings as a pendulum with two horizontal springs of negligible mass and constants k_1, k_2 acting at the bottom end. Both springs are relaxed when the rod is vertical. What is the period of small oscillations?

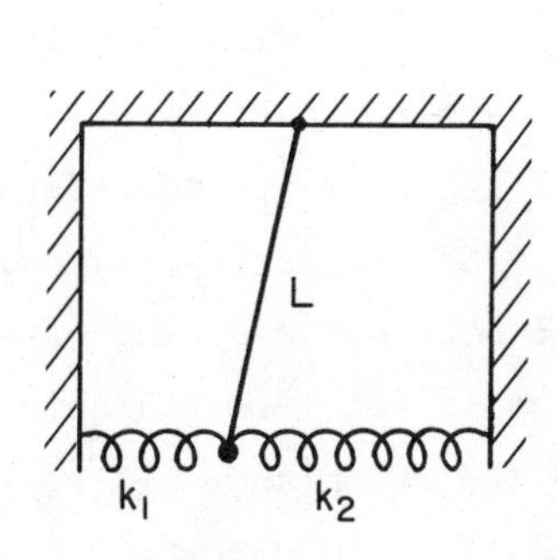

A-3.

In terms of the maximum amplitude A, how far from the equilibrium position is a simple, undamped mechanical harmonic oscillator when its kinetic energy is exactly equal to its potential energy?

A-4.

Two particles A and B execute harmonic motion of the same amplitude (10 cm) on the same straight line. For particle A, $\omega_A = 20\ s^{-1}$; for B, $\omega_B = 21\ s^{-1}$. If at t = 0, they both pass through x = 0 in the positive x-direction (hence are then "in phase"),

a) How far apart will they be at t = 0.350 s?

b) What is the velocity of B relative to A at 0.350 s?

A-5.

A vertical U tube manometer of constant internal cross-section A contains a total length of liquid L. Find the period of oscillation of the liquid. Neglect friction and assume that the amplitude of oscillation is such that the two liquid surfaces remain within the straight vertical portions of the tube.

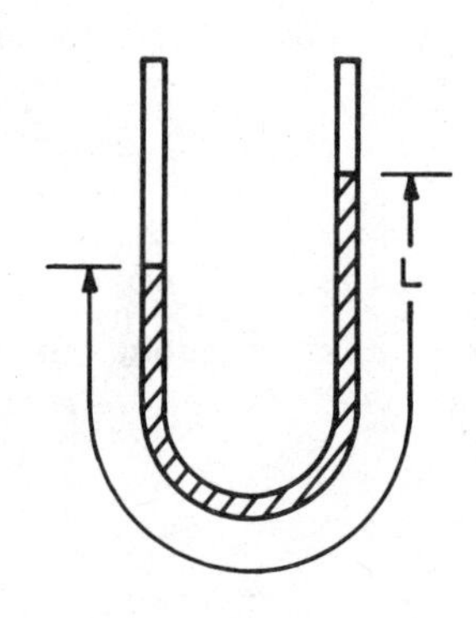

A-6.

In its initial stages, a colony of bacteria grows at a rate proportional to the number of bacteria present. Write the differential equation which expresses this relationship.

B-1.

A flat disc of radius R, mass M, is suspended at its rim with a torsion wire, which has a torsional constant K. What is the period of torsional oscillation?

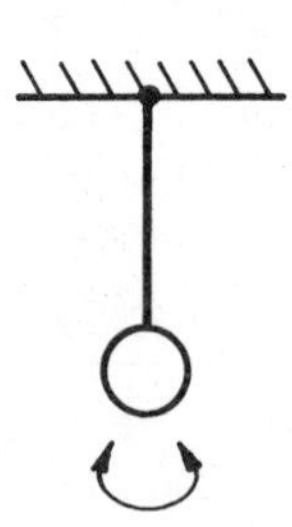

B-2.

A frame made of stiff wire of uniform cross section and density consists of a semi-circular arc ACB with its diameter AB. It is hung from a frictionless pin P passing through a hole at the midpoint of its diameter, and is set into vibration as a pendulum in its own plane. If the diameter of the frame AB is 50 cm, what is the period of the oscillating motion for small arcs?

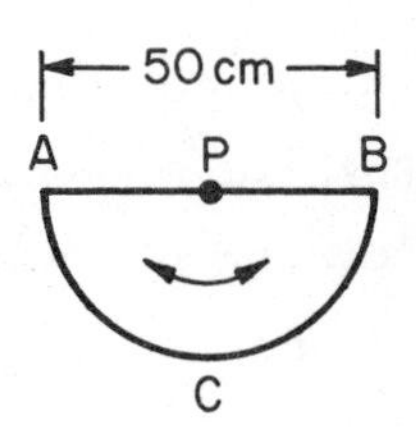

B-3.

Consider an ideal wheel of mass M, and moment of inertia I_c about its frictionless axle. The wheel is suspended from a hanger of length d, of negligible mass and moment of inertia, which is free to move in the plane of the wheel about a pivot point at X. (See figure.) The hanger and wheel are released from rest simultaneously when the hanger makes an angle θ_0 with the vertical through X. ($\theta_0 \ll 1$). For each of the two cases below, A and B,

a) Find the period of the motion of the hanger;

b) Find the angular acceleration $\ddot{\theta}$ when $\theta = \theta_0$; and

c) Find the angular velocity $\dot{\theta}$ when $\theta = 0$.

A. When the wheel is free to turn without friction about the axis C.

B. When the wheel and hanger are locked together and constrained to move together about X as a rigid body.

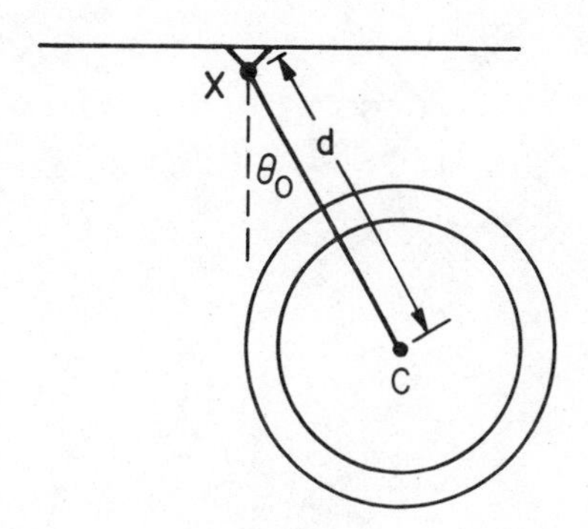

B-4.

Two uniform, circular plane wheels of equal mass 1.00 kg are mutually pivoted about a horizontal axis A, perpendicular to both bodies and passing through their centers of mass. The radii of gyration k of the two bodies are also equal: k = .20 m. Body 2 is pivoted about a fixed horizontal axis B, a distance k from its CM. Initially, body 2 is motionless and body 1 is rotating at angular velocity ω_0 about the common axis. A small latch pin C, fixed in body 1, suddenly drops into a hole in body 2, stopping their relative motion. It is observed that the resulting pendular motion of the system has an amplitude of 90° each side of the vertical. Find ω_0.

B-5.

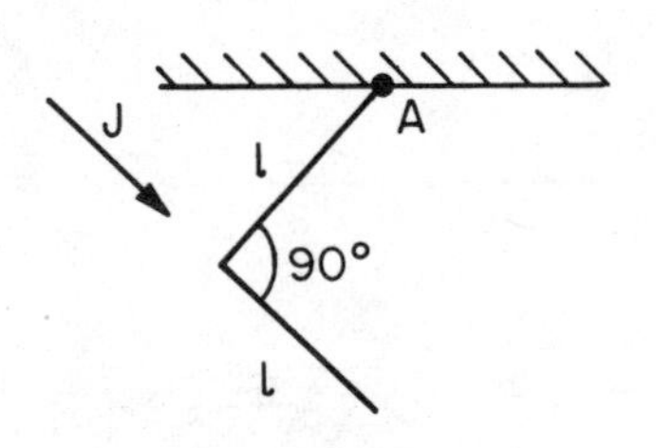

An L-shaped uniform, rigid bar of mass M with legs each of length ℓ hangs from its upper end A, pivoted to swing freely in its own plane.

a) At what angle θ (with vertical) does it hang when at rest?

b) If an impulse J is applied at the elbow in the direction shown, producing thereafter undamped, small oscillations, find $\theta(t)$ if J was applied at t = 0.

B-6.

The gravitational force felt by a particle embedded in a solid uniform sphere, due to the mass of the sphere only, is directly proportional to the distance of the particle from the center of the sphere. If the earth were such a sphere, with a narrow hole drilled through it along a polar diameter, how long would it take a body dropped in the hole to reach the surface at the opposite side of the earth?

B-7.

Derive the equations of motion and find the period of oscillation for the two systems shown.

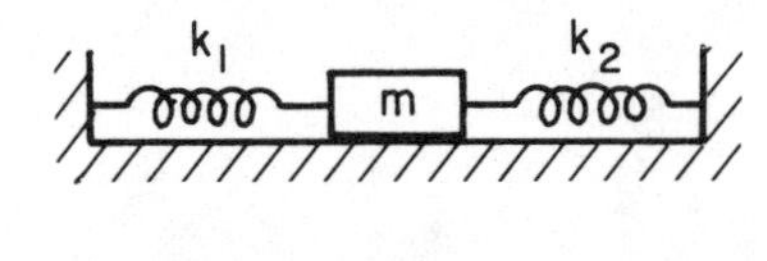

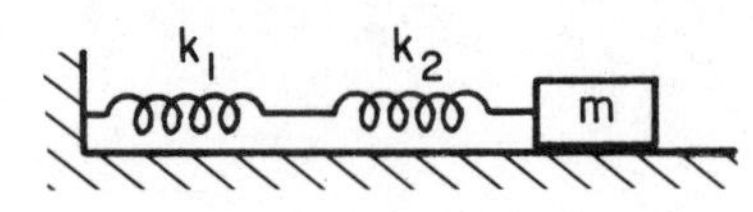

m moves on in a straight line on a frictionless horizontal plane under the influence of two springs with spring constants k_1 and k_2, respectively. The springs exert no force at the equilibrium point.

B-8.

Two particles, of mass 3M/4 and M, are connected by a massless spring of free length L and force constant k. These masses are initially at rest L apart on a horizontal frictionless table. A particle of mass M/4, moving with speed v along the line joining the two connected masses, collides with and sticks to the particle of mass 3M/4. Find the amplitude and period with which the spring between the two masses vibrates.

B-9.

Two unequal masses (m_1 = m; m_2 = 2m) rest on a frictionless table. If the spring (spring constant K) is compressed a distance d, with m_2 resting against the wall, and then the system is released from rest, find:

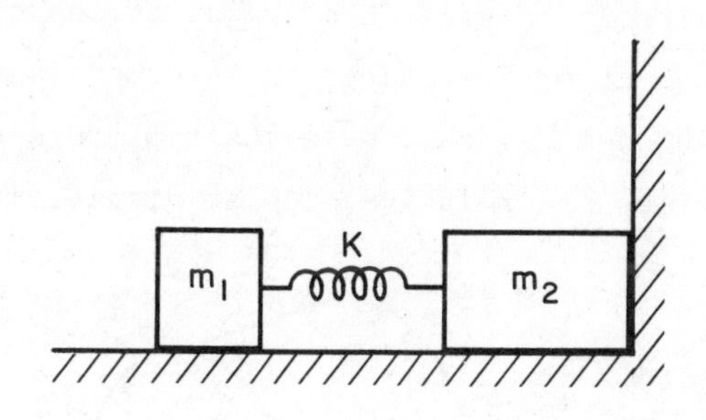

a) How far mass m_1 moves before m_2 starts moving.

b) After m_2 has lost contact with the wall, what is the velocity of the C.M. and amplitude of oscillation?

B-10.

Two gliders of different mass are sliding along a horizontal air trough with velocity v_0. They are held together with a clamp which compresses a spring of force constant K between them. The spring is displaced by an amount X from its uncompressed position. The clamp suddenly gives way (or is released) and the compressed spring forces the two masses apart. Neglect the mass of the spring. Let the masses of the gliders (M_1 and M_2) be unequal. Find the final velocities of gliders M_1 and M_2.

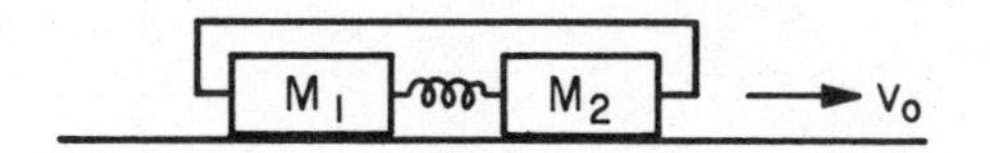

B-11.

Given the undamped horizontal mechanical oscillator shown. Find the maximum amplitude of oscillation such that the upper mass will not slip on the lower mass. The coefficient of friction between the masses is μ.

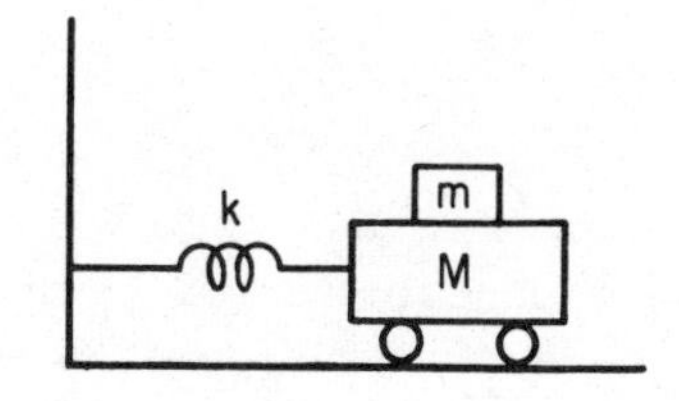

B-12.

A 200 gram mass oscillates on a horizontal guide under the influence of a light spring. Its maximum kinetic energy is 10^6 ergs, and its period is 1 s.

a) What is the total system energy?

b) What is the force constant of the spring?

c) What is the amplitude of the oscillation?

B-13.

The rotating element of a jet engine consists of a turbine disc (with blades) having a moment of inertia I_1 and a compressor (with blades) having a moment of inertia I_2 connected together by a shaft of torsional stiffness k (the torque in the shaft is k times the relative angular displacement between turbine and compressor).(B = bearings.)

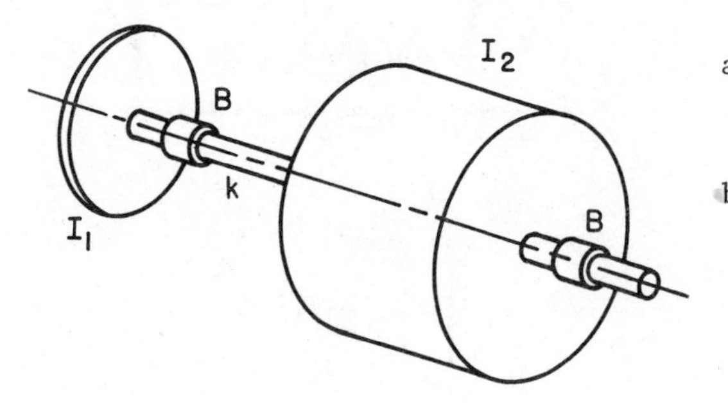

a) What is the frequency of torsional oscillation of the engine rotor?

b) What is the ratio of the amplitudes of torsional oscillations of the turbine and compressor?

C-1.

The position of the fluorescent spot on an oscilloscope screen is frequently determined by two harmonic voltages applied to the x and y axis, respectively.

$$x = A_x \cos(\omega t + \delta_x)$$

$$y = A_y \cos(\omega t + \delta_y)$$

Sketch and discuss the curve defined by the motion of the fluorescent spot for the following cases:

a) $\delta_x = \delta_y$

b) $\delta_x = \delta_y + \frac{\pi}{2}$

$A_x = A_y$

c) $\delta_x = \delta_y + \frac{\pi}{2}$

$A_x \neq A_y$

d) $\delta_x = \delta_y - \frac{\pi}{4}$

$A_x = A_y$

e) $\delta_x = \delta_y - \alpha$

$A_x \neq A_y$

C-2.

The bifilar pendulum shown in the figure consists of a rod of length L, mass M, suspended by two thin threads of length ℓ which are separated by the distance $d < L$. Find the period of oscillation for small amplitudes.

a) If the rod swings like an ordinary pendulum

b) If it oscillates about its CM.

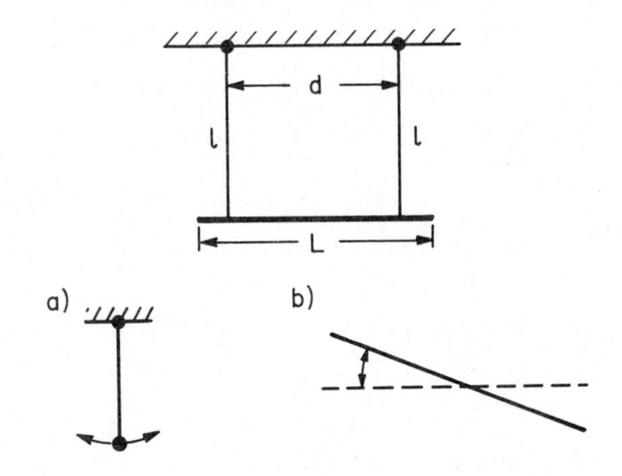

C-3.

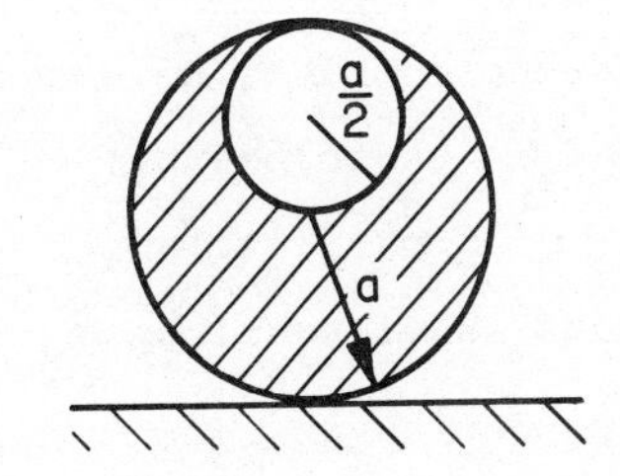

A solid circular cylinder of radius a has a hole of radius 1/2 a drilled through it parallel to its axis and 1/2 a from it, as shown in the figure. The cylinder is placed on a horizontal plane on which it rolls without slipping. Find the period of oscillation for small displacements from its equilibrium position.

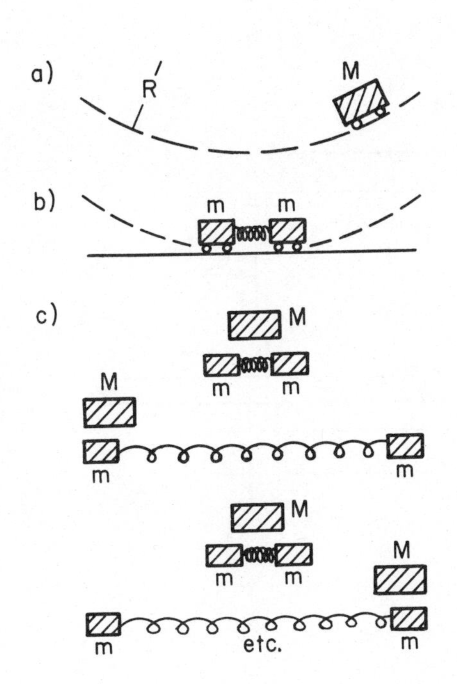

C-4.

A mass M, on small frictionless wheels, is allowed to oscillate transversely in a cylindrical trough of radius R, with an amplitude A $\ll$ R, as shown in a). Then two identical masses m, also mounted on small, frictionless wheels, are connected by a compressed, massless spring of spring constant K, are placed on a horizontal surface adjacent and parallel to the path of M as shown in b). At the instant M passes the bottom of the trough the cocked spring is released and the subsequent motion at quarter cycles for M is shown in c). What is the value of m?

C-5.

Two gliders in a frictionless air-trough have respective masses m_1 and m_2. They are connected by a massless spring of spring constant k. They are pulled apart a distance A over the rest length of the spring and then released from rest.

a) Find the oscillation periods of m_1 and m_2.
b) Compare the period with the one of a single mass oscillator. Which physical concept, typical for relative motion of two bodies, do you discover?
c) Find the energy of oscillation.
d) How do m_1 and m_2 share this energy?

C-6.

A simple pendulum consists of a mass M at the end of a massless rod of length L, freely pivoted so as to be able to swing in a full 360° arc. The period of the pendulum for small oscillations is 2π sec. If the pendulum is carefully balanced at its top (unstable) equilibrium position and is then given a tiny push of 1 mm s^{-1}, how long does it take the mass to move 10 cm? (assume the usual "linear system" approximations are valid over this distance, but not of course for the full circular swing.)

C-7.

One end of a torsion rod is fastened to the center of a turntable which moves on frictionless bearings about its vertical axis of symmetry; and the other end of the rod is clamped at a point on the extended axis. The torque constant of the rod is κ, the total moment of inertia of the system is I. Initially the turntable executes an undamped angular simple harmonic motion of maximum amplitude θ_0. A dart of mass m falls vertically onto the turntable at a distance a from the axis when the turntable is passing through the equilibrium position; its needle point becomes firmly embedded, essentially instantaneously. Find θ_0', the new maximum amplitude. Neglect any spin of the dart about its axis, and assume its thickness is small compared with a.

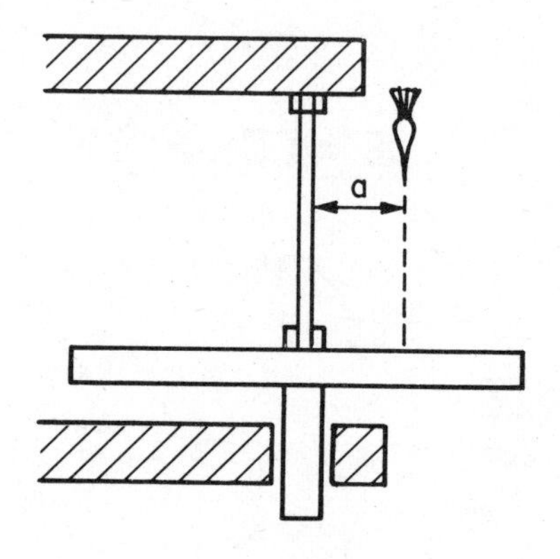

C-8.

A certain rigid body of mass M is supported on a frictionless horizontal axis which lies a distance d from the CM. The moment of inertia about the axis of rotation is I.

a) Write the differential equation which describes the variation of the angle Θ with time, where Θ is measured from the equilibrium position of the body.

b) If the body undergoes small oscillations, so that $\sin\Theta \approx \Theta$, what is their period?

In the preceding exercise, the moment of inertia of the rigid body about its CM is I_c. Find an expression for the period of small oscillations as a function of d(and I_c), and thus show

a) that there are two values of d, say d_1 and d_2, which correspond to a given period,

b) that the period is $t_0 = 2\pi \frac{d_1 + d_2}{g}$ in terms of d_1 and d_2,

c) that the period has a minimum value when $d = \sqrt{I_c/M}$. Find this minimum period.

C-9.

A certain linear spring has a free length D. When a mass m is hung on the end, it has a length D + A. While it is hanging motionless with mass m attached, a second mass m is dropped from a height A onto the first one, with which it collides inelastically. Find the period, amplitude, and the maximum height (above the original equilibrium position) attained in the resulting motion.

C-10.

A 20 g weight hanger with a 5 g weight on it is hung from a vertical spring of negligible mass. When the spring is displaced from equilibrium the system is found to vibrate in vertical S.H.M. with a period of $\pi/3$ s. If the 5 g weight is replaced by a 25 g weight, how far can the spring be displaced from equilibrium before release if the weight is not to jump off the weight hanger?

CHAPTER 18

Algebra

Refer to The Feynman Lectures on Physics, Vol. I, Ch. 22

The most general kind of number which satisfies the rules of elementary algebra is a complex number. Complex numbers may be written as a sum of a pure real (positive or negative) number and a pure imaginary number.

(complex number) u = (real number) x + (imaginary number)iy

$i = \sqrt{-1}$ is called the unit imaginary number

$1 = \sqrt{+1}$ is called the unit real number.

Any algebraic equation is still true if the sign of i is changed throughout. This is called taking the complex conjugate. If $u = x + iy$, then the complex conjugate of u, written u^*, is $u^* = x - iy$.

The rules of algebra, applied to complex numbers, show that

I. $(a + ib) + (c + id) = (a + c) + i(b + d)$

II. $(a + ib)(c + id) = (ac - bd) + i(ad + bc)$

III. $u = \sqrt{uu^*} = \sqrt{x^2 + y^2}$ is called the magnitude of u.

A real number raised to an imaginary power is complex, and has unit magnitude. The real and imaginary parts behave like a sine and cosine function as the magnitude of the imaginary power increases. Specifically,

IV. $e^{i\Theta} = \cos\Theta + i\sin\Theta$.

1.

In the equation

$$u + iv = (a + ib)(c + id)$$

let $b/a = \tan\alpha$ and $d/c = \tan\beta$. Using Eq. II and formulas of trigonometry, show that

a) $\sqrt{u^2 + v^2} = \sqrt{a^2 + b^2}\ \sqrt{c^2 + d^2}$

b) $v/u = \tan(\alpha + \beta)$.

2.

Work the above exercise using Eq. IV.

3.

Show that $\cos\Theta = (e^{i\Theta} + e^{-i\Theta})/2$

$\sin\Theta = (e^{i\Theta} - e^{-i\Theta})/2i$

4.

Show that

$$(a + ib)/(c + id) = [ac + db + i(bc - ad)]/(c^2 + d^2)$$

5.

The quantities cosh Θ and sinh Θ, defined as

$$\cosh \Theta = (e^{\Theta} + e^{-\Theta})/2$$

$$\sinh \Theta = (e^{\Theta} - e^{-\Theta})/2$$

are called the hyperbolic cosine and hyperbolic sine of Θ. Show that

$$\cos i\Theta = \cosh \Theta$$

$$\sin i\Theta = i \sinh \Theta$$

and

$$\cosh^2\Theta - \sinh^2\Theta = 1$$

6.

Using the fundamental formula of differentiation

$$df/dx = \lim_{\Delta x \to 0} \frac{f(x + \Delta x) - f(x)}{\Delta x}$$

Show that

$$d(e^{\alpha x})/dx = \alpha e^{\alpha x}.$$

7.

a) By successive differentiation, or otherwise, show that e^x may be represented by the infinite series

$$e^x = 1 + x + x^2/2! + x^3/3! + \ldots$$

b) Show that cos x and sin x may be represented by the infinite series

$$\cos x = 1 - x^2/2! + x^4/4! + \ldots$$

$$\sin x = x - x^3/3! + x^5/5! + \ldots$$

(These series are of considerable value in calculating e^x, cos x, and sin x for $x \ll 1$, although they converge for all x.)

B-1.

Find the complete algebraic solution of the equation

$$y = \sqrt[n]{1}$$

where n is an integer.

B-2.

Using the properties of $e^{in\Theta}$ and the binomial theorem, show that

$$\cos n\Theta = \cos^n\Theta - \frac{n(n-1)}{2!} \times \cos^{n-2}\Theta \sin^2\Theta + \ldots$$

B-3.

a) From the relation $e^{i(\Theta + \Phi)} = e^{i\Theta} \cdot e^{i\Phi}$, prove the trigonometric formulas giving the cosine and sine of the sum of two angles.

b) Interpret geometrically the result of multiplying one complex number, $Ae^{i\Theta}$, by another complex number, $Be^{i\Phi}$.

C-1.

From the following table of successive square roots of 11, find (to 3 places) $\log_{11}2$; $\log_{11}7$

Root r	$r\sqrt{N}$	$\log r\sqrt{N}$
1	11.000	1.00000
2	3.3167	0.50000
4	1.8212	0.25000
8	1.3495	0.12500
16	1.1617	0.06667
32	1.0778	0.03333
64	1.0382	0.01667
128	1.0195	0.00833

(Check your result by $\log_a N = \log_a b \log_b N$ where a and b are any two bases.)

CHAPTER 19

Forced Oscillations with Damping

Refer to the Feynman Lectures on Physics, Chs. 23, 24, and 25.

A-1.

Sketch the transient "coasting" motion of (a) an undamped oscillator, (b) an underdamped oscillator, and (c) an overdamped oscillator, all of which start from rest at the same time from the same displaced position.

A-2.

What is the resonance frequency of an L-C circuit having 10 mH inductance and 1 μF capacitance?

A-3.

Find the impedance of a 1.00 H inductance in series with a resistance of 377 Ω, at a frequency of 60 Hz.

A-4.

A certain coil has a resistance of 20 Ω. When it is connected to a 60 Hz voltage source of 10 V rms amplitude, it is observed that a current of 0.3 A rms flows. Find the inductance of the coil.

A-5.

An inductance-capacitance series circuit is to be resonant for a frequency of 1.0×10^4 Hz. If $L = 7.6 \times 10^{-2}$ H, what should C be?

A-6.

Find the impedance $\hat{Z}$ of an inductance L and a capacitance C as a function of ω when they are connected

a) in series, and

b) in parallel.

Discuss your answers qualitatively.

A-7.

Two capacitors, C_1 and C_2 are connected

a) in series

b) in parallel.

Find the effective capacitance for these two cases.

A-8.

Two inductances L_1 and L_2 are connected
a) in series
b) in parallel.
Find the effective inductance for these two cases.

A-9.

A resonant circuit is composed of two inductances, L and 3L, and two capacitors, C and 3C, all connected
a) in series
b) in parallel.
Find the resonant frequencies for these two cases.

A-10.

The "time constant" of a resistance-capacitance series circuit is RC; that of an inductance-capacitance series circuit is $\sqrt{LC}$; from dimensional considerations what would you expect the time constant of a resistance-inductance series circuit to be?

A-11.

What is the approximate Q of a 1000 cps tuning fork? (Use your experience.)

B-1.

a) Show that the differential equation of motion of a mass m on a spring whose force constant is k, and having a frictional force $-m\gamma v$ is

$$d^2x/dt^2 + \gamma dx/dt + \omega_0^2 x = 0$$

where $\omega_0^2 = k/m$.

b) Solve this equation (using complex variables) by assuming a solution of the form $x = e^{\alpha t}$ and thus show that the general solution is

$$x = e^{-1/2\ \gamma t}(A \cos\sqrt{\omega_0^2 - \gamma^2/4}\ t + B \sin\sqrt{\omega_0^2 - \gamma^2/4}\ t)$$

if $\gamma < 2\omega_0$.
c) What is the solution if $\gamma > 2\omega_0$?
d) At $t = 0$, the position and velocity of the mass m are $x = x_0$ and $\dot{x} = v_0$. Find the coefficients A and B.

B-2.

The gliders used with a linear air track lose speed mainly because of the frictional drag of the thin air film which supports them. This viscous force is proportional to the velocity. Write and solve the differential equation of motion of a glider on a level track. How should the velocity vary with

a) time

b) distance?

B-3.

A certain glider on a tilted air track has a magnet embedded in it, and this magnet generates eddy currents in the track which react back on the magnet, giving a retarding force precisely proportional to the velocity: $F = -m\gamma v$. If the glider starts from rest, find (as a function of the angle of tilt of the track, and the drag coefficient γ of the magnet)

a) the terminal velocity attained,

b) the velocity as a function of time,

c) the position as a function of time.

B-4.

A tourist on an ocean cruise inadvertently drops his camera of mass 1.0 kg from rest 20 m above the surface of the water. On impact the camera loses half its kinetic energy. After entering the water, it is subjected to a buoyant force equal to half its weight, and a drag force of 1/3 kg s^{-1} times v, its speed in the water. How far below the surface is the camera 3.0 s after it enters the water?

B-5.

The pivot point of a simple pendulum having a natural period of 1.00 s is moved laterally in a sinusoidal motion with an amplitude 1.00 cm and period 1.10 s. With what amplitude should the pendulum bob swing after a steady motion is attained?

B-6.

An object of mass 5.0 kg is found to oscillate with negligible damping when suspended from a spring which causes it to perform 10 complete cycles in 10.0 seconds. Thereafter, a certain small magnetic damping is applied, proportional to the velocity of motion and the amplitude decreases from 0.20 m to 0.10 m in 10 cycles.

a) Write the equation of motion, with the coefficients of d^2x/dt^2, dx/dt, and x represented by numbers in MKS units.

b) What is now the period of the motion?

c) In how many cycles (starting from 0.20 m amplitude) will the amplitude reach 0.05 m? 0.02 m?

d) What is the approximate maximum rate of dissipating energy by damping during the first cycle?

B-7.

A capacitor of capacitance C is initially charged to a voltage V_0, and at $t = 0$ it is connected across a resistor of resistance R. Write the differential equation for V, the voltage across the capácitor, as a function of t, and solve it by assuming an exponential solution.

B-8.

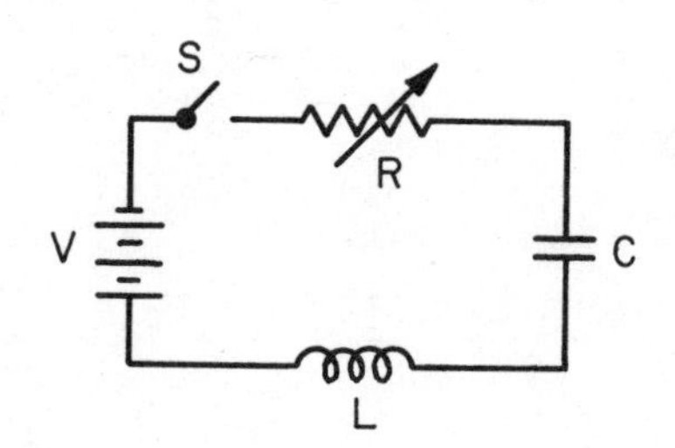

An uncharged capacitance C, "pure" inductance L, and variable ohmic resistance R are connected to a battery of potential difference V. Write the equation pertaining to the circuit and graph the voltage across C as a function of time after the switch S is closed for various values of R.

B-9.

Write down and solve the differential equations which describe the steady-state current which flows when a sinusoidal voltage of angular frequency ω is applied to

a) an inducatnace L; and

b) a capacitance C.

Thus find the (complex) impedance of an inductance L and a capacitance C.

B-10.

Draw the phasor diagram (including $V_{in} = V_0$, $\hat{I}$, $\hat{V}_R$, $\hat{V}_L$, $\hat{V}_c$) for a series R-L-C circuit driven at resonance.

B-11.

Draw phasor diagrams for the voltages and currents for a voltage $V_0 \cos \omega t$ applied to the following circuits:

a) a resistance R and inductance L in series

b) a resistance R and inductance L in parallel

c) a resistance R and capacitance C in series

d) a resistance R and capacitance C in parallel.

B-12.

The circuit shown has the following characteristics:

$V(t) = V_0 \cos \omega t$

$V_0 = 10$ volts

$\omega = 25 \times 10^3 \text{ rad s}^{-1}$.

$L = 4 \times 10^{-3}$ H

$C = 4 \times 10^{-7}$ F

$R = 160\ \Omega$

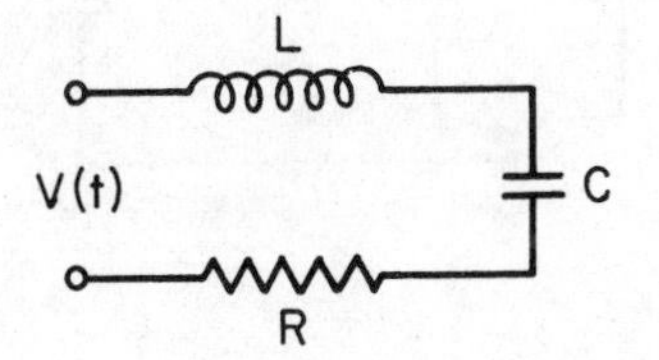

Consider the steady-state oscillations of this circuit.

a) What is the amplitude of the current?

b) What is the phase shift of the current with respect to the applied driving voltage?

c) Draw a phasor diagram, showing the voltage across the resistor, capacitance, and inductance.

B-13.

In the circuit shown, the driving frequency $\omega = 1/\sqrt{LC}$. What is the current through R? What is the current through L?

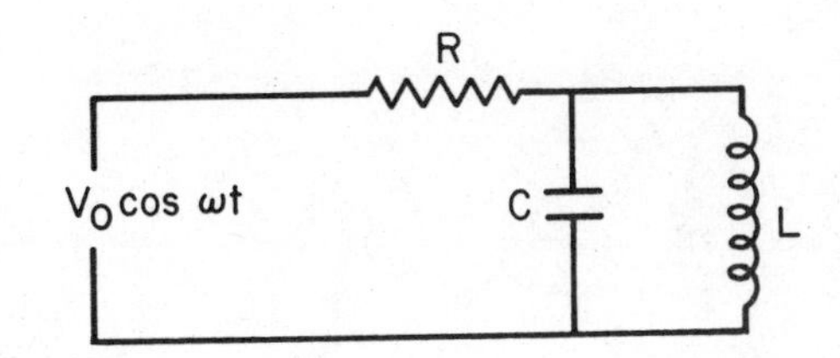

B-14.

The series RLC series circuit shown contains a generator supplying an alternating voltage of fixed frequency ω. The capacitor is variable.

a) For a value $C = C_1$, the current I_1 is found to be in phase with the applied voltage. What is C_1, in terms of L and ω?

b) The capacitance is then changed to $C = C_2$, so that the voltage is observed to lead the current I_2 by a phase angle of 45°. What is C_2 in terms of C_1, R, and ω?

c) What was the ratio I_1/I_2 ?

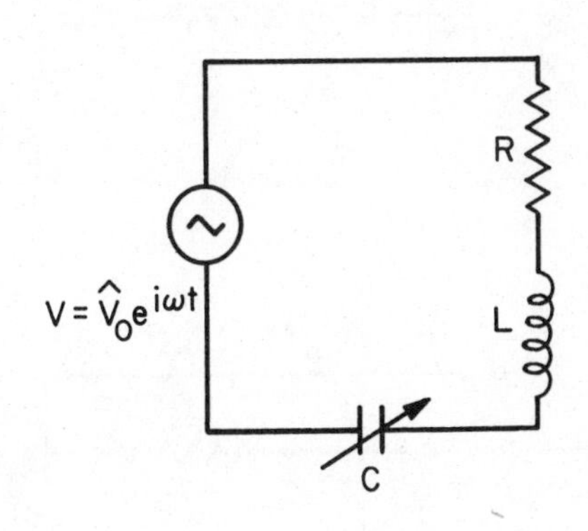

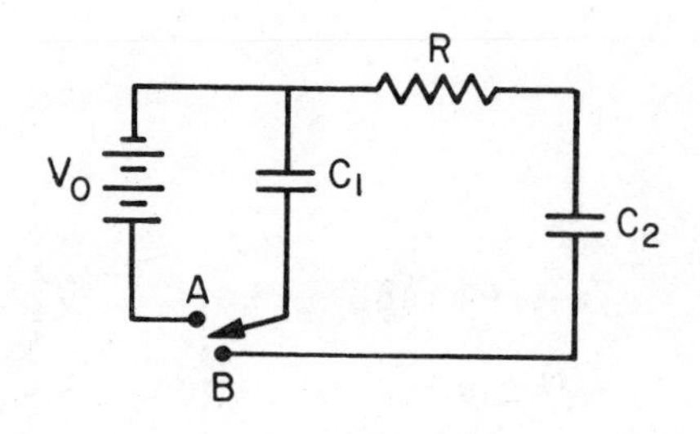

B-15.

Originally the switch was at A, but at t = 0 it is thrown to B. After a long time

a) how much energy has been dissipated as heat in the resistor?

b) what voltage, if any, remains on the capacitors?

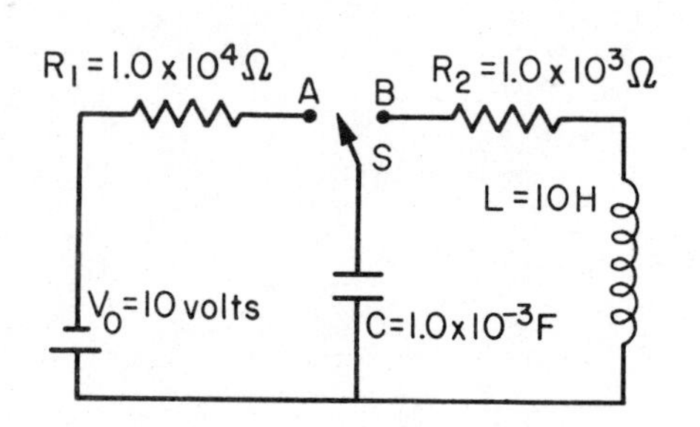

B-16.

In the circuit shown with the switch S open at $t < 0$, the capacitor is uncharged.

a) After the switch is closed at A, how long does it take the voltage across the capacitor to reach 8.0 volts?

b) At the instant the voltage across C reaches 8.0 volts, the switch is thrown to B. What is the initial value of the current that starts through L?

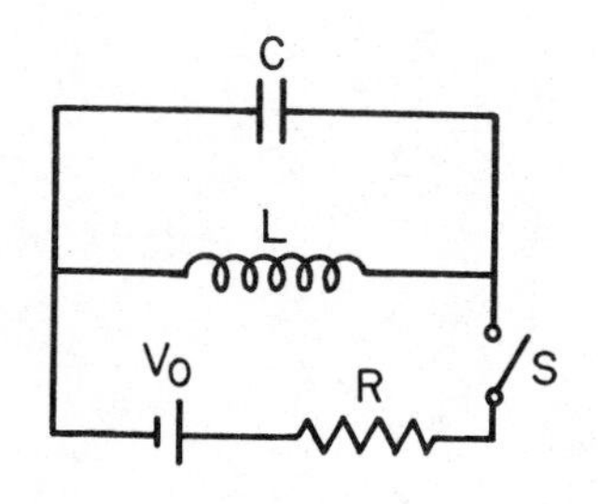

B-17.

In the circuit shown, the switch S is initially closed, and a steady current $I = V_0/R$ is flowing. At t = 0, S is suddenly opened. Find the maximum voltage that is subsequently observed on the capacitor.

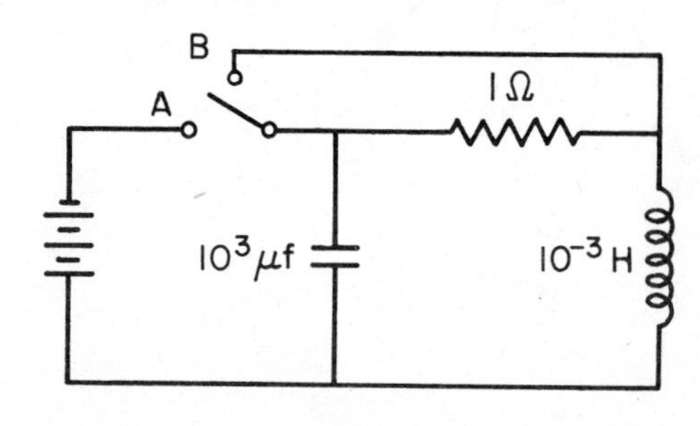

B-18.

Given the circuit shown, with the switch initially in position A. If the switch is suddenly changed to position B, what maximum voltage will subsequently appear on the capacitor?

B-19.

In order to suppress the 120 Hz "hum" from the power supply rectifier of an amplifier, a "smoothing filter" is used. In its simplest form, this consists of a resistance in series with a capacitance, as shown in the figure. If the applied voltage has a DC component V_0 and a 120 cycle component of amplitude V_2, find the corresponding voltages at the terminals of the capacitor, for $r = 10^3 \Omega$ and $C = 10\ \mu F$.

B-20.

A spar buoy of uniform cross-section floats in a vertical position with a length L submerged when there are no waves on the ocean.

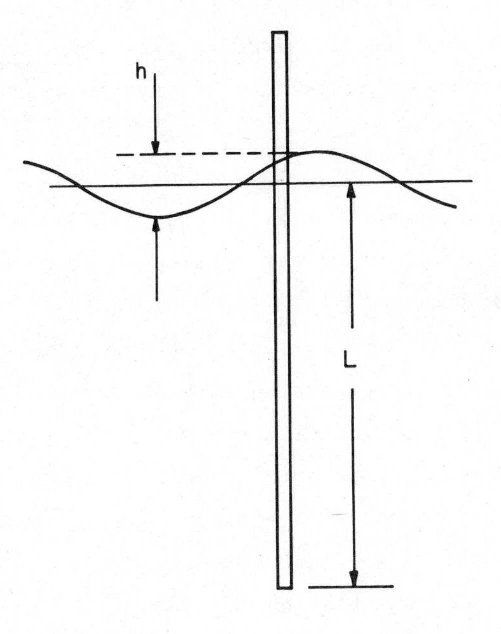

a) What is the amplitude (with respect to the mean ocean surface) of the vertical motion of the buoy when there are sinusoidal waves of height h (crest to trough) and period T on the ocean? Neglect fluid friction and non-vertical motions of the buoy.

b) If the undisturbed submerged length is 100 feet, the wave height 10 feet, and the wave period 5 seconds what is the amplitude of the buoy motion.

c) What must the total length of the bouy be so that the crests of the waves in (b) will just reach the top of the buoy?

B-21.

The diagram shows the rotating element of a high speed centrifugal gas compressor. The impeller of mass M is rigidly mounted on a shaft of negligible mass and is located midway between the bearings B. When the compressor is not running the center of mass of the impeller is located eccentrically with respect to the centerline between the bearings by a small amount e (greatly exaggerated in the diagram). The elastic bending stiffness of the shaft is k (a transverse force F applied to the center of the shaft would produce a transverse displacement of $x = F/k$ at that point on the shaft).

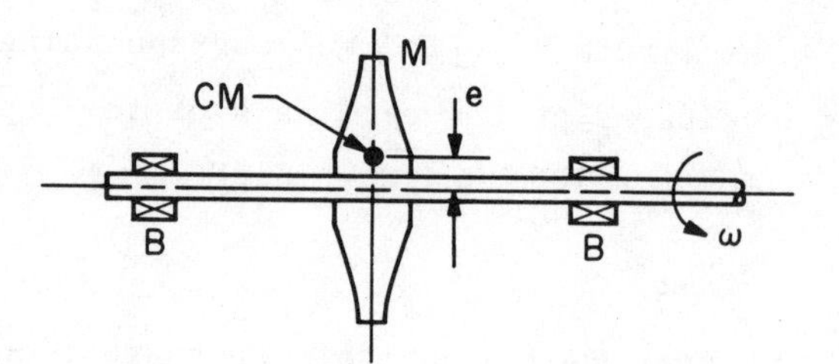

a) What is the circular frequency, ω_0, of bending vibrations of the system when the machine is not running?

b) What is the bending deflection of the shaft when the machine is running at angular speed ω?

c) What is the critical speed at which the compressor will fail?

d) What is the critical speed, if the eccentricity is reduced by a factor of two?

e) If, by rapid acceleration through the critical speed, a speed much greater than the critical speed is achieved without causing failure, where is the CM located with respect to the centerline between the bearings?

C-1.

Damped harmonic oscillator: A mass m is suspended from a spring of force constant k in a medium which exerts a damping form $- m\gamma\, dx/dt$.

a) For the case of underdamped motion find the complete solutions for the position $x = x(t)$ of m for all times $t \geq 0$ for the following driving forces:

1)

$$F = \begin{cases} 0 \text{ for } t < 0 \\ F_0 = \text{const. for } t \geq 0 \end{cases}$$

2) no driving force, but at $t = 0$ an impulse $J = J_x$ is imparted to mass m.

3)

$$F = \begin{cases} 0 \text{ for } t < 0 \\ F_0 \cos \omega_0 t \text{ for } t \geq 0 \end{cases} \qquad \omega_0 = \sqrt{\frac{k}{m}}$$

b) If the oscillator is driven by a sinusoidal force $F = F_0 \cos \omega t$ and we consider long times, what is the frequency ω^* for which the amplitude reaches a maximum?

Note:

Remember that the complete solution contains both steady-state and transient motion and that the initial conditions determine the constants of integration.

C-2.

A mass m, attached to two equal horizontal springs of force constant k/2, slides on a table top whose coefficient of friction is μ, assumed constant. The mass is pulled aside a distance A from the center point and is then released from rest.

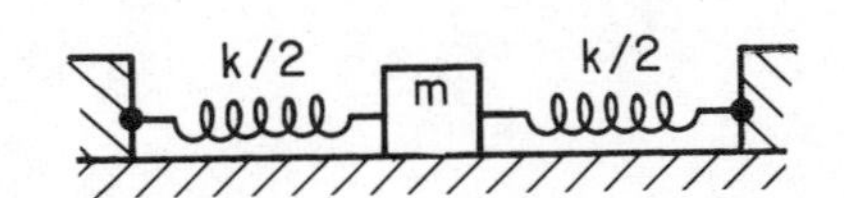

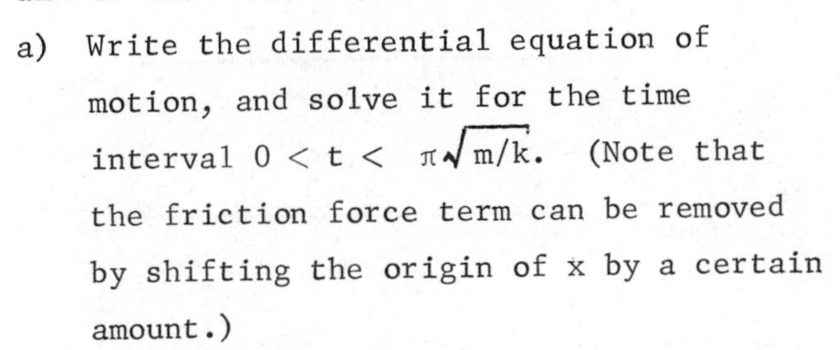

a) Write the differential equation of motion, and solve it for the time interval $0 < t < \pi\sqrt{m/k}$. (Note that the friction force term can be removed by shifting the origin of x by a certain amount.)

b) How large must A be if the mass comes to rest permanently at a distance B from the center, after crossing $x = 0$ 0, 1, 2, ... times?

C-3.

A particle of mass m and electric charge q is situated in an alternating electric field along the x axis.

$$E = E_0 \cos \omega t$$

The particle also experiences a force proportional to the third derivative of its x-position:

$$F_\alpha = +\alpha \dddot{x}$$

Find the amplitude and phase of the oscillation of the particle in the steady state. This model gives an approximate description of a charged particle which scatters radiation.

C-4.

The circuit shown constitutes what is called a relaxation oscillator. It consists of a neon bulb connected across a capacitor, and the capacitor is charged through a resistor from a DC voltage source. The neon tube has infinite resistance as long as the voltage across it is less than 60 V. If the voltage attains or exceeds this value, the neon tube breaks down and then has negligible resistance, discharging the capacitor. The neon tube then "goes out", and returns to its infinite resistance state. If C = .10 μF, R = $10^6\ \Omega$, and V_0 = 80 V, find the frequency at which the neon tube flashes.

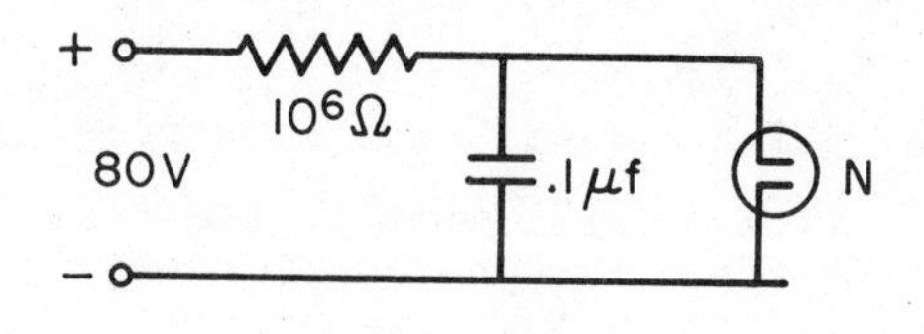

C-5.

In many instances it is desirable to have an electronic circuit which will "differentiate" a function with respect to time. A simple circuit to accomplish this is shown in the figure. Show that the output voltage of this circuit (if negligible current is allowed to flow into the output circuitry) is

$$V_{out}(t) = RC\,\frac{dV_{in}}{dt}$$

provided $|V_{out}| \ll |V_{in}|$

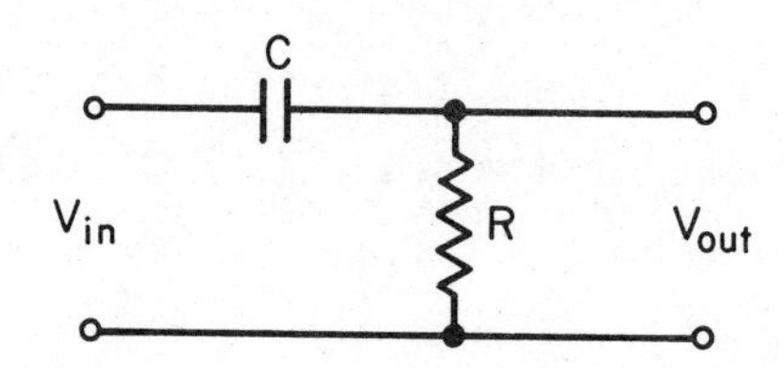

Solve for V_{out} in the above circuit for the case in which $V_{in} = V_0 \cos \omega t$, and thus test the validity of the result of the preceding exercise as a function of ω.

C-6.

Invent a simple circuit which will "integrate" a function, and discuss its properties.

C-7.

In electronic circuits it is often desired to provide a sinusoidal voltage of constant amplitude but variable phase. A circuit which accomplishes this is called a phase-shifting network. One example of such a network is shown in the figure. Show that the voltage measured bewteen terminals A and B has half the amplitude of the input voltage, and a phase which may be adjusted between 0° and 180° by changing the resistance R'.
Hint: a phasor diagram is helpful.

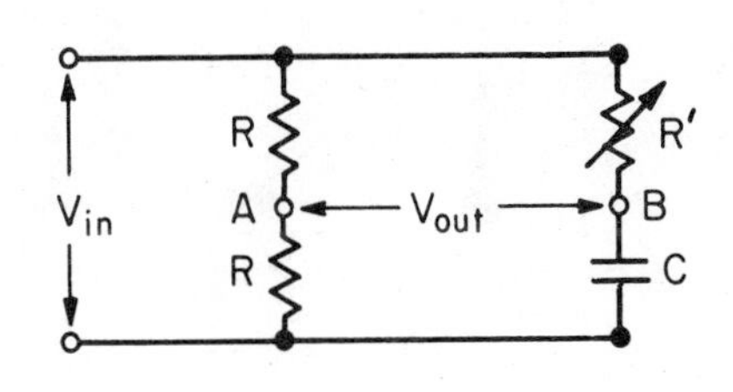

C-8.

The ignition system of a gasoline engine is shown in the diagram. When the breaker points, S, are closed the battery voltage, V_0, produces a current in the primary winding of the coil which has an inductance L and internal resistance R. The secondary winding of the coil has 100 times as many turns as the primary winding so that the voltage across the spark plug gap, P, is 100 times the voltage across the primary winding of the coil. The breaker points are opened by the distributor cam (not shown) each time the arm D is in contact with one of the spark plug circuits, as shown. C is the capacitance of the condenser which is connected across the breaker points. Typical values of the circuit constants are $V_0 = 12$ V, $C = 0.25$ µF, $R = 6\Omega$, $L = 2$mH.

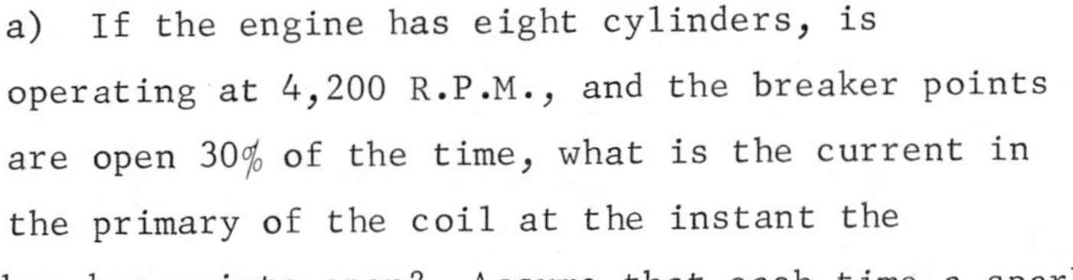

a) If the engine has eight cylinders, is operating at 4,200 R.P.M., and the breaker points are open 30% of the time, what is the current in the primary of the coil at the instant the breaker points open? Assume that each time a spark occurs the currents in the system decay to zero before the breaker points close. Also, recall that each cylinder fires every other revolution of the engine.

b) When the breaker points open what maximum voltage would be produced across the spark plug gap, if a spark did not occur?

c) How much time elapses between the instant the breaker points open and the instant of maximum spark plug voltage?

C-9.

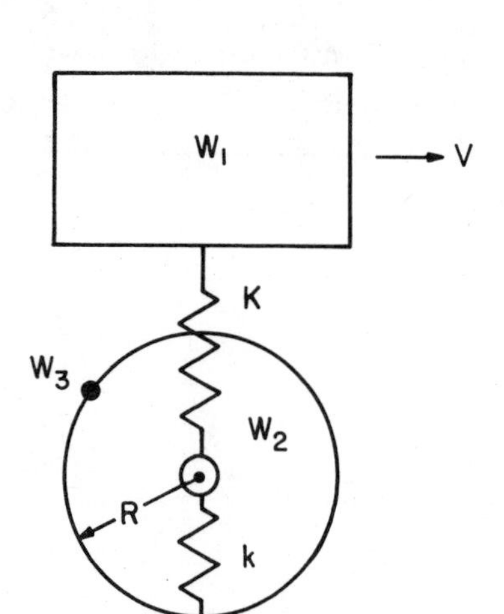

Calculate the speed of an automobile at which an unbalanced wheel will begin to hop off the ground. W_1 is the portion of the autombile weight supported by the wheel. W_2 is the unsprung weight (wheel + tire + brake assembly + etc.). W_3 is the unbalanced weight which is assumed to be very small compared to W_2 and to be located at the tire tread radius R. (For example, W_3 might be the weight of rubber worn off one spot on the tire during a "wheels-locked" panic stop). K is the stiffness constant of the suspension system given by $K = W_1/\delta_1$ where δ_1 is the static deflection of the wheel spindle with respect to the frame of the automobile. k is the stiffness constant of the tire, given by $k = (W_1 + W_2)/\delta_2$, where δ_2 is the static deflection of the wheel spindle with respect to the road. Neglect the influence of the shock absorbers and the small vertical motion of the automobile body (these influences turn out to be negligible in this problem for typical automobiles). Assume the following typical numerical values:

$W_1 = 750$ lbs; $W_2 = 75$ lbs; $W_3 = 2$ oz. $= 1/8$ lb;

$R = 14$ inch.; $\delta_1 = 6$ inch.; $\delta_2 = 1\ 1/2$ inch.

CHAPTER 20

Geometrical Optics

Refer to The Feynman Lectures on Physics, Vol. I, Chs. 26 and 27.

A-1.

When we stand before an ordinary plane mirror, our image appears to be reversed, right for left: that is, the image of our right hand looks like the left hand of the "person" in the mirror. Why does the mirror not also reverse top for bottom? What is reversed by the mirror?

B-1.

A man can walk at 5 ft/sec on a sidewalk, but only 3 ft/sec on a "uniformly rough" field. He starts at A, 140 ft from a wall, and goes to B, 120 ft south of the sidewalk along the wall.

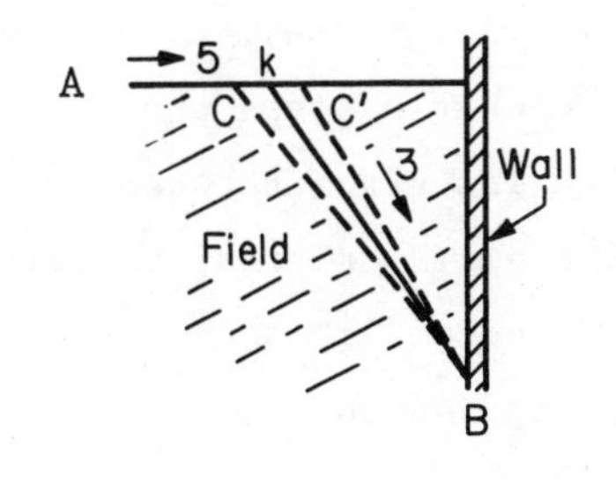

a) What route AKB must he follow to do this in least time?
   (Note: It is legitimate to assume the "law of refraction" to apply to this problem. However, if you have enough courage, you might try to solve it without such an assumption!)
b) What is his least time?
c) What time do alternate routes ACB and AC'B require, if CK = KC' = 10 ft?

B-2.

Light from source S sends a narrow beam perpendicular to a screen 1.0 m away. The ray strikes the screen at P. If a lucite slab of index of refraction 1.50 and thickness 0.20 m is inserted so that the beam strikes it at angle of incidence 30°,

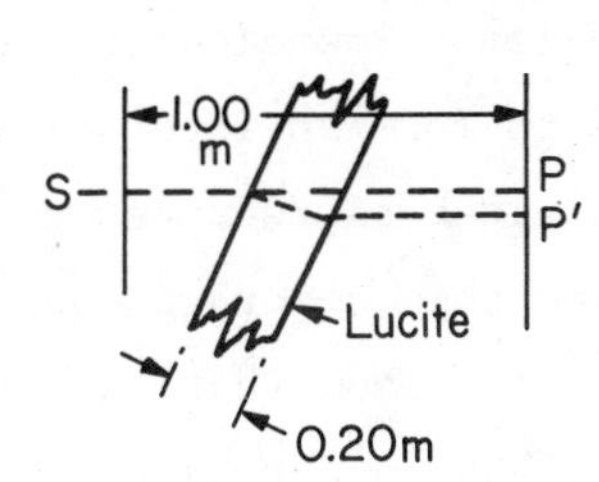

a) Find the lateral displacement of the ray, PP';
b) Find the percent increase in time of path SP' over the original path in air, SP.

B-3.

A hungry sportsman encounters a circular rain barrel 80 cm in diameter with 100 cm depth of water in it, and in passing he notices a fish inside adjacent to the wall and diametrically opposite him. The fish is part way from the bottom to the top of the barrel, and the ray from the fish to the man's eye emerges from the water at the axis of the barrel, making an angle of 60° with the vertical axis. If the man's eye is straight above the edge of the barrel, at what angle with this line of sight must he shoot his gun in order to hit the fish? (Neglect the deflection of the bullet as it enters the water.)

B-4.

It is well known that when light goes from one transparent medium into another, not all of the light is refracted, but some is reflected, and very little, if any, is absorbed or scattered. What happens when a beam of light strikes the interface between two media, if the light beam is originally moving in the more dense medium? Discuss and sketch the situation for various angles θ.

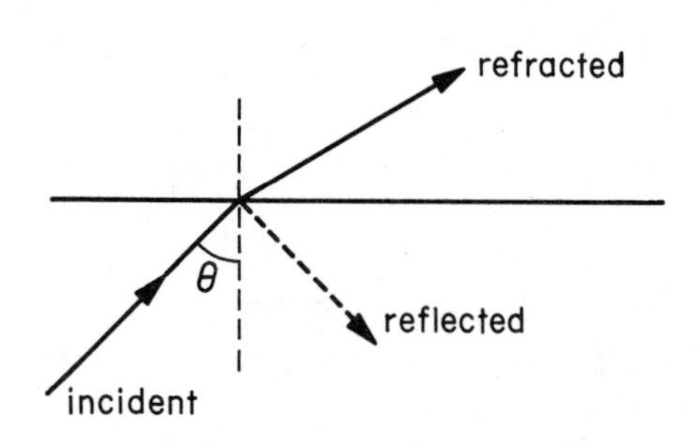

B-5.

Two plane mirrors intersect each other so as to form a perfect internal right angle, with the line of intersection vertical. Make a sketch to explain why, in such a mirror, we "see ourselves as others see us".

B-6.

Three mutually perpendicular mirrors intersect so as to form an internal right-angled corner. A light ray strikes one of the mirrors, and thence perhaps one or both of the other two. Show that, after all reflections have occurred (assuming the mirrors to be very large in extent) the ray is traveling exactly opposite to its original direction, but displaced laterally. Do you know of a practical application of such a "corner reflector"?

B-7.

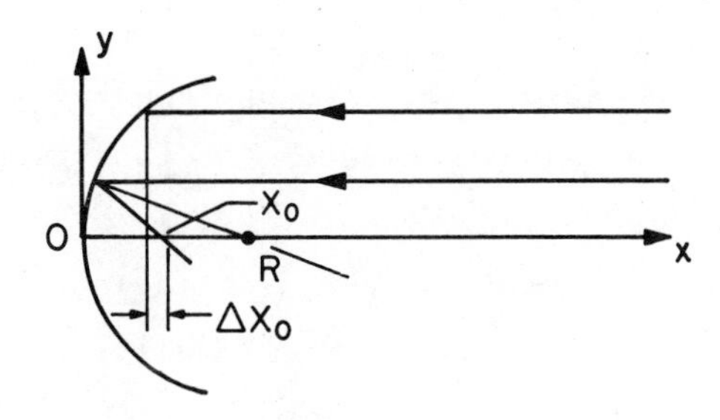

A bundle of light rays, parallel to and close to the axis, fall on a concave spherical mirror of radius R.

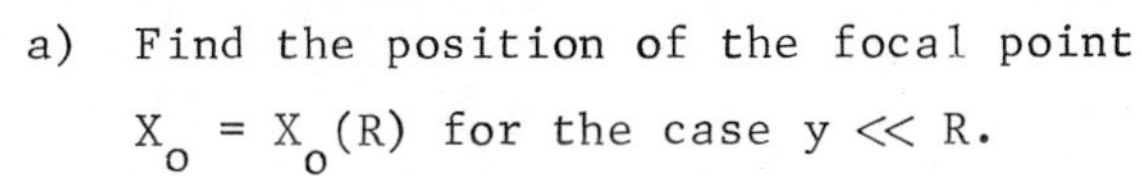

a) Find the position of the focal point $X_o = X_o(R)$ for the case $y \ll R$.

b) For $y/R = 0.2$ (note $y \ll R$ no longer holds) find the image point $X = X_o + \Delta X_o$ and determine the value of $\frac{\Delta X_o}{X_o}$, the relative aberration of the mirror.

Hint: $(1 - a^2)^{-1/2} \approx 1 + 1/2\ a^2$

B-8.

The solar disk subtends an angle of approximately 32 minutes at the earth. Find the position and diameter of the solar image formed by a concave spherical mirror of radius r = 400 cm.

B-9.

The 200-inch Hale telescope, used in one of its several optical arrangements, has a focal length of 160 m. What should be the distance between the focal plane for distant stars and

a) the moon

b) an artificial earth satellite at a slant range of 300 km?

B-10.

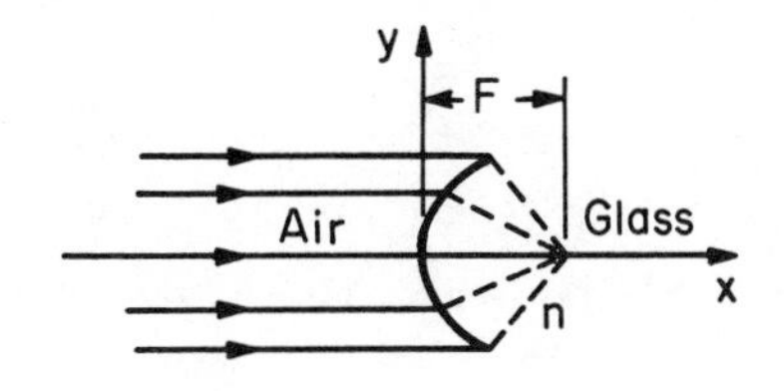

A parallel beam of light in air is to be brought to a point focus by a single refracting surface which bounds a region of index n. Find the proper shape for this surface. (y is the normal distance from the axis) Lenses are often made spherical. Under what conditions is this acceptable?

B-11.

The outer diameter of a piece of glass capillary tubing is D, and its index of refraction is n. When viewed from the side, the small capillary bore appears to have a diameter d'. What is its true diameter d ?

B-12.

A certain glass sphere has a radius of 2 cm and refractive index n = 1.50. If a point source of light is placed 12 cm from the center, where will the image be formed?

B-13.

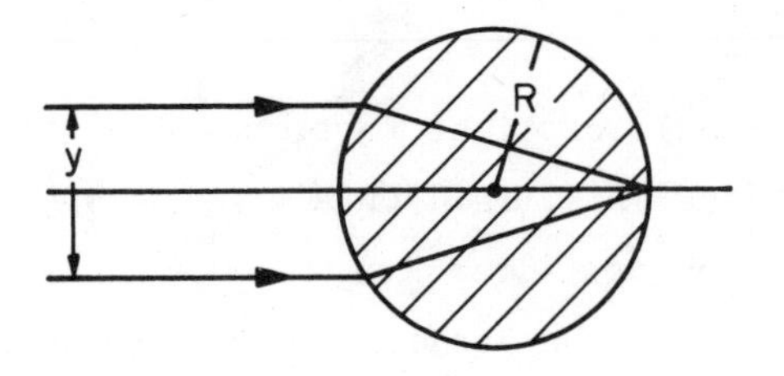

In the calibration of a photometric instrument it is necessary to determine that two parallel light rays are exactly a distance y apart. This is done by letting both rays fall normally and symmetrically on a glass rod, of radius R and index of refraction n = 1.60, and then adjusting the separation of the rays until they come exactly to a focus at the opposite circumference of the rod. In terms of R, what is y?

B-14.

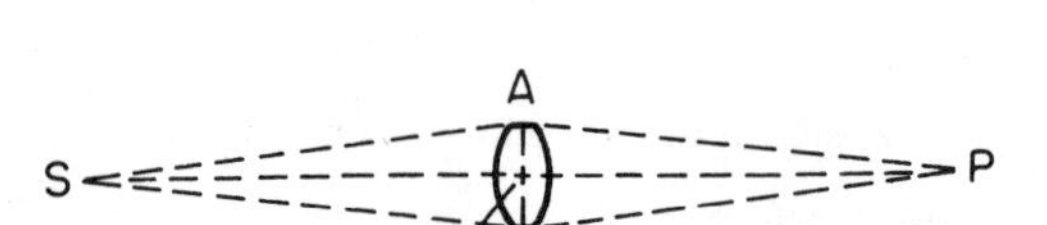

S is a source of light. P is its image produced by a lens. SC = CP = 1.00 m. AC = BC = 0.10 m. The lens ACB is 3.0 mm thick at its edge, with index of refraction n = 1.6. For the ray SCP to take just the same time as the rays SAP and SBP, how thick should the lens be at C?

B-15.

A lens of focal length F produces a real image of a distant object, and this image is viewed through a magnifying glass of focal length f. If the eye is focused at infinity while viewing, find the apparent angular magnification of the system.

B-16.

Two thin lenses L and L', of focal lengths f and f', are separated by a distance D. Find the equivalent focal length F of the combination, and the distances Δ, Δ' of the principle planes from the respective lenses L and L'.

B-17.

The typical human eye can focus on objects lying between about 25 cm and infinity. A simple thin magnifying lens of focal length f = + 5 cm is placed directly in front of the eye.

a) Between what two limiting positions should an object be placed to be seen clearly?
b) Determine the angular magnification for each of these positions.

B-18.

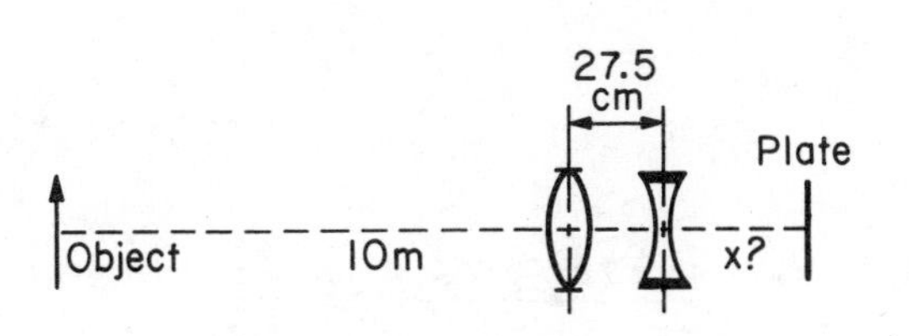

A telephoto combination consists of a positive lens of focal length $f_1 = +30$ cm and a negative lens of focal length $f_2 = -10$ cm. The separation between the two lenses is 27.5 cm. Make a ray diagram which shows where a photographic plate should be placed in order to photograph an object 10 meters in front of the first lens.

B-19.

A simple astronomical telescope has an objective lens 4.0 cm in diameter with 10.0 cm focal length, and an eye lens with 2.0 cm focal length. The two lenses are placed on a common axis 12.0 cm apart. The telescope is to be used to observe stars as much as 5.7°($\tan^{-1}$ 0.1) off-axis. How large must the eye lens be in order to collect all the light from the objective? (The cure is to place a "field lens" at the focal plane.)

B-20.

A luminous disk of diameter D is held perpendicular to the axis of a convex lens, and its real image is focused on a fixed screen. When the disk is at a distance L_1 from the lens, the diameter of the image is d_1. The disk is now moved to a closer distance L_2 from the lens, and the screen is moved to refocus the image. The diameter of the new image is d_2.

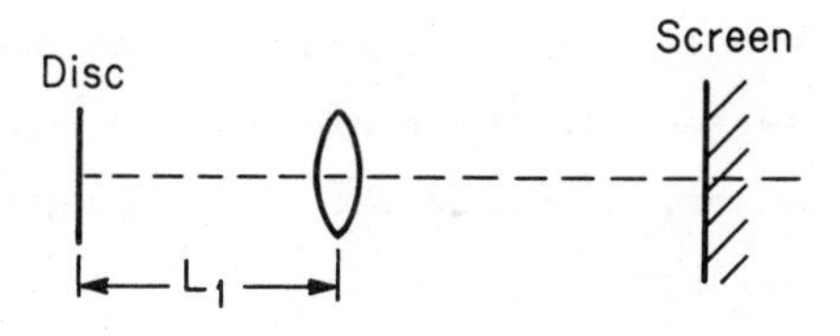

a) Is $d_1 > d_2$ or $d_2 > d_1$?

b) Must the screen be moved toward or away from the lens to form the image in the second case?

c) What is the focal length of the lens?

C-1.

A certain beam of light is converging toward a focus at a certain point P. It is desired to insert a single reflecting surface passing through a given axial point Q which will re-image the light to a new point focus at a given point P'. Find the shape of the required surface. Let the distance QP' = D and QP = d. Note that there are two cases to be considered, in which the mirror intercepts the rays (1) before they pass through P, or (2) after passing through P.

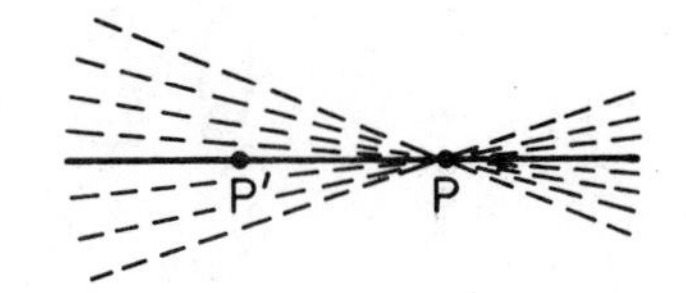

C-2.

a) Referring to the figure, establish that the equation of a parabolic curve of focal length f is $y = x^2/4f$.

b) A bucket of fluid of density ρ is rotating uniformly with angular velocity ω about a vertical axis. Show that the upper surface of the fluid assumes a paraboloidal shape, and find the focal length of the paraboloid.

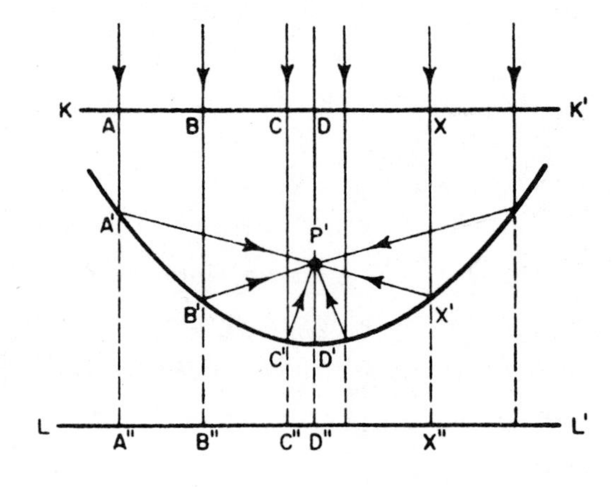

CHAPTER 21

Electromagnetic Radiation. Interference

Refer to The Feynman Lectures on Physics, Vol. I, Chs. 28 and 29.

1.

Interpret the following two problems in complex numbers geometrically, and show that the absolute value of A in each case is as given:

a) $A = re^{i\Theta/2} + re^{-i\Theta/2}$; $|A| = 2r\cos\frac{\Theta}{2}$

b) $A = \sum_{n=0}^{N} re^{in\Theta}$; $|A| = r\,\dfrac{\sin\frac{N+1}{2}\Theta}{\sin\frac{\Theta}{2}}$

B-1.

A charge q traverses a circular path of radius a at an angular velocity ω. Evaluate the electric field at a great distance R from the charge, at an angle Θ with respect to the axis of the circular path. Find the intensity of the radiation at a great distance R in the plane of the circle and on the axis. Assume that $\omega a \ll c$.

B-2.

The power per unit area delivered by an electromagnetic wave is proportional to the mean-square electric field strength. Find what fraction of the total power radiated by an oscillating charge falls on a unit area normal to the radius vector R at an angle Θ with respect to the axis of oscillation. Evaluate this power in Wm^{-2} for a vertically oriented dipole suspended from a cosmic ray radiosonde balloon at an altitude of 25 km and at a horizontal distance of 25 km from the receiver, if the transmitter is radiating 0.5 W total.

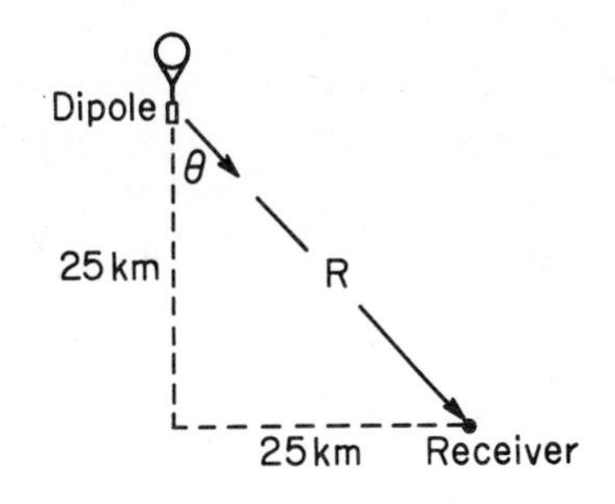

B-3.

Two vertical antennas are arranged as shown and are driven in phase. The antennas are driven so that one would, if alone, radiate a certain intensity I_0 in all horizontal directions, and the other, an intensity $2\ I_0$. What should the observed intensities in the various directions shown in the figure be?

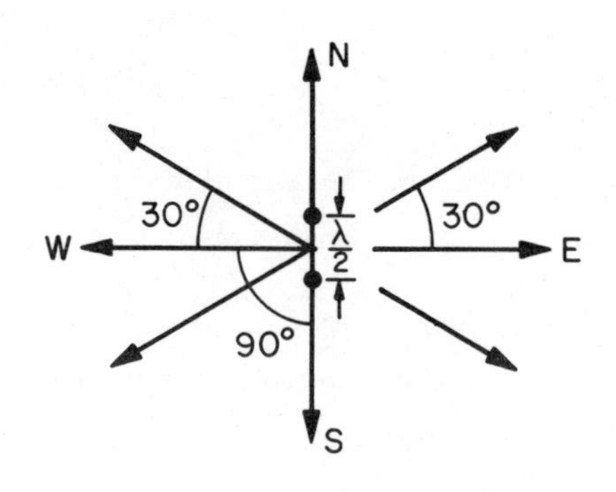

B-4.

Four identical dipole radiators are aligned parallel to one another and are equally spaced along a line at a distance 2.50 cm apart. They are driven at a frequency of 3.00×10^9 Hz and are phased so that, starting from one end, each successive dipole lags the preceding one by 90°. Find the intensity pattern of the radiation at a great distance in the equatorial plane (perpendicular to the dipole axes), and sketch this function in polar coordinates. Such a diagram is called the radiation pattern or lobe pattern of an antenna system.

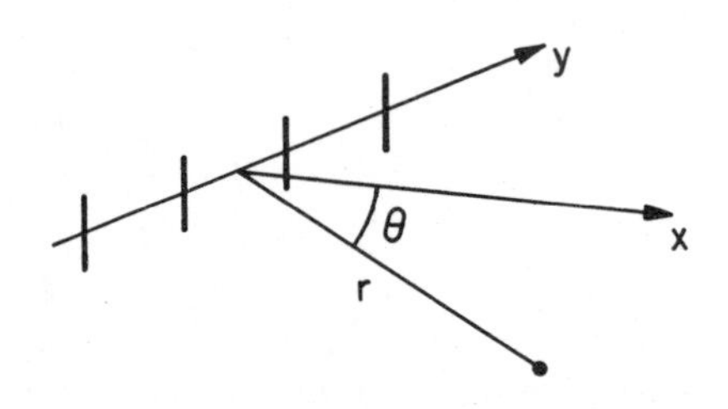

B-5.

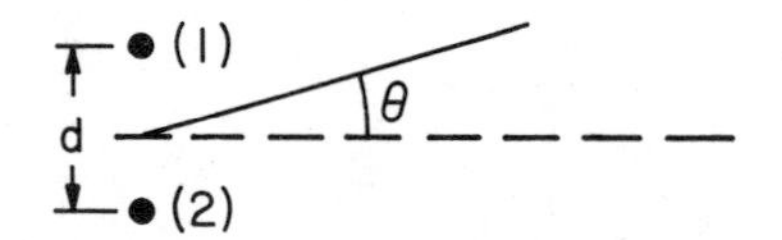

Two parallel dipoles are situated a distance $d = \lambda/2$ apart, and are oscillating with the same frequency and amplitude.

a) Find $I = I(\theta)$ (the lobe pattern) in the equatorial plane and sketch the pattern in a polar diagram if the oscillators are in phase.

b) Find by what fraction of a period oscillator (2) must lag oscillator (1) so that an observer at $\theta = 210^{\circ}$ will see maximum signal. For which value of θ will there be no signal? Sketch the lobe pattern.

B-6.

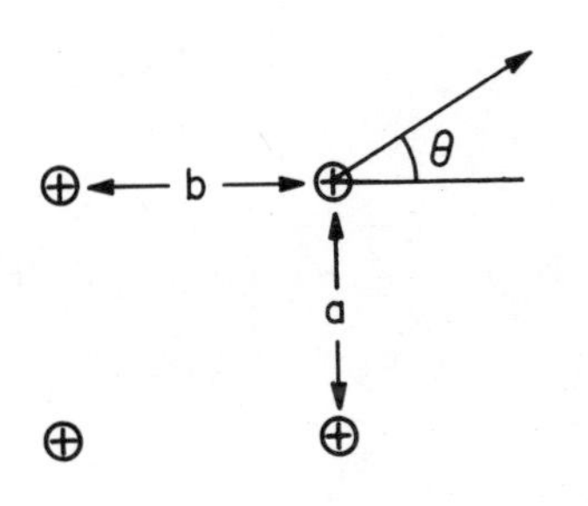

Four vertical dipoles are located at the corners of a horizontal rectangle of sides a,b as shown. If they are driven in phase, at wavelength λ, what minimum values (> 0) should a,b have to produce maximum intensity in the direction $\theta = 30^\circ$ far from the charges?

B-7.

An observer is at distance R from two identical charges, q, which are both passing through the origin at $t = 0$. The first charge moves only along the z-axis, and $z(t) = d \sin \omega t$; the second charge moves only along the x-axis, and $x(t) = d \sin \omega t$. What is the electric field $\vec{E}(t)$ at the two following points:

a) $x = R/\sqrt{2}$, $y = 0$, $z = R/\sqrt{2}$;

b) $x = 0$, $y = R$, $z = 0$. $(R \gg c/\omega)$ $(\omega d \ll c)$.

B-8.

A field engineer testing radiation patterns is flying in a helicopter at a ground speed of 120 mi. hr^{-1} at low altitude in a circular pattern of 2.0 mi radius about the mid-point between two vertical dipole transmitting antennae that lie in a north-south line. For the frequency being used for the test, the antennae are a half wavelength apart. Normally the antennae are operated in phase. However, the transmitter operator decided to play a joke on the field engineer, by changing the phase relation between the antennae at such a rate that no change in radiation intensity could be observed aboard the helicopter. If he started this change when the helicopter was due east of the antennae at what rate was he changing the phase relation when the helicopter was θ° north of east of the antennae?

B-9.

Two electric dipoles, A and B, are situated one-half wavelength apart and are perpendicular to one another and to the line joining their centers, as shown in the figure. They are driven at the same frequency and phase, but dipole B has twice the amplitude of dipole A. Find the intensity and the direction of the $\vec{E}$ vector of the radiation at a great distance from the dipoles in the directions C, D, and E (all in x-y plane) indicated.

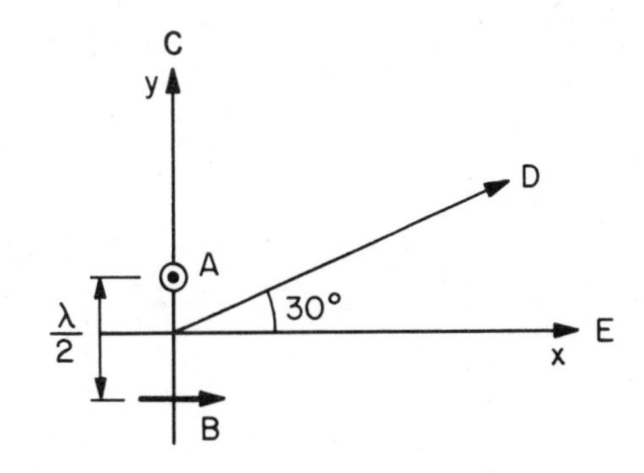

B-10.

A double line of N equally spaced oscillating dipoles is situated as shown. All dipoles in row A are driven in the same phase, and all those in row B lag 90° in phase behind those of row A. Sketch the radiation pattern in the equatorial plane at a great distance from the array.

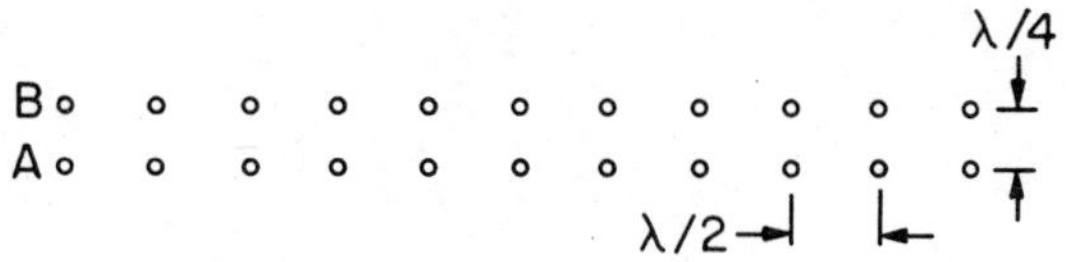

B-11.

The electrons in a long, straight, fine wire of length L are all oscillating along the wire with angular frequency ω, small amplitude $\underline{a}$, and in the same phase. Find the electric field at a great distance $R (R \gg L)$, at an angle θ with respect to an axis coincident with the wire.

CHAPTER 22

Electromagnetic Radiation. Diffraction

Refer to The Feynman Lectures on Physics, Vol. I, Ch. 30.

1.

Consider n equally spaced dipole radiators, each of length a, and separation d, along a straight line, oscillating along the line at the same amplitude A and frequency ω, but with successive phase shifts α. Each dipole radiator consists of a large number of atomic dipoles. Show that the diffraction pattern of the intensity at large distance at an angle θ is given by:

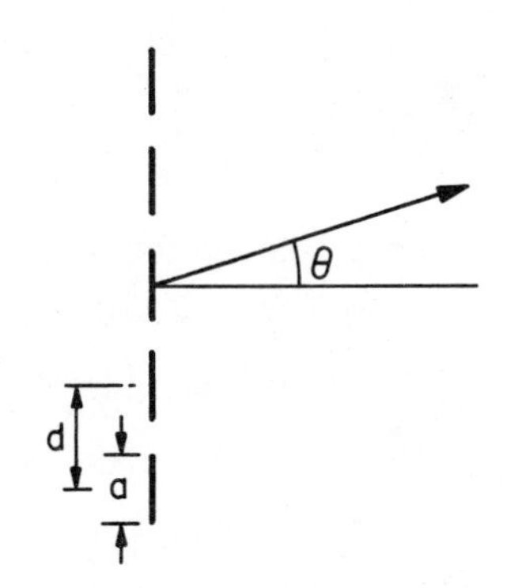

$$I = I_0 \frac{\sin^2 \frac{\beta}{2}}{\left(\frac{\beta}{2}\right)^2} \frac{\sin^2 \frac{n\varphi}{2}}{\sin^2 \frac{\varphi}{2}}$$

where $\varphi = \alpha + \frac{2\pi d}{\lambda} \sin \theta$

$\lambda = \frac{2\pi c}{\omega}$

$\beta = \frac{2\pi}{\lambda} a \sin \theta$

and I_0 is the intensity of a single dipole at the angle θ.

A-1.

A certain spectral line has a wavelength of 5500 Å and a "width" of 10^{-3} Å. What is the Q of the atomic oscillator?

A-2.

Under what conditions will an illuminated slit cast a "geometrical" shadow? (i.e., such that diffraction effects are negligible.)

B-1.

An automobile with the customary two headlights (considered as point sources) is approaching from a distance on a straight road. The lights on the car are situated 120 cm apart. How far from an observer would the car be when he could just be sure he was seeing two lights and not one? Take aperture of iris of eye as 0.5 cm and effective wavelength of light as 5500 Å . Would the fact that the light is "white" (a mixture of wavelengths) make it easier or harder to resolve the two sources?

B-2.

The wavelengths of the D-lines of sodium are 5889.95 Å and 5895.92 Å, respectively. How large a grating having 600 lines mm^{-1} is needed to resolve these lines in the first order spectrum?

B-3.

A point source of light L emitting a single wavelength λ is situated a small distance d above an ideal plane mirror. A screen stands at the end of the mirror at distance D from L. (D >> d). Find the relative intensity of light on the screen as a function of Z, the plane of the mirror being at z = 0. (Note: a mirror changes the phase of the light it reflects by $\pi = 180^{\circ}$.)

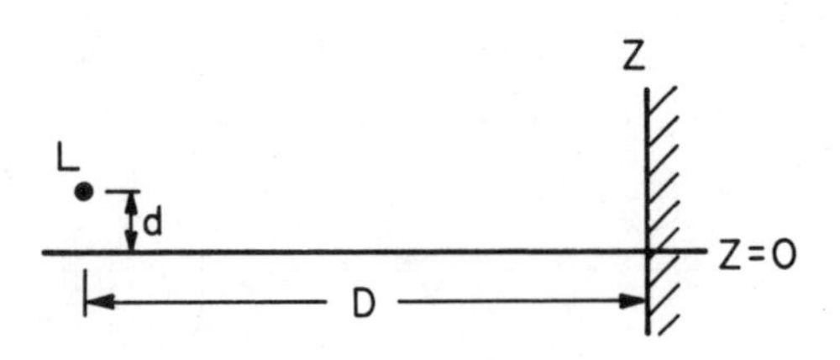

B-4.

Parallel light of wavelength λ is normally incident from the left on a circular hole in a screen and the resultant intensity is observed at a point on the axis of the hole at $z = 10\lambda$ to the right.

a) What radius should the hole have to produce maximum intensity at the observation point?

b) By what fraction is the intensity reduced if the screen is removed?

B-5.

a) Calculate the transmitted diffraction pattern $I(\theta)/I_{max}$ for a screen having 2 parallel slits of width a = 6 cm, separated by a distance d = 12 cm, which is exposed to a parallel beam of λ = 3 cm microwave radiation.

b) How many orders of principal maxima are there and for which values of θ?

c) What is $I(\theta)/I_{max}$ at the position of the principal maxima?

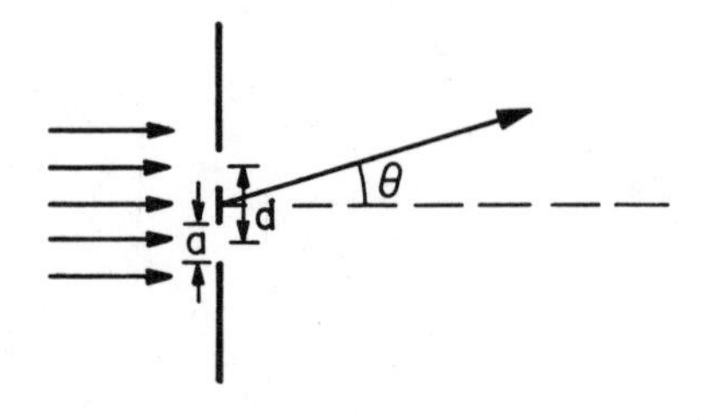

C-1.

The wavelengths of spectral lines are commonly measured to 0.001 Å using spectrographs whose resolving power may be only .010 Å. Are any basic laws of physics being violated in the process? Explain.

C-2.

A Fabry-Perot interferometer consists of a pair of very accurately flat surfaces, parallel to each other at a distance D apart. The surfaces are coated so as to reflect a fraction R^2 of the intensity of the light incident on them normally, and to transmit a fraction T^2 of the intensity. Light of intensity I_0 and wavelength λ is incident upon one surface from the left (see figure). Part of this beam is transmitted directly through the system, but some of the light is reflected from the second surface, then from the first surface, and is thence transmitted. In general, the outgoing beam is made up of light which has been reflected 0, 2, 4, 6, ... times and transmitted through 2 films, all summed together. How should the transmitted intensity depend upon D, λ, R, and T?

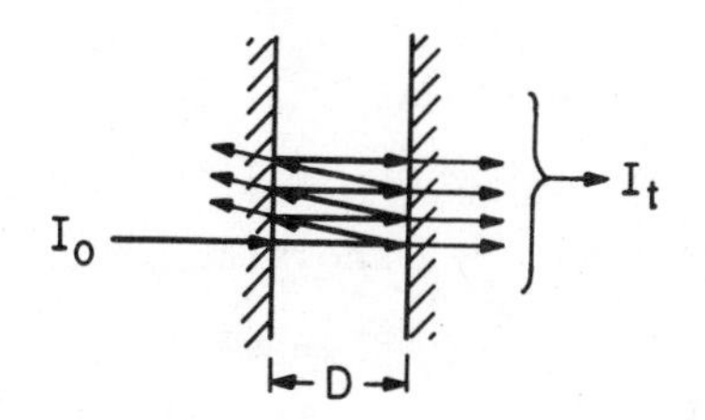

Note: Narrow-band optical filters, called interference filters, operate on this same principle, but the two reflecting surfaces are made by high-vacuum coating a piece of glass with several layers, accurately controlled in thickness, or clear materials having various indexes of refraction.

C-3.

A common type of grating spectrograph is constructed as shown in the figure. Light from a source L passes through a narrow slit S, thence through a collimator lens (or mirror) C_1 which renders it parallel (so that it strikes the grating as would plane waves from infinity). This parallel light is then diffracted by the grating G ; the diffracted light which proceeds in a certain range of angular directions strikes another lens C_2, called the camera lens, and is focused in a plane P, where the spectrum appears as a band, perhaps crossed

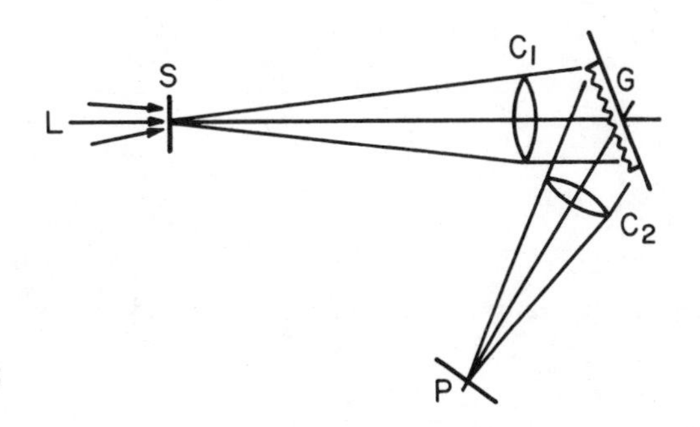

by narrow spectrum lines at various places. Let the length and width of the slit be h and w, the focal lengths of C_1 and C_2 be F_1 and F_2, the angles between the grating normal and the axes of C_1 and C_2 be Θ_i and Θ_d, and the number of lines per mm on the grating be N.

a) How wide will the spectrum band appear at P?

b) What wavelength(s) will appear on the axis of C_2 at P?

c) How far apart in the focal plane at P will two spectral lines appear whose wavelength differs by 1.00 Å? This quantity is often called the <u>dispersion</u> of the instrument.

d) If the slit width w is much larger than the collimator lens resolution $1.22 \lambda F_1/A_1$, where A_1 is the aperture, how wide should a spectral line at P be?

C-4.

The spectrograph at the 150 ft solar tower telescope of the Mt. Wilson Observatory is of the Littrow type, shown schematically in the figure. In this arrangement, a single lens acts as both the collimator and camera lens, and $\theta_i = -\theta_d$ (nearly). The spectrum is formed in a strip adjacent to the slit. The focal length of the Mt Wilson instrument is F = 23 m, and the grating has a ruled area 15 cm x 25 cm with 600 lines mm^{-1}. The fifth order spectrum is commonly used.

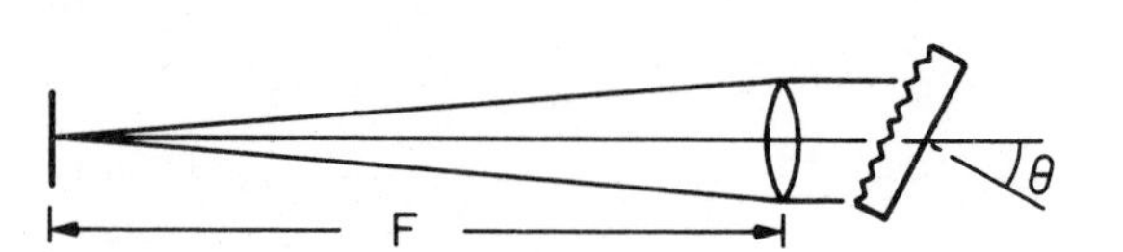

a) At what angle Θ should the grating be tilted to bring the line λ5250.218 of neutral iron in coincidence with the entrance slit in the fifth order spectrum?

b) What other wavelengths in the range λ3600 - λ7000 will also be coincident with the slit?

c) Suggest a simple way to remove the unwanted orders, leaving only the fifth order.

d) What is the dispersion of the instrument at fifth order λ5250?*

e) What is the minimum Δλ which can theoretically be resolved at fifth order λ5250 by this instrument?

* Note that, although $\theta_i = \theta_d$ at λ = 5250 Å, θ_i is fixed while θ_d depends upon λ.

C-5.

When the grooves of a diffraction grating are shaped in such a way as to throw most of the incident radiation into a particular direction, the grating is said to be blazed for this direction. Suppose it were possible to shape the grooves perfectly in a sawtooth shape as shown, each groove surface being tilted at a certain angle θ_b.

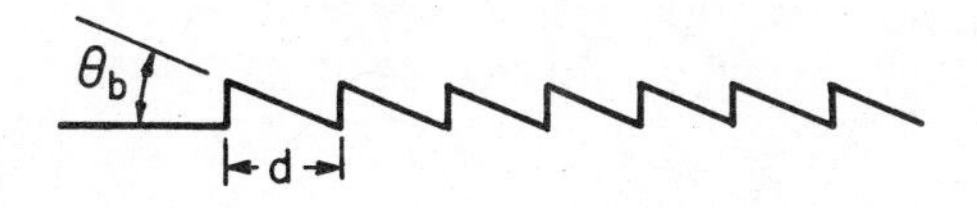

a) Use the notion of the diffracted beam being the radiation emitted by oscillators in the material, which are driven in phase with the incoming radiation, to deduce in what direction the diffracted beam would most intense if $\theta_i = 0$. (Assume white light.)

b) Estimate the approximate angular range over which the blaze would extend.

CHAPTER 23

Electromagnetic Radiation. Refraction. Dispersion. Absorption

Refer to The Feynman Lectures on Physics, Vol. I, Ch. 31.

A-1.

Is red light or blue light deflected most by a prism, and for what physical reason?

B-1.

Find the index of refraction of aluminum for x-rays of wavelength 1.56×10^{-8} cm. Assume that all of the electrons in aluminum have natural frequencies very much less than the frequency of the x-rays.

B-2.

The index of refraction of the ionosphere for radio waves of frequency 100 M Hz is $n = 0.90$. Find the density of electrons per cubic centimeter in the ionosphere.

B-3.

Noting that the electric field of a light wave traveling through a medium of refractive index n is $E = E_0 e^{i\omega(t - nz/c)}$,

a) Show that, if $n = n' - in''$, $E = E_0 e^{-n''\omega z/c} e^{i\omega(t - n'z/c)}$

b) Use the equation $n - 1 = \dfrac{Nq^2}{2\epsilon_0 m} \dfrac{1}{\omega_0^2 - \omega^2 + i\gamma\omega}$

to find the rate at which the intensity of a beam of radiation whose frequency is exactly equal to the natural frequency ω_0 of an atom is attenuated.

C-1.

It was deduced that the instantaneous energy flux of a wave is $S = \epsilon_0 c E^2$ watts per square meter:

a) Find the total rate at which energy is radiated by an electron which is oscillating with amplitude x_0 and angular frequency ω.
b) Compare the energy radiated per cycle with the stored energy $\frac{1}{2} m\omega^2 x_0^2$, and thus find the damping constant γ_R. This process is called radiation damping.
c) An excited atom gives out radiation having a certain wavelength λ. Calculate theoretically the expected breadth $\Delta\lambda$ of the spectral line, if the breadth arises solely from radiation damping. (Think of the atom as being a tiny damped oscillator having a large Q.)

CHAPTER 24

Electromagnetic Radiation. Radiation Damping. Scattering

Refer to The Feynman Lectures on Physics, Vol. I, Ch. 32.

A-1.

What is the wavelength dependence of the scattering of light by free electrons?

B-1.

A beam of light is passing through a region containing N scatterers per unit volume, each of which scatters the light with a cross section σ. Show that the intensity of light remaining in the beam, as a function of the distance x traversed, is

$$I = I_0 e^{-N\sigma x}$$

B-2.

Using the scattering formula

$$\sigma = \frac{8\pi}{3}\left(\frac{e^2}{m_e c^2}\right)^2 \frac{\omega^4}{(\omega^2 - \omega_0^2)^2}$$

and the formula previously derived for the index of refraction of a gas, show that the quantity $N\sigma$ can be written as

$$N\sigma = \frac{2}{3\pi}\frac{(n-1)^2}{N}\left(\frac{2\pi}{\lambda}\right)^4$$

(This was one of the first ways used to estimate Avogadro's number, using the scattering of the blue sky.)

B-3.

The inner corona of the sun (called the K-corona) is sunlight that has been scattered by free electrons. The apparent brightness of the K-corona at one solar radius from the sun's limb is about 10^{-8} that of the solar disc, (per unit area). Estimate the number of free electrons per cm^3 near the sun.

B-4.

How much is the blue light ($\lambda = 4500$ Å) of the sun attenuated in going through the atmosphere when the sun is

a) at the zenith, and

b) 10° from the horizon?

B-5.

A short straight piece of copper wire placed in the beam of electromagnetic waves sent out by a radar antenna will "scatter" some of the wave. The electric field of the wave sets up a motion of the electrons in the wire and this motion results in the radiation of the "scattered" wave. For a short piece of wire (length $\ll \lambda$) we can assume that the average displacement of the electrons in the wire is along the axis of the wire and is proportional to the component of the electric field parallel to the wire. That is, if there are N electrons in the wire and d is their average instantaneous displacement, then $d = \chi E_{\parallel}$, where $E_{\parallel}$ is the component of the electric field of the wave parallel to the wire. We would like to know (in terms of χ and N):

a) What is the maximum scattering cross-section of the wire?

b) How does the scattering cross-section depend on the orientation of the wire?

C-1.

A new radiation is discovered (called x-rays because they are new and mysterious), and are suspected of being transverse waves like light. Scattering of these rays by electrons in matter has been observed. How could you prove they are transverse waves and can be polarized?

C-2.

Show that if the equation of motion of a charged oscillator is assumed to be

$$md^2x/dt^2 + \omega_0^2 x - (2e^2/3c^3)d^3x/dt^3 = F(t)$$

the third-derivative term will correctly describe the rate of loss of energy by radiation (the radiation resistance) at any frequency.

Hint: Assume $F(t) = A \cos \omega t$ and find the amount of power absorbed from the driving source.

C-3.

Interstellar space is believed to be populated by clouds of tiny dust grains composed of carbon, ice, and small amounts of other elements. Estimate the minimum mass per unit area (g cm^{-2}) of such dust needed to obscure our view of stars behind it by, say a factor 100 (i.e., 5.0 stellar magnitudes). Note that the dust grains may remove starlight by scattering as well as by simple absorption.

CHAPTER 25

Electromagnetic Radiation. Polarization

Refer to The Feynman Lectures on Physics, Vol. I, Ch. 33.

A-1.

Is the light obliquely reflected from a lake (e.g., light of the rising sun or moon) polarized with its electric field in a vertical or horizontal plane?

A-2.

Photographers often use a yellow filter or polaroid filter to make the clouds stand out against the sky. Explain the physical reasons for these techniques in both cases.

A-3.

Two polaroid sheets are set with their axes at right angles. A third sheet is then inserted between them with its axis at an angle θ with the first polaroid. What intensity should be transmitted by this combination, if the polaroids are ideal (50% transmission of incident unpolarized light and no transmission through crossed polaroids).

B-1.

Discuss the intensity and polarization of the radiation emitted by an electron moving at constant speed in a circular path, particularly for points (a) on the axis of the circle; and (b) in the plane of the circle.

B-2.

Assume that when a beam of plane polarized light strikes a polaroid sheet, a fraction α^2 of the intensity is transmitted if the polaroid axis is parallel to the polarization axis, and a fraction ϵ^2 is transmitted if the two axes are at right angles. (If the polaroid were ideal, α^2 would be unity and ϵ^2 would be zero.) Unpolarized light of intensity I_0 is normally incident on a pair of polaroid sheets with an angle θ between their axes. What intensity should be transmitted? (Ignore reflection effects.)

B-3.

A vacationing freshman from CIT, strolling with a girl friend, sees the moon, 10° above the horizon, reflected in a calm lake. Nostalgically recalling "Feynman, Chapter 33", he attempts to calculate how bright the image should appear, compared with the moon itself. He assumes the radiation from the moon to be (nearly) unpolarized. What result should he expect to get?
Show that the reflected intensity approaches 100 percent for grazing incidence.

B-4.

Show that Brewster's angle (the angle of incidence i for which the reflected ray is linearly polarized) is such that $\tan i = n$.

B-5.

If light falls perpendicularly on the plane facet of a diamond ($n = 2.40$),
a) What fraction of the incident radiation is reflected?
b) What is Brewster's angle for diamond?

B-6.

Consider plane polarized light traveling through a series of n polarizers, each rotated clockwise through an angle θ/n with respect to the one before it and the first polarizer rotated at an angle θ/n clockwise with respect to the initial plane of polarization. Find the intensity and polarization of the light that passes through the polarizers, if the initial intensity is I_0.

B-7.

Linearly polarized light is sent through a quarter-wave plate followed by a polaroid plate. The direction of polarization makes an angle θ with the optical axis of the quarter-wave plate. As the polaroid is rotated, one observes maxima and minima of the emerging light intensity. What is the ratio I_{max}/I_{min} for $\theta \leq 45^{\circ}$? Assume normal incidence.

B-8.

A piece of crystal quartz, whose indices of refraction are $n_0 = 1.553$ and $n_e = 1.544$ is ground to a thin sheet, 0.12 mm thick, in such a way that its optic axis is parallel to the faces of the sheet. If it is now sandwiched between crossed polaroids so that its optic axis is at 45° with those of the polaroids, what wavelength(s) of visible light (4000-7500 Å) will be transmitted through the system with maximum intensity?

B-9.

The indices of refraction of crystalline quartz for light of wavelength 600 mμ are $n_0 = 1.544$ and $n_e = 1.553$, for the ordinary and extraordinary rays, respectively. If a crystal of quartz is cut parallel to its optic axis, one may take advantage of the maximum difference in speed of the ordinary and extraordinary rays as they enter normally and progress through the crystal. What thickness of crystal is required to shift the relative phases of these two rays by 90°, for light of the above wavelength? Suppose the indices of refraction for light of wavelength 410 millimicrons are $n_0 = 1.557$ and $n_e = 1.567$, and that the crystal of quartz is cut as a quarter-wave-plate for wavelength 600 millimicrons. Describe fully the state of polarization of emergent light of this shorter wavelength which is linearly polarized before entry into the crystal.

C-1.

You are given a polished plate of black obsidian and are asked to measure the index of refraction of the material. How would you proceed, and what precision would you expect to attain?

PART III

CHAPTER 26

Electromagnetic Radiation. Relativistic Effects

Refer to The Feynman Lectures on Physics, Vol. I, Ch. 34.

1.

A disc of radius A rolls without slipping on a horizontal plane. Find the equations of the path followed by a point at a radius $R \leq A$ from the center of the disc in terms of A, R, and the angle θ through which the disc has turned. Let x be measured from the center of the disc vertically and z be measured horizontally. Show that

$$z = A\theta + R \sin \theta$$

$$x = R \cos \theta$$

A-1.

Discuss the polarization properties of synchrotron radiation and bremsstrahlung.

A-2.

If you were to make measurements of the electromagnetic radiation emitted by an astronomical object, like the Crab nebula, how would you distinguish between synchrotron radiation and bremsstrahlung?

A-3.

Assume that you are looking along the x-axis of your coordinate system at a small section of the Crab nebula , and observe synchrotron radiation polarized in the z-direction. What is the direction of the magnetic field? Discuss.

A-4.

Consider an electron circling with relativistic velocity in a uniform magnetic field. Sketch the electric field strength as function of time (over at least two cycles) for an observer looking

a) in a direction along the magnetic field

b) in a direction perpendicular to the magnetic field.

A-5.

Is the radiation pressure of a given light beam greater on a black or on a mirror surface? Explain.

A-6.

Bradley (1728) observed the aberration of light by which stars appear to be displaced in the sky because of the earth's motion in its orbit. The telescope must be pointed "forward" a maximum of 20.5" arc for stars near the pole of the ecliptic. If one considers the velocity of light as known, 3.00×10^8 m/sec, to what value of the radius of earth's orbit does this observation lead?

B-1.

As suggested on p. 34-10 of Vol. I of The Feynman Lectures on Physics, derive the expression $\sin \theta = v/c$ for the aberration of starlight, using the Lorentz transformation.

B-2.

A man in a rocket ship traveling at 0.5 c observes a star at exactly 90° to his direction of motion. A certain line in the spectrum of the star appears to be at frequency ν_0. He now reverses the ship and retraces his path at the same speed. Where does he now see the star and what is the frequency ν_1 of the spectral line?

B-3.

A space probe is moving radially away from an observer. The observer directs a radar beam of frequency ν_o towards the probe and finds the frequency of the returning reflected beam to be ν'. What is the speed of the space vehicle relative to the observer? (Assume that in the rest frame of the vehicle the beam is reflected without change in frequency.)

B-4.

Spectrograms of the radiation coming from opposite ends of the sun's equatorial diameter show a shift of 0.1 Å for the H_α line 6564.7 Å. What is the peripheral speed of the sun at its equator?

B-5.

The D-lines of sodium (laboratory wavelength, 589.0 mμ) are observed to be shifted to 588.0 mμ in the spectrum from a certain star. What is the star's velocity relative to the observer? Is the nonrelativistic Doppler formula sufficiently accurate in this case?

B-6.

The Caltech astronomer M. Schmidt measured the wavelengths of certain spectral lines from a distant quasar and found that they were red-shifted by $\Delta\lambda \approx 2\lambda$. With what speed is the quasar presumably receding?

C-1.

If $z = ct$ in Problem 26-1, find the transverse acceleration of d^2x/dt^2 of the point. This is the retarded acceleration needed for calculating the radiation from a particle moving in a circular path of radius R.

a) Express the result in terms of the observable quantities R, v (the speed of the particle in its path), and x (the apparent transverse position of the particle at the time of observation).

b) Find the ratio of the radiation intensities that will be observed as the particle moves toward and away from the observer in its circular path.

C-2.

An electron initially at rest at $x = 0$, $z = 0$ is given (for times $t > 0$) an acceleration a in the x-z plane at an angle θ with respect to the z-axis. Calculate (relativistically) the electric field $\vec{E}(t)$ at a point $z = R_0$, where R_0 is a "large" distance. Express your answer in terms of a, the true acceleration, θ, and $\beta = v/c$, where v is the true velocity of the electron.

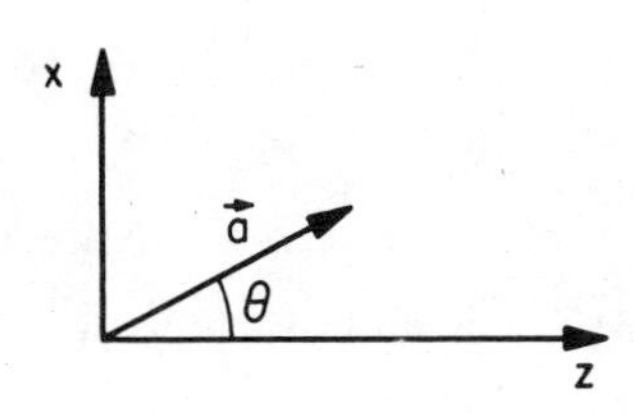

C-3.

A disc of area A and thickness d is illuminated by normally incident light of wavelength λ and intensity I_0. Calculate the force due to radiation pressure for the three following cases.

a) The disc is opaque and non-reflecting.

b) The disc has a refractive index $n = 1.5$. (Answer accurate to 10 percent is sufficient.)

c) The disc has a complex refractive index $n = 1 - in_2$. (n_2 = real.)

C-4.

A spherical balloon of radius 30 m is made almost perfectly reflecting on the outside to avoid solar heating. When the balloon is moving freely in space at 1.0 A.U. from the sun, what force results from the reflection of solar radiation?

C-5.

In one proposed means of space propulsion, a thin sheet of highly reflecting plastic film would be used as a radiation pressure "sail". A plane sheet 100 m square is available, and the mass of the spaceship is 10^3kg. If the spaceship initially travels in a circular orbit of 1 A.U. radius about the sun, describe how to use the "sail" to increase the mean radius of the orbit, and find at what rate the orbit radius will grow. (Hint: Maximize the power transferred to the spacecraft by radiation pressure.)

C-6.

Assume that interplanetary space is populated by small grains of "dust", of mean specific gravity ρ and of roughly spherical shape of radius R.

a) Show that, for any size dust grain, the ratio of the gravitational attraction toward the sun to the radiation pressure away from the sun is independent of the distance from the sun.

b) Using the fact that the solar radiation intensity at the earth's orbit is $1374\ \mathrm{W\ m^{-2}}$, and assuming the absorption cross-section to be πR^2, find for what radius R the radiation pressure and gravitational attraction will just balance.

c) Considering the results of Chapter 32 of Vol. I, The Feynman Lectures on Physics, can the effective cross-section of a dust grain be appreciably greater than πR^2?

CHAPTER 27

Quantum Behavior: Waves, Particles, and Photons

Refer to The Feynman Lectures on Physics, Vol. I, Chs. 37 and 38.

A-1.

Compare qualitatively the x-ray diffraction patterns of two crystals having the same size and shape unit cells, but different atomic arrangements within their unit cells.

A-2.

A parallel beam of electrons with momentum p_o passes through a slit of width W. What is the approximate angular spread of the beam after the slit?

A-3.

a) Thermal neutrons have kinetic energy $T \simeq \frac{1}{40}$ eV. What is the wavelength associated with such neutrons?

b) What is the wavelength associated with electrons of kinetic energy

i) 1 keV

ii) 1 MeV

c) What wavelength would be associated with an object of mass 50 g traveling at 1000 m s^{-1}?

d) Which has a shorter wavelength, a 1 MeV x-ray or an electron having a total energy E_{tot} = 1 MeV?

A-4.

Light of wavelength 4100 Å produces electrons of 1.0 eV maximum kinetic energy in a certain photoelectric cell. What is the longest wavelength to which the cell will respond?

A-5.

The energy (kinetic plus potential) of an electron in the ground state of an H-atom is - 13.6 eV. If a free electron is captured by a proton to form a hydrogen atom in the ground state, what is the wavelength of the photon emitted in this process? Does the emitted radiation fall into the visible, infrared, or ultraviolet region of the spectrum?

A-6.

A μ^- meson ($m_\mu = 206\ m_e$) and a proton may form a (hydrogen-like) μ^--mesonic atom. Estimate the Bohr radius for this atom in Å.

A-7.

It is desired to estimate the minimum possible energy of a harmonic oscillator, for which the energy is determined by $E = p^2/2m + \beta x^2/2$. According to the uncertainty principle, the momentum p can be reduced only at the cost of an increase in the mean displacement, so the condition of minimum energy implies a compromise between these two contributions. What should the minimum energy be?

A-8.

A spectral line (λ = 5000 Å) due to an electron transition from an excited state to the ground state of an atom is observed to have a spread in wavelength of 0.01 Å. On the average, how long does the atom exist in the excited state?

A-9.

Free neutrons are observed to decay into protons and electrons. A conceivable model for a neutron would be an electron-proton bound state. If the neutron has an estimated radius of 1×10^{-15} m, evaluate the approximate kinetic energy (in MeV) for a bound electron in such a model. Discuss your opinion of this model.

A-10.

For small time intervals the rest mass of a particle may be indeterminate because of the uncertainty principle. For example, inside the atomic nucleus a proton may emit a (virtual) π^o-meson ($m_{\pi^o} = 270\ m_e$) which is then reabsorbed within a short time. Estimate the size of a nucleus by considering the distance π^o may travel before it is reabsorbed (within the nucleus). Make sure your arguments are self-consistent.

A-11.

In Chapter 32 (p. 32-3) of Vol. I of the Feynman Lectures on Physics it is discussed that an excited atom would radiate away its energy at a certain rate, which has the effect both of limiting the "lifetime" of an excited state and of introducing a finite width to the corresponding spectral line. Show that these effects, interpreted as uncertainties in the energy and the time of measurement of a photon (or of momentum and position) are consistent with the uncertainty principle.

A-12.

a) Check by your own dimensional analysis the "Bohr radius" of the hydrogen atom.

b) Show by the uncertainty principle that the energy needed to remove an electron from its associated proton in hydrogen is on the order of a few electron volts.

A-13.

a) An x-ray of wavelength 500 Å is absorbed by a hydrogen atom in its ground state. Find the kinetic energy of the ejected electron in electron volts.

b) What is the minimum frequency of x-ray radiation that will ionize unexcited hydrogen?

B-1.

An orchardist found it was easy to set two trees in line, but harder to set three. However, by practice and careful surveying, he set out 64 small trees on a square E-W, N-S grid, 8 trees to a row, and 8 rows, with a 6.0 x 6.0 m basic square. Standing at one corner of his orchard, he observed 3 lines of 8 trees each, counting the tree in the corner where he stood, 2 lines of 4 each, and 4 lines of 3 each.

a) What was the least angle between two adjacent lines of these nine lines?

b) What was the greatest distance between two successive trees in any one of these lines?

c) In an "infinite orchard" set out on this basic grid, each of these lines would appear from the air as one of a set of parallel lines well populated with trees. The distance between adjacent lines of any set could be considered as its "grating space". Find the grating space for successive sets from the south front of the orchard to the 45° line.

B-2.

The sodium and chlorine atoms of an NaCl crystal are alternately spaced at the corners of a cubic lattice whose Na-to-Cl closest spacing is d = 2.82 Å. Find the largest five interplanar spacings for the NaCl crystal, and find at what angles first-order Bragg reflections should occur for these planes, if x-rays of wavelength 1.50 Å were used.

B-3.

In the ultraviolet spectrum of hydrogen one observes a series of lines known as the Lyman series. The wavelengths of the three longest-wavelength lines of this series are 1216 Å, 1026 Å, and 973 Å. Compute the wavelengths of three other possible lines in the spectrum of hydrogen that could be "predicted" on the basis of this information alone, together with the Ritz combination principle. Two of these lines are in the visible region (Balmer series), and one is a line in the infrared (the first line of the Paschen series).

B-4.

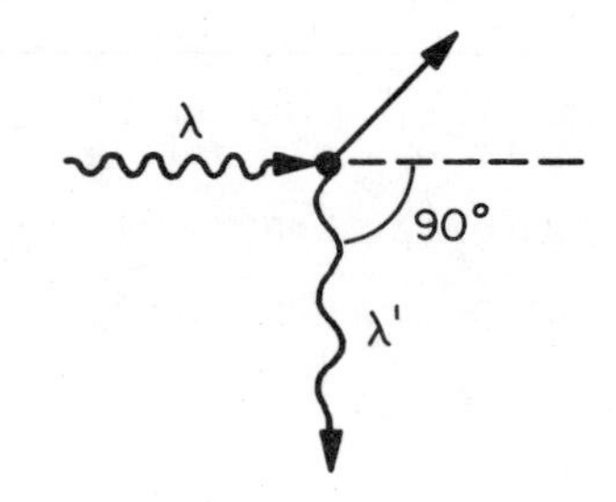

A photon of wavelength $\lambda = 3$ Å (x-ray) is scattered at an angle of 90° by a free electron, which was originally at rest. What is the kinetic energy T (in eV) of the recoil electron?

B-5.

A "monochromatic" neutron beam of "thermal" (1/40 eV) neutrons impinges on a crystal with lattice spacing d = 1.2 Å between planes parallel to the surface.

a) At what angles does Bragg reflection occur?

b) Below what critical energy E_c will diffraction no longer take place?

B-6.

Consider electron diffraction by a crystal of Bragg plane spacing d = 1.2 Å. The diffraction setup allows you to use electron beams of energy

I) $E_k = 10$ keV

II) $E_k = .5$ MeV

a) At what angle does the 1st order diffraction maximum occur in each case?

b) If you were to use this setup for a very accurate determination of the crystal spacing d, which beam would you use and why?

C-1.

A certain atom returns from an excited state (E_1) to the ground state (E_0) by the emission of a photon. The atom emits this photon over a typical time of 10^{-8} s.

a) If the emitted photon has a wavelength of 5000 Å, what is the half-width ($\Delta\lambda$) of the wave train representing this photon?

b) The wavelength of the photon is to be determined by means of a perfect diffraction grating placed perpendicular to the direction of propagation. If the grating spacing is such that the first order maximum is at 45°, how wide (in meters) must the grating be to permit a measurement of the half-width $\Delta\lambda$ found in (a)?

c) What is the energy difference ($E_1 - E_0$) in eV between the excited state and the ground state of the atom?

C-2.

In a simple, non-relativistic model of the hydrogen atom, it is assumed that:

1. The force between the electron and the proton is given by

$$\vec{F} = - \frac{e^2}{4\pi\epsilon_0 r^3} \vec{r}$$

and,

2. The electron moves in a circular orbit about the proton such that the product of the electron's momentum and the radius of the orbit (angular momentum) is given by

$$pr = n\hbar$$

where $n = 1,2,3,...$ and $\hbar$ = Planck's constant $/2\pi$.

a) Compute the radius of the nth orbit and the angular velocity of the electron in the nth orbit.

b) What are the electron's kinetic energy, potential energy and total energy in the the nth orbit?

c) An atomic electron can lose energy by making a quantum jump from a higher to a lower orbit and emitting a photon. What does this model imply about the energies which a photon, emitted by a hydrogen atom, can have?

CHAPTER 28

Kinetic Theory of Gases

Refer to The Feynman Lectures on Physics, Vol. I, Ch. 39.

A-1.

How should the pressure P of a gas vary with n, the number of atoms per unit volume, and $\langle v \rangle$, the average speed of an atom? (Should P be proportional to n and/or $\langle v \rangle$, or should it vary more, or less, rapidly than linearly?)

B-1.

If an ideal gas is compressed adiabatically, then PV^γ = constant. On the other hand, under all conditions, PV/T = constant. Combine these to deduce how P and T, or V and T, are connected during an adiabatic compression.

B-2.

a) Two samples of gas, A and B, of the same initial volume, V_0, and at the same initial absolute pressure, P_0, are suddenly compressed adiabatically, each to one-half its initial volume. How does the final pressure of each sample compare with its initial pressure, if γ_A is 5/3 (monatomic) and γ_B is 7/5 (diatomic)?

b) Find the ratio of works required to perform the two compressions described.

B-3.

Two containers of volume $V_1 = V_2 = V$ are connected by a small tube with a valve. Initially, the valve is closed and the two volumes contain monatomic gas at pressures P_1 and P_2 and temperatures T_1 and T_2, respectively. After the valve is opened, what will be the final pressure and temperature inside the joint volume? (Neglect heat lost from the system.)

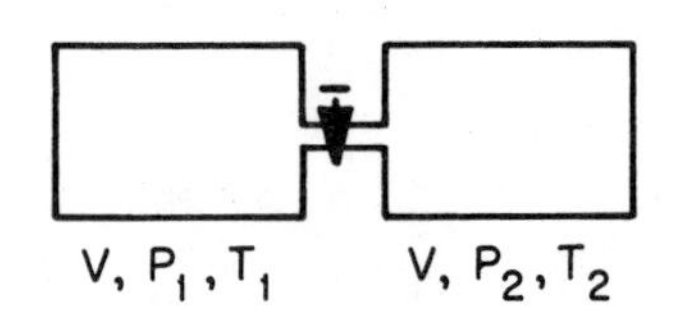

B-4.

a) Imagine a tall vertical column of gaseous or liquid fluid whose density varies with height. Show that the pressure as a function of height follows the differential equation $dP/dh = -\rho(h)\,g$.

b) Solve this differential equation for the case of an ideal gaseous atmosphere of molecular weight μ, in which the temperature is constant as a function h.

B-5.

A cylinder with a leakless, frictionless piston contains 1 m^3 of a monatomic gas ($\gamma = 5/3$) at gauge pressure 1 atmosphere (1.01×10^5 N m^{-2}). The gas is slowly compressed at constant temperature until the final volume is only 0.4 m^3. How much work must be done to accomplish this compression?

B-6.

A bicycle pump is being used to inflate a tire to a pressure of 50 lb in^{-2} gauge pressure, starting with air at atmospheric pressure, 14.7 lb in^{-2} at $20^\circ C (293^\circ K)$. If $\gamma = 1.40$ for air, at what temperature centigrade is the air as it leaves the pump? Neglect heat losses to the walls of the pump.

B-7.

A 50 liter tank is connected to a 15 liter tank through a short tube which contains a pressure release valve which will only allow gas to pass from the larger tank to the smaller tank if the pressure in the larger tank exceeds the pressure in the smaller tank by 88 cm of Hg. If at $17^\circ C$ the larger tank contains gas at atmospheric pressure and the smaller tank is evacuated, what will be the pressure in the smaller tank when both tanks are $162^\circ C$?

B-8.

Two bulbs of volumes 200 cm^3 and 100 cm^3, respectively are connected by a short tube containing an insulating porous plug that permits equalization of pressure but not of temperature between the bulbs. The system is sealed at $27^\circ C$ when it contains oxygen under a pressure of 760 mm Hg. The small bulb is immersed in an ice bath at $0^\circ C$ and the large bulb is placed in a steam bath at $100^\circ C$. What is the final pressure inside the system? Neglect thermal expansion of the bulbs.

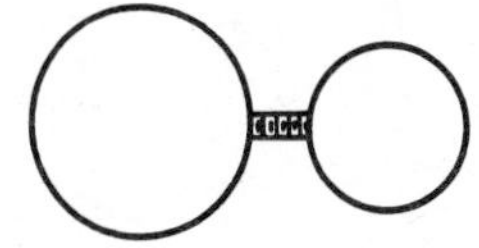

B-9.

A mole of ideal monatomic gas in a non-insulated container with a movable piston is originally at P_1, V_1, and $T_1 = 27^\circ$. Then the gas is slowly heated using a total of 8.31 W h of energy and at the same time allowed to expand at constant pressure to a new state P_1, V_2, and T_2. From evaluation of the new energy content of the gas and the work done by the gas during expansion, find

a) T_2 b) V_2/V_1.

C-1.

Helium gas is contained in one half of each of two identical containers, and the other half of each container is evacuated. The two halves of each container are separated by a piston which has a small stopcock through it. (See the figure). Two experiments are now performed:

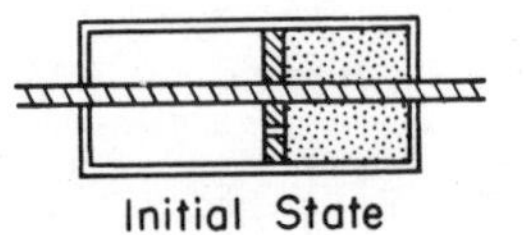
Initial State

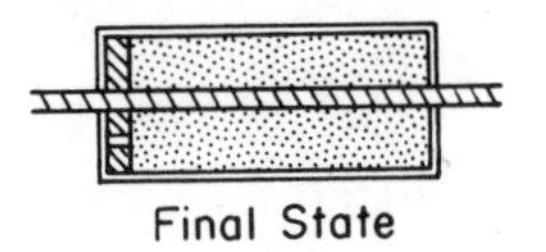
Final State

a) The stopcock is opened in one piston and the gas is allowed to flow through to the other side until equilibrium is reached. The piston is then very slowly moved to one end of the container.

b) The piston of the other container is very slowly allowed to move into the evacuated end of the container, and then the stopcock is opened. Compare quantitatively the final state of the gas in the two containers. (Ignore heat loss through walls, and friction).

C-2.

An atmosphere in which the pressure and density as a function of height satisfy the relation $P\,\rho^{-\gamma}$ = constant is called an adiabatic atmosphere.

a) Show that the temperature of such an atmosphere decreases linearly with height, and find the constant of proportionality. This temperature gradient is called the adiabatic lapse rate. Evaluate this temperature gradient for the earth's atmosphere.

b) Use an argument based on energy considerations to show that an atmosphere having less or more temperature gradient than the adiabatic lapse rate will be stable or unstable against convection, respectively.

C-3.

A cylinder, filled with argon, is equipped with a spring loaded piston of mass m and area A. At equilibrium, the argon is at total pressure P_0, the piston is at distance L_0 from either end of the system and the spring (constant = K) is com-

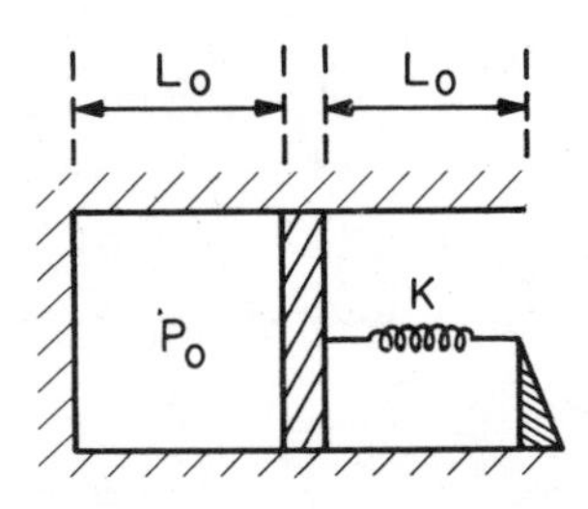

pressed by x_0 (its free length being $L_0 + x_0$). Find the frequency of small oscillations ($x \ll L_0$) of the piston if the gas compresses isothermally.

Hint: You may use $1/(1 + x) \approx 1 - x$ for $x \ll 1$.

C-4.

At ordinary temperature nitrogen tetroxide is partially dissociated into nitrogen dioxide as follows:

$$N_2O_4 \rightleftarrows 2\ NO_2$$

Into an evacuated flask of 250 cm^3 volume 0.90 g of liquid N_2O_4 at 0^oC is introduced. When the temperature in the bulb has risen to 27^oC the liquid has all vaporized and the pressure is 960 mm Hg. What percent of the nitrogen tetrocide has dissociated?

CHAPTER 29

Principles of Statistical Mechanics

Refer to The Feynman Lectures on Physics, Vol. I, Chs. 39 and 40.

A-1.

What is the v_{rms} of an object of mass m in a gas of temperature T?

A-2.

Sketch the Maxwellian distribution $f(v_x)$ vs. v_x and f(v) vs. v for two different temperatures T_1 and T_2 $(T_2 > T_1)$.

A-3.

Consider the molecules of a certain diatomic gas to be rigid dumbbells, free to rotate and move around, but not to vibrate. What is the (classical) specific heat at constant volume?

B-1.

The molar heat capacity at constant volume of a substance, C_v, is the amount of energy needed to raise the temperature of one mole of the substance by one degree, while holding the volume constant. What is the molar heat capacity at a constant volume of a) an ideal monatomic gas? b) an ideal diatomic gas?

B-2.

In the atmospheric pressure law $n = n_0 e^{-\frac{mgh}{kT}}$; $\frac{kT}{mg} = \frac{RT}{\mu g} = h_0$ is called the scale height, where μ is the molecular weight. Evaluate the scale height for the earth's atmosphere and the sun's atmosphere, given $\mu_\oplus = 29$, $T_\oplus = 300^\circ K$, $\mu_\odot = 1.5$, $T_\odot = 5500^\circ K$, $g_\odot = 2.7 \times 10^2$ m s^{-2}.

B-3.

Consider a long, closed cylinder of length L, cross section A, standing upright in the earth's gravitational field. It is filled with an isothermal, homogeneous, diatomic gas of N molecules, each having mass m. What is the pressure at the two ends of the gas tube?

Note: Obviously: $P(h = 0) - P(h = L) = \frac{Nmg}{A}$.

B-4.

An isothermal atmosphere in a constant gravity field confined in an infinitely tall column of uniform cross-sectional area A contains equal numbers, N, of two types of molecules, one of mass m_1 and one of mass m_2, $(m_2 > m_1)$.

a) Find the fraction of molecules that have mass m_1 as a function of height above the ground $(h = 0)$. What are the maximum and minimum values of this fraction and at what values of h do they occur?

b) If you are at a distance above the ground where about 63.2 percent $(1-1/e)$ of the molecules of m_2 are below you, what fraction of the molecules m_1 are below you at the same elevation?

B-5.

The Maxwellian distribution law is of the general form $dN/dv = Av^2e^{-bv^2}$. This may be transformed to $y = x^2e^{-x^2}$.

a) Graph this equation for $0 \leq x \leq 3.0$ to show how an increasing $y = x^2$ curve is suppressed by the exponential.

b) Find its maximum ordinate.

c) See how closely the area under your curve comes to

$$\int_0^\infty x^2e^{-x^2}\,dx$$

B-6.

According to the Maxwell-Boltzmann distribution law, the fraction of molecules in a given volume having speed v in the range dv is given by

$$f(v)\,dv = A\,v^2\exp\left(-\frac{mv^2}{2kT}\right)dv$$

From this distribution, calculate the fraction $F(E)dE$ having kinetic energy E in the range dE.

B-7.

The speed distribution function for a group of N particles is given by

$$f(v)dv = kvdv \quad (0 < v < V)$$

$$f(v)dv = 0 \qquad v > V$$

a) Find k

b) Find the average speed and the root-mean-square speed.

B-8.

In a gas at thermal equilibrium, what fraction of the molecules striking a surface have kinetic energies greater than a) average? b) three times average?

B-9.

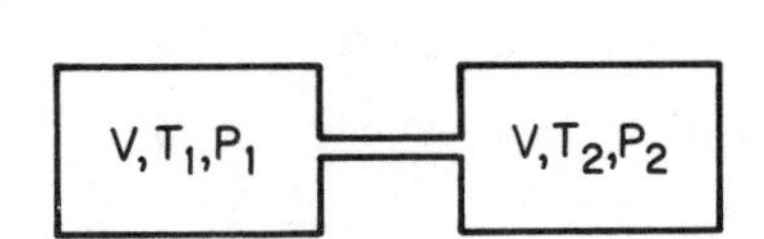

Two containers of equal volume ($V_1 = V_2 = V$) are connected by a small "pinhole" tube. The containers are kept at constant temperatures T_1 and T_2, respectively. All gas molecules have the same mass m.
Find $P_1/P_2 = f(T_1,T_2)$, the ratio of the pressures inside the containers as function of T_1 and T_2 only.

B-10.

A furnace at temperature T contains n atoms of mass m per unit volume, some of which escape through a small hole of area A. (The hole is small enough so that equilibrium inside the oven is not disturbed).

a) What is the number of atoms leaving through the area A per second, having speeds between v and v + dv?
b) What is their rms velocity? (If different from v_{rms} inside oven, explain why.)

C-1.

Na^{23} vapor in a gas discharge tube emits a strong yellow line at 5890 Å. If the vapor is at room temperature, estimate roughly how many angstroms broad this line will appear, due to Doppler shifts caused by thermal motion.
(Useful information: for Na^{23}, $mc^2 \simeq 23 \times 10^9$ eV.)

C-2.

The observability of an absorption spectrum series depends on the number of atoms in the lowest energy state for the series. If the lowest energy state for the Lyman series of hydrogen is - 13.6 eV, and the lowest energy state for the Balmer series is - 3.4 eV, at what temperature of the gas will the number of atoms available to produce a Balmer absorption spectrum equal 1/e times the number of atoms available to produce Lyman absorption? (This is the basis for one way to estimate the temperature of a star.)

C-3.

The ground state of the hydrogen atom has 4 substates which have the same, or very nearly the same, energy. Similarly, the first excited state, 10.2 eV higher, has 16 such substates. What is the ratio of the numbers of atoms in these two states at the surface of the sun, where $T = 5700^{o}K$?

C-4.

In a radiometer, the molecules of a gas at low pressure bombard a set of thin, light vanes which are black on one side and shiny on the other. When radiation strikes these vanes, the absorbed energy is carried away principally by the molecules striking the blackened side of each vane, and the vanes turn as a result of this unbalanced force*. Consider a vessel in which there are n molecules of mass m per unit volume, at an absolute temperature T. A thin vane of unit area inside the vessel is absorbing radiant energy at a rate Π watt, and this energy is being carried off (isotropically) by the molecules striking one side of the vane. Estimate roughly the unbalanced force on the vane for air at room temperature.

*(The blackened side is rougher than the shiny side, which causes the molecules striking the rough side to become trapped for a short time before rebounding, while the molecules striking the shiny side rebound at once. The trapped molecules therefore tend to come to thermal equilibrium with the vane, while those bouncing directly away do not.)

C-5.

a) Air at NTP is flowing at speed v through a smooth pipe of constant cross-sectional area A. As it passes a wire grid which offers negligible resistance to the flow, it is heated; the energy input is W watts. It ultimately emerges from the tube at a speed v'. Write equations for conservation of mass, energy, and momentum as the air traverses the tube, and thus find:

a) v'

b) the final temperature T

c) the thrust* F.

*This is basically a jet engine.

Hint: For simplicity, you may consider a "low-efficiency" engine with equal intake and exhaust pressures.

b) Discuss the approximate performance of an aircraft jet engine in the light of part (a), if the engine consumes 100 kg of air and 2.00 kg of kerosene per second. The heat of combustion of kerosene is about 4.65×10^{7} J kg^{-1}. What complications might invalidate your result?

CHAPTER 30

Equipartition. Applications of Kinetic Theory

Refer to The Feynman Lectures on Physics, Vol. I, Chs. 41 and 42.

· A-1.

Calculate the following:

a) The temperature T for which kT is equal to 1 electron volt.

b) The value of kT in electron volts for room temperature.

c) The wavelength of a photon corresponding to a quantum jump of 1 eV.

A-2.

Activation energies, heats of vaporization, heats of formation or dissociation, etc., are commonly expressed in Joules per g-mole or in electron volts per atom. How many Joules per g-mole is 1 eV/atom?

B-1.

Over the temperature range 0 - 300°C the heat of vaporization of mercury changes by only 3 percent, and is about 0.61 eV/atom on the average. How much error will one make in calculating the vapor density of mercury at 0°C, if the heat of vaporization at 300°C is used instead of the correct 0°C value?

Moral: A small percentage error in a large exponent can have a large effect.

B-2.

Find the relative intensities of light of wavelength 0.31 μ for two black-body sources at temperatures of 2000°K and 4000°K.

C-1.

a) Plot the vapor density of mercury vs. 1/T on semi-log paper, (data are available in the Handbook of Chemistry and Physics) and from this plot, deduce the heat of vaporization of mercury. Check your results against the tabulated value.

b) Do the same for water.

(Note: Chemists use an energy unit called a kilocalorie. 1 kilocalorie = 4186 J.)

C-2.

The distribution law for black-body radiation is:

$$I(\omega)d\omega = \frac{\hbar\,\omega^3 d\omega}{\pi^2 c^2 (e^{\hbar\omega/kT} - 1)}$$

By changing the variable from ω to $z = \hbar\omega/kT$, show that:

a) The total radiation intensity, integrated over all frequencies, is proportional to the fourth power of the absolute temperature.

b) The frequency ω_m at which $I(\omega)$ has its maximum value is proportional to the absolute temperature.

C-3.

Consider a quantized oscillator (e.g., an atom) which can have the following four energy states:

$$E$$
$$E + \Delta E - \epsilon$$
$$E + \Delta E$$
$$E + \Delta E + \epsilon$$

For simplicity, you may consider ϵ negligible, saying that the oscillator has one energy state E and 3 energy states $E + \Delta E$.

a) If you have N_0 such oscillators, what is the specific heat C_v of the system at temperature T?

b) What is C_v for $T \to \infty$? Give a physical explanation.

CHAPTER 31

Transport Phenomena. Applications of Kinetic Theory

Refer to The Feynman Lectures on Physics, Vol. I, Ch. 43.

A-1.

The transfer of what molecular physical quantity gives rise to

a) Heat conduction

b) Viscosity?

A-2.

The cross section for collision of slow neutrons in hydrogen is about 20×10^{-24} cm^2. What is the mean free path of such neutrons in hydrogen at N.T.P.?

B-1.

The "diameter" of an oxygen molecule is roughly 3Å. Estimate the mean free path and the mean time between collisions for oxygen gas at NTP.

B-2.

A "Dewar" (e.g., Thermos-Bottle) is a double-walled evacuated chamber used for thermal insulation. Assume the requirement for good insulation in a Dewar with wall separation D is that $\ell \geq 10$ D, where ℓ is the mean free path of the residual gas in the Dewar.

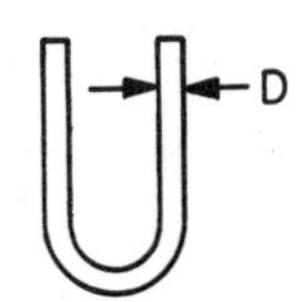

a) If D = 1 cm and the residual gas is oxygen, what pressure (in mm Hg) would be allowable in the Dewar at room temperature?

b) What is the ratio of the conductivities of the Dewar gas for the two pressures P_1 = 400 mm Hg and P_2 = 200 mm Hg? (D = 1 cm; oxygen)

B-3.

Two gases, A and B, are at density ρ_A and ρ_B at a certain temperature T_0. A particular ion is observed to have a mobility μ_a in gas A, and μ_b in gas B. What mobility would you expect the ion to have in a mixture of these gases, at density $\rho_A + \rho_B$ and temperature T_0?

B-4.

When a temperature gradient exists in a material, an energy flow proportional to the temperature gradient results. (Ignore convection.) The coefficient of proportionality, reduced to a unit area and unit temperature gradient, is called the thermal conductivity, K. Thus $dE/dt = KA\, dT/dx$. Show that, in the absence of convection, the thermal conductivity of a gas is

$$K = kn_0 v\ell/(\gamma - 1) = kv/(\gamma - 1)\,\sigma$$

Hint: Interpret thermal conductivity as a transport of internal (heat) energy U across a plane, from one mean free path on either side.

B-5.

When a velocity gradient exists in a fluid, such that the velocity changes with distance at right angles to the flow direction, a drag results, called viscosity. In a gas, this is due to the transport of momentum across a plane, from roughly one mean free path on either side. If the flow is in the x-direction and there is a gradient of v_x in the y-direction, then the drag force per unit area on a plane perpendicular to y is

$$F/A = \eta\, dv_x/dy$$

Show that, for a gas the coefficient of viscosity, η, is approximately,

$$\eta = n_0 vm\ell$$
$$= vm/\sigma$$

B-6.

Notice that the thermal conductivity and the viscosity of a gas are both independent of the pressure. Devise a suitable modification of the formulas for the energy transfer between two surfaces whose temperature are T and $T + \Delta T$, situated a distance D apart, if $\ell \gg D$. Do the same for the momentum transfer between two such surfaces, moving at speeds U and $U + \Delta U$.

C-1.

A certain vessel contains 10^{24} molecules of a gas for which the mean free path is ℓ. For approximately what path length L will no single molecule in the container go farther than L before it suffers its next collision?

C-2.

The resistivity of nearly pure silicon as a function of temperature is shown in the figure. Make a quantitative deduction concerning the nature of the current flow in this substance above and below 300°C.

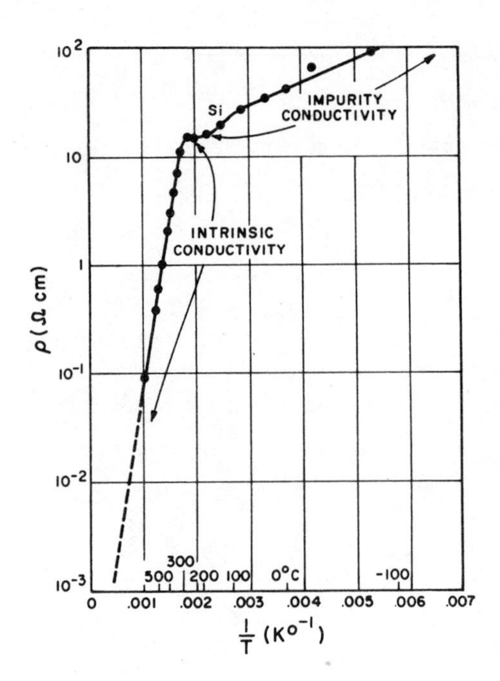

C-3.

In "laminar" flow the viscosity of a liquid alone determines the speed with which it can be transported through a pipe between two reservoirs at different pressure ($P_1 > P_2$). In the figure, the liquid flows through a cylindrical pipe of radius a, length ℓ. ($\ell \gg \lambda$ = mean free path). The liquid has coefficient of viscosity η. Show that the amount of liquid flowing from reservoir 1 to reservoir 2 per second in the steady state is given by

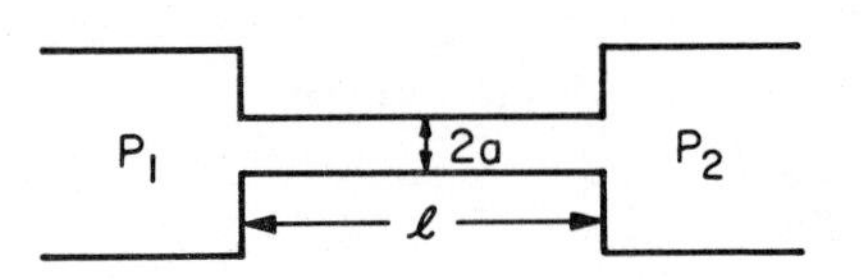

$$V = \frac{\pi a^4}{8\eta} \frac{P_1 - P_2}{\ell}$$

Hint: the forces acting on a "thread" of liquid must sum to zero. This gives $v = v(r)$. (See figure.)

C-4.

The figure shows a single gap spark chamber with gap spacing d between two aluminum plates. A charged cosmic ray particle ionizes the neon gas molecules along its path. At time t later, a high voltage pulse is applied between the plates and a spark is observed along the particle path. In order to keep the chamber free of spurious electrons and ions which exist from earlier cosmic rays, a DC voltage, V_D, is applied between the plates. This "clearing voltage" also sweeps out the electrons and ions from the track of interest.

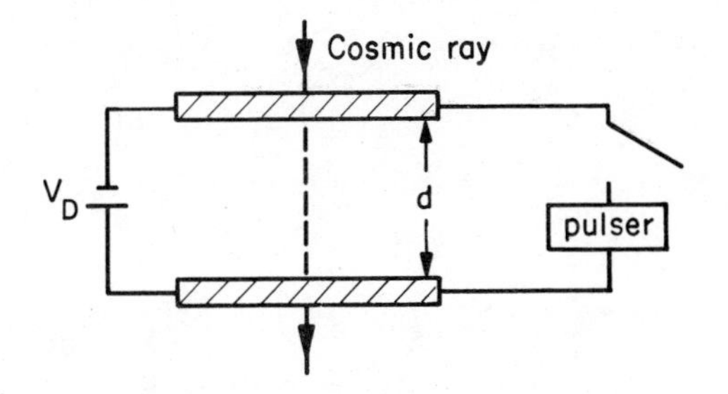

a) At what voltage, V_D, will the space be completely cleared of (a) electrons, and (b) neon ions when the pulse occurs?

b) A spark chamber with spacing, d = 0.63 cm, is observed to give no tracks for an applied V_D of 80 V when $t = 0.4 \times 10^{-6}$ s. Are the electrons essential to the formation of a spark? (Justify your answer.)

Note: Geometric cross section of neon is $\sim 4 \times 10^{-16}$ cm^2, density of neon is $\sim 3 \times 10^{19}$ molecules/cm^3

$m_e c^2 \approx 5 \times 10^5$ eV

$m_{Neon} c^2 \approx 2 \times 10^{10}$ eV

$kT \approx 1/40$ eV at room temperature.

CHAPTER 32

Thermodynamics

Refer to The Feynman Lectures on Physics, Vol. I, Ch. 44.

A-1.

An ideal reversible Carnot engine is run backwards to serve as a refrigerator. If it takes in heat at 250°K and ejects it at 350°K to the outside, for every Joule of heat removed from the box, how many joules are ejected to the outside?

A-2.

If a refrigerator is to be maintained at -3°C, and the outside air is at 27°C, what minimum amount of work has to be done to remove a joule of heat from inside the refrigerator?

A-3.

Two reversible engines operate on Carnot cycles between the same minimum and maximum volume, maximum and minimum pressure, maximum and minimum temperature. One engine uses helium as working substance, the other uses air. Which engine delivers more work per cycle?

A-4.

In a modern steam power plant using superheated steam, the temperature in the steam generator is 600°C. The intake river water used to cool the condenser is at 20°C. What maximum efficiency could such a plant have?

B-1.

An insulated container with a movable, frictionless piston of mass M and area A, contains N grams of helium gas in a volume V_1. The external pressure is P.

The gas is very slowly heated by an internal heating coil until the volume occupied by the gas is $2V_1$.

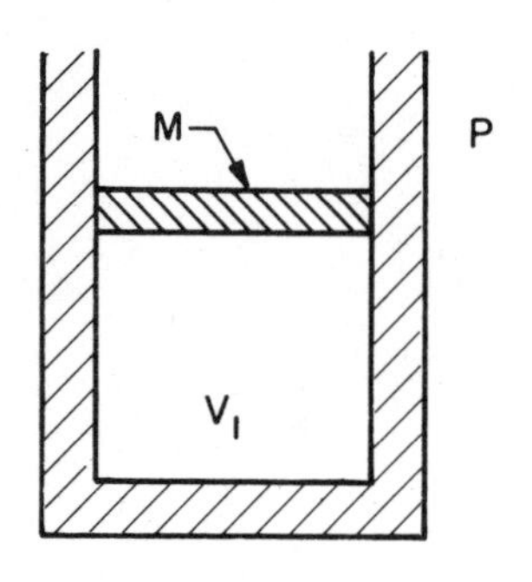

a) What are the initial temperature, T_i, and the final temperature, T_f, of the gas?

What are:

b) The work, W, done by the gas;

c) The change in the internal energy of the gas, ΔU;

d) The heat supplied to the gas, ΔQ?

B-2.

An ideal gas with coefficient γ, is initially at the condition $P_0 = 1$ atm, $V_0 = 1$ liter, $T_0 = 300^\circ K$. It is then:

1. Heated at constant V until P = 2 atm.
2. Expanded at constant P until V = 2 liters.
3. Cooled at constant V until P = 1 atm.
4. Contracted at constant P until V = 1 liter.

a) Draw a P-V diagram for this process.

b) What work is done per cycle?

c) What is the maximum temperature the gas attains?

d) What is the total heat input in steps 1 and 2?

e) What is the combined change in entropy during steps 1 and 2?

B-3.

An ideal engine operates with a perfect gas with $\gamma = 4/3$ in the cycle shown ($A \to B \to C \to D$). At A, P = 1 atm., V = 22.4 liters, T = $300^\circ K$. At C, P = 2 atm., V = 33.6 liters, T = $900^\circ K$.

a) How much work is done per cycle?

b) What is the temperature at B?

c) How much heat input is required for $A \to B$?

d) How much heat input is required for $B \to C$?

e) If the engine works from heat reservoirs at 900° and 300° only, what is the maximum efficiency with which the engine may be operated using the given cycle?

f) What is the maximum efficiency for any engine working between these temperatures?

B-4.

A sample of ideal gas with $\gamma = 4/3$ is taken successively from condition A(1. atm.press. 22.4 liter vol. at $300^\circ K$) to condition C (2 atm.press., 33.6 liter vol. at $900^\circ K$) by two routes, ABC and ADC.

a) Show that the change in entropy is the same by both paths.

b) Compute this change.

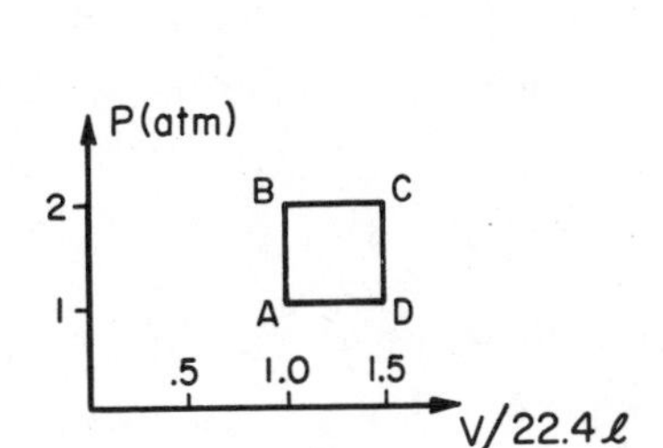

B-5.

In an ideal reversible engine employing 28 g nitrogen as working substance ($\gamma = 7/5$) in a cyclic operation abcd without valves the temperature of the source is 400°K, of the sink 300°K. The initial volume of gas at point a is 6.0 liters and the volume at point c is 18.0 liters.

a) At what volume V_b should the cylinder be changed from heat input (isothermal expansion) to isolation and adiabatic expansion (from V_b to V_c)? At what V_d should the adiabatic compression begin?

b) How much heat is put in on the $V_a \rightarrow V_b$ part of the cycle?

c) How much heat is extracted during the $V_c \rightarrow V_d$ part?

d) What is the efficiency of the engine?

e) What change in entropy per gram occurs in the working substance during $a \rightarrow b$? $c \rightarrow d$?

Hint: You should find that in a Carnot cycle for an ideal gas the expansion ratios V_b/V_a and V_c/V_d are equal.

B-6.

One mole of gas in a container is initially at a temperature 127°C. It is suddenly expanded to twice its initial volume without heat exchange with the outside. Then it is slowly compressed, holding the temperature constant, to its original volume. The final temperature is found to be -3°C. What is γ for the gas and what change in its entropy, if any, has occurred?

B-7.

A gas of coefficient γ in a cylinder of volume V_0 at temperature T_0 and pressure P_0 is compressed slowly and adiabatically to volume $V_0/2$. After being allowed to come to temperature equilibrium (T_0) at this volume, the gas is then allowed to expand slowly and isothermally to its original volume V_0. In terms of P_0, V_0, T_0, what is the net amount of work the piston does on the gas?

B-8.

Translate the ideal Carnot cycle abcd on a p-V diagram between T_1 and T_2 and (p_a, V_a) (p_c, V_c) into a temperature entropy diagram with corresponding points ABCD.

B-9.

The first earth settlers on the moon will have great problems in keeping their living quarters at a comfortable temperature. Consider the use of Carnot engines for climate control. Assume that the temperature during the moon-day is 100°C, and during the moon-night is -100°C. The temperature of the living quarters is to be kept at $20^{\circ}C$. The heat conduction rate through the walls of the living quarters is 0.5 kw per degree of temperature difference. Find the power which has to be supplied to the Carnot engine during the day and the night.

B-10.

Two "identical" bodies of constant heat capacity, originally at temperatures T_1 and T_2, respectively, are used as reservoirs for a Carnot engine operating in infinitesimal reversible cycles. If the bodies remain at constant pressure and undergo no phase changes,

a) Show that after the engine comes to rest, the final temperature $T_f = \sqrt{T_1 T_2}$.

b) Find the total work done by the engine.

Hint: Recall that ΔQ is related to ΔT and consider what happens to the entropy in a reversible cycle.

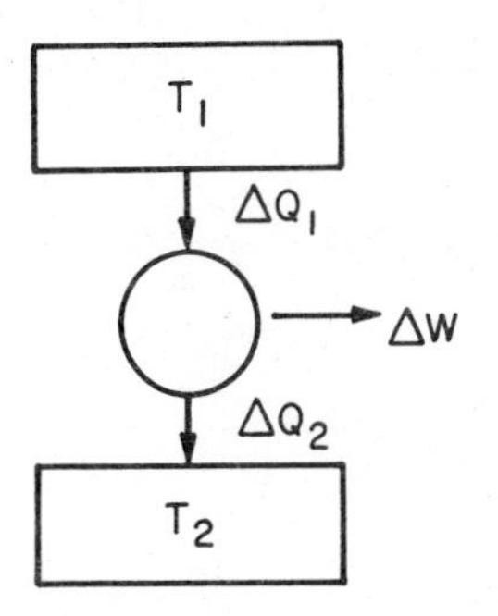

B-11.

A careless experimenter left the valve of a tank of helium slightly open over the weekend. The gas, originally at 200 atm. slowly escaped isothermally at $20^{\circ}C$. What change in entropy per kg of gas occurred?

C-1.

The ideal gas turbine engine cycle consists of adiabatic compression from A to B, addition of heat at constant pressure from B to C, adiabatic expansion from C to D, and rejection of heat at constant pressure from D to A, all carried out in a reversible manner.

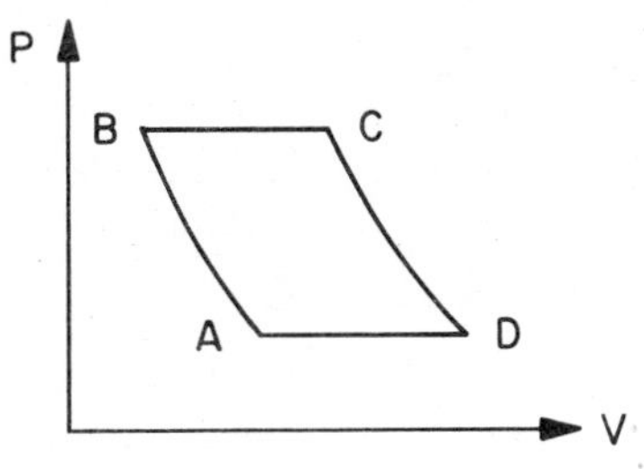

Assume that the working fluid in the engine is an ideal gas with ratio of specific heats γ, and that $\dot{N}$ moles pass through the engine per unit time. Assume further that the maximum gas temperature, T_c, is fixed by the maximum temperature which the hot parts of the engine can withstand and that the minimum gas temperature, T_A, is fixed by the ambient air temperature.

a) Find the power produced by the engine as a function of the pressure ratio, $p = \frac{P_B}{P_A}$.

b) At what pressure ratio is the power a maximum?

c) What is the maximum power?

d) What is the efficiency at maximum power?

e) What is the volume flow rate of air ($\gamma = 7/5$) at atmospheric conditions ($P_A = 1.013 \times 10^5 \text{ Nm}^{-2}$, $T_A = 300^oK$) in such an engine, if it produces 1 megawatt of power and the maximum temperature is $T_c = 1200^oK$?

f) What is the efficiency of the engine in (e)?

g) What is the pressure ratio of the engine in (e)?

CHAPTER 33

Illustrations of Thermodynamics

Refer to The Feynman Lectures on Physics, Vol. I, Chs. 45 and 46.

A-1.

How does the total radiation intensity in a black body cavity depend on temperature?

A-2.

In a molecular gas, the number of molecules in a closed container is independent of temperature. Is the same true for a "photon gas"? Explain.

A-3.

Calculate c_v, the specific heat of a "photon gas", at constant volume.

A-4.

A DC current of 10 A flows through a resistor of 10 Ω which, is kept at the constant temperature of 10°C.

a) What is the entropy change of the resistor (in cal/$^\circ$K/s?)

b) What contribution is made to the entropy change of the universe?

B-1.

For an ideal gas, whose internal energy depends only upon T, show that the difference between the molar heat capacities at constant pressure and at constant volume is equal to the gas constant R: $C_p - C_v = R$.

B-2.

The latent heat of vaporization of water is about 2.44×10^6 J kg^{-1}, and the vapor density at 100°C is 0.598 kg m^{-3}. Use the Clausius-Clapeyron Equation to find the rate of change of the boiling temperature with altitude near sea level in $^\circ$C per km. Assume the temperature of the air is 300°K.

B-3.

The top layers of the water in a lake are initially at 0°C. A cold breeze starts to blow, keeping the surface of the lake at a temperature ΔT below 0°C. Find the rate of increase of the thickness of the ice, assuming that the heat loss required to lower the temperature of the ice which has already formed is much less than that required to form new ice. (Assume also that the temperature in the ice changes linearly with depth.) Using your result, calculate the thickness of the ice one hour after freezing begins if $\Delta T = 10^{\circ}C$. (Thermal conductivity of ice: $K = 2.0$ J/s m$^{\circ}$C Latent heat of ice formation: $L = 3.3 \times 10^{5}$ J/kg.)

B-4.

Two volumes of gas are separated by a stopcock, which is opened at time $t = 0$. $V_2 = 2V_1$. What is the change in entropy of (a) the gas; (b) the surroundings; and (c) the universe after a very long time for the two following cases:

1. for: V_1 contains 1 mole of helium
   V_2 contains 2 mole of Argon
2. V_1 contains 1 mole of helium
and also V_2 contains 2 mole of helium?

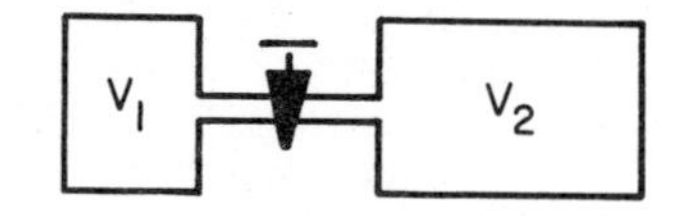

B-5.

Calculate the change in entropy when radiation (photon gas) is:

a) Expanded isothermally.

b) Heated at constant volume, and use your results to find $S(V,T)$ for a photon gas.

B-6.

Sunlight beats down perpendicularly on a large black paved field in Equatorial Africa. If the surface radiates as a black body, what maximum temperature does it attain? (Solar constant, 1395 watts/m^2).

B-7.

The sun radiates approximately like a black body of temperature 5700°K. If a perfectly black copper sphere is irradiated by sunlight at a distance of one astronomical unit from the sun, what equilibrium temperature will it attain? (The sun's diameter subtends an angle of $0.^{\circ}50$ at the earth.)

B-8.

Black body radiation in an isothermal cavity of volume V_0 is compressed at constant temperature until the volume is decreased to $V_0/2$. By what factor is the radiation pressure changed?

B-9.

A thin spherical shell of negligible heat capacity and radius R has a black interior surface and an exterior surface with absorption coefficient A for black body radiation. The shell floats in empty space and at time $t = 0$ contains a "photon gas" at temperature T_0. Find the temperature T for times $t \geq 0$.

B-10.

a) Consider a thin black spherical shell of radius R, containing an ideal monatomic gas at temperature T_0. If the sphere contracts adiabatically to radius R/2, by what factor F would the radiation intensity change as seen by a very distant observer if you neglect gravitational changes of the gas in the compression?

b) If in part (a) you include gravitational effects, would F be larger or smaller and why?

B-11.

Consider a thin, black spherical shell (of negligible heat capacity) of radius R containing black body radiation at temperature T_0. If the sphere contracts adiabatically to radius R/2, by what factor F will the radiation intensity change as seen by a very distant observer?

B-12.

A blackened solid copper cylinder 2.0 cm long and 10.0 cm^2 in the base area is suspended by a thin insulating fiber at the center of an evacuated hollow spherical cavity 25.0 cm in radius, and having blackened walls. The walls of the cavity are maintained at a constant temperature of 27^oC.

a) If the copper cylinder is in thermal equilibrium with the cavity, at what rate is it radiating energy to the cavity walls? Give answer in joules/sec.

b) If the cylinder is heated to 150° and then allowed to cool, what is its rate of temperature decrease as it passes through temperature 127^oC? (Assume that at any instant all parts of the copper are at the same temperature.)

$\rho_{Cu} = 8950$ kg m^{-3}, $C_p(Cu) = 390$ J/kg^oC.

B-13.

The density at the center of the sun is about 80 g cm^{-3} and the central temperature is about $13 \times 10^{6\,o}K$. The matter is composed almost entirely of protons and electrons. Find the gas pressure and the radiation pressure at the center of the sun.

C-1.

At 0^oC, the specific volume of saturated water vapor is 206 m^3/kg. What is the latent heat of vaporization in J kg^{-1} at this temperature? (Determine dp/dT from tables, calculate L, compare with tabular value.)

C-2.

a) Use a thermodynamic argument to show that, if a substance expands when it freezes, its freezing temperature must decrease with increasing pressure.

b) Estimate the lowest temperature of the ice on a skating rink for which ice skating would be possible.

C-3.

If a certain object absorbs a fixed fraction A of all radiation incident upon its surface and reflects the rest, show that, at temperature T, it emits an amount $A \sigma T^4$ per unit area.

C-4.

A black body of radius r at temperature T is surrounded by a thin shell of radius R, black on both sides. Find by what factor this radiation shield reduces the rate of cooling of the body.
(Consider space between sphere evacuated, with no thermal conduction losses.)

C-5.

A black spherical shell at a certain position in interplanetary space has equilibrium temperature T_0. If the same object were copper-plated, would its new equilibrium temperature be higher, lower, or equal to T_0? Typical values for the reflectivity of copper as function of wavelength are:

λ(micron)	.305	.385	.450	.550	.600	.700	1.00	3.0	9.0
R(λ)	.25	.29	.37	.48	.72	.83	.90	.97	.98

$$R(\lambda) = \frac{I_{reflected}}{I_{incident}}$$

Consider the sun a black body radiator of 5700°K. Also, see Problem C-3.

CHAPTER 34

The Wave Equation. Sound

Refer to The Feynman Lectures on Physics, Vol. I, Ch. 47.

A-1.

The compressive elastic property of a liquid is measured by M, the bulk modulus, where M is defined by

$$dP = -M\frac{dV}{V} .$$

dV/V is the fractional change in volume brought about by a dP change in external pressure. By dimensional analysis, determine the speed of sound propagation in a liquid as a function involving M.

A-2.

Two identical ropes of small mass hanging from a support are stretched by weights of 1 kg and 2 kg, respectively. What is the ratio of the wave velocities for transverse waves along the two ropes?

A-3.

Find the ratio of the speed of sound in helium to that in hydrogen at the same temperature.

A-4.

Two whistles of the same length are blown (a) with air cooled to liquid air temperature (-180°C) and (b) with heated air. One whistle gives a pitch just one octave above the other (twice the frequency). What should be the temperature of the air blowing the whistle (b)?

B-1.

Show that $u = Ae^{i(\omega t - kx)}$ satisfies the wave equation

$$\partial^2 u/\partial x^2 = (1/v^2)\partial^2 u/\partial t^2$$

provided ω and k satisfy the relation $\omega = vk$.

B-2.

A uniform, perfectly flexible string of density σ kg m^{-1} is stretched with a tension T. Derive the wave equation governing the lateral displacement y and deduce the speed of propagation of disturbances along the string. Assume that $\partial y/\partial x \ll 1$ at all points and times, and consider only vibration in a plane. Note that the component of the string tension in the lateral direction is very nearly $T\, \partial y/\partial x$.

B-3.

A crude musical instrument is constructed by stretching a wire of negligible mass under tension, T, between two points and firmly attaching a mass, M, to the wire at a distance x from one end. The mass is displaced from equilibrium by a small distance $A(A \ll x,\ A \ll \ell - x)$, and then allowed to vibrate.

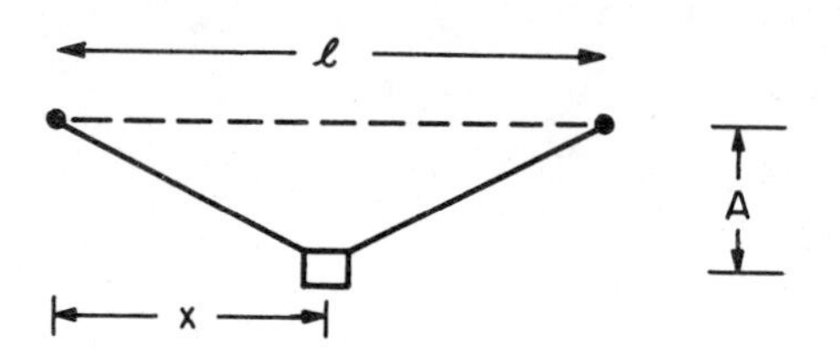

a) Find the frequency of the sound.

b) Write the equation for the displacement of the mass from equilibrium as a function of time.

c) As x is varied, what are the minimum and maximum frequencies available? Neglect the effects of gravity.

B-4.

A sound wave passes through a gas of density ρ_0 and pressure P_0. The displacement of the gas molecules is described by the equation $\xi = \xi_m \cos(\omega t - kx)$.

a) Find the equation for the pressure in the gas as a function of x and t.

b) Find the kinetic energy of motion due to the sound wave in a volume of gas with area A in the YZ plane and of length λ along the X-axis.

B-5.

A light, flexible diaphragm is located at a node of an organ pipe in which the sound level is 120 db at a frequency of 100 cps. The medium is air at N.T.P.

a) What is the amplitude of the diaphragm's motion (in cm)?

b) What is the amplitude of the temperature change in the gas?

C-1.

If one inhales helium and speaks, the voice sounds unnatural and high in pitch. If all your resonant cavities ("the empty parts of your head") were filled with helium instead of air, by about what factor would every resonant frequency be increased? If you were to sing a tune, what effect would the helium have on the key in which you sing? Discuss.

C-2.

Pinch a single length of rubber band about 5 cm long between the fingernails of your two hands; twang it to observe the pitch; then stretch it 2x, 3x, 4x, 5x its original length without changing the mass of band between fingernails, twanging it as you proceed. Discuss the results observed. Why does not a violin string do the same thing if you increase its length?

C-3.

Consider a steady, plane sound wave of frequency 1000 Hz in which the pressure peaks are ± 1 dyne cm^{-2} from the prevailing atmospheric pressure of 1×10^6 dynes cm^{-2}.

a) What change in density accompanies such a wave?

b) What maximum particle displacement X_m?

c) What intensity?

(Take the velocity of sound as 340 m/sec.)

CHAPTER 35

Linear Wave Systems : Beats, Modes

Refer to The Feynman Lectures on Physics, Vol. I, Chs. 48 and 49.

A-1.

If you write the wave equation as

$$\frac{\partial^2 y}{\partial x^2} = \frac{1}{C^2}\frac{\partial^2 y}{\partial t^2}$$

What are the phase velocity v_{ph} and group velocity v_g in terms of C?

A-2.

If in a medium the phase velocity differs from the group velocity, we speak of dispersion. Do we find dispersion in

i) an audible sound wave in air?

ii) a stretched copper wire?

iii) a water wave?

A-3.

The phase velocity of a water wave of wavelength λ is, neglecting surface tension and the effects of finite depth,

$$V_{ph} = \sqrt{g\lambda/2\pi}$$

Show that the group velocity is one half the phase velocity. What are the group and phase velocities of a wave of wavelength 1000 m?

A-4.

Six gliders of mass m each, connected by identical springs, are constrained to move in a linear air trough. How many independent modes of oscillation are there?

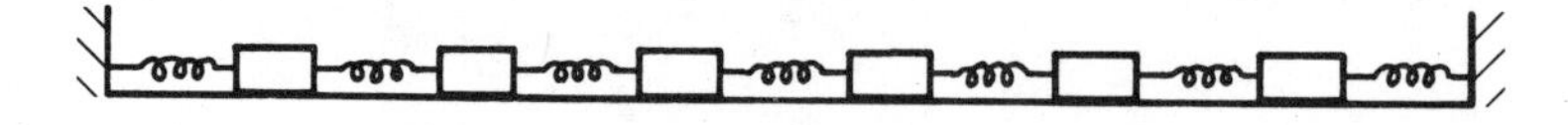

A-5.

Write the solution of the wave equation, $u = u(x,y,t)$ describing the vibrational mode of the rectangular plate shown, which is clamped at the edge.

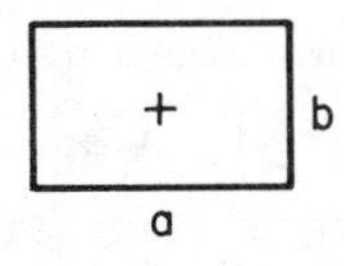

B-1.

Use the idea of infinitely long, periodic wave trains moving in opposite directions to deduce what will happen if an ideal, uniform stretched string of length L, held firmly at both ends, is pulled aside a distance A (normal to its length) at its mid-point and then released. Sketch a few representative views of the appearance of the string at various times throughout a half-cycle of the motion.

B-2.

If surface tension in included, the phase velocity of a surface wave on a liquid of density ρ and surface tension T is

$$V_{ph} = \left(\frac{2\pi T}{\lambda\rho} + \frac{g\lambda}{2\pi} \right)^{1/2}$$

if the depth is sufficiently great. Find the group velocity of such a wave.

B-3.

Find the phase velocity of ripples of wavelength 1.0 cm

a) in water (surface tension 70 dyne cm^{-1});

b) in alcohol (surface tension 26 dyne cm^{-1}).

B-4.

Find the wavelength, frequency, and speed of ripples on water which advance with minimum speed.

B-5.

Two sources of sound S_1 and S_2 are situated 10 m apart. On the same line at A and B are two observers. S_1 emits a steady plane wave whose excess pressure is given by $p_e = A \cos (200\ t)$; and S_2 emits a steady plane wave for which $p_e = A \sin (210\ t)$. The distance intervals, S_1S_2, S_2A and AB are each 10 m. For parts a) and b), take the speed of sound as 340 m/sec.

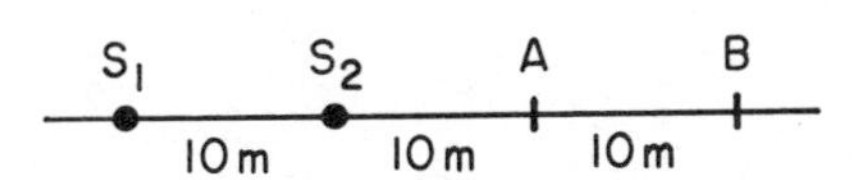

a) How many beats per second does each observer hear?

b) What is the time interval between the maximum pulses heard by A and those heard by B?

c) If there were dispersion in the medium such that the wave of higher frequency went at 341 m/sec and that of lower went at 340 m/sec, with what speed would beats formed by the two sounds advance from A to B?

B-6.

A long diesel freight train is traveling uphill at a speed of 5.0 m s^{-1} on a straight track. As it approaches a tunnel in a sheer vertical wall, the engineer gives a long steady blast of the horn, whose principal frequency is 340 cycles s^{-1}. Both the horn itself and its echo from the wall are heard a) by the engineer; b) by a person on the ground near the caboose. How many beats per second does each person hear?

B-7.

Show that the function

$$f(x,y,z,t) = Ae^{i\omega t} \sin l\pi x/a \sin m\pi y/b \sin n\pi z/c$$

where

$$\omega^2 = v^2\pi^2(l^2/a^2 + m^2/b^2 + n^2/c^2)$$

and l, m, n are integers ≥ 1,

a) satisfies the three-dimensional wave equation (with propagation velocity v).

b) is equal to zero at x = 0 and x = a, y = 0 and y = b, and z = 0 and z = c.

c) oscillates sinusoidally in time.

d) If a:b:c = 1:2:3 evaluate the lowest ten frequencies in terms of the lowest frequency ω_0. List them in order of increasing frequency and plot them roughly on a vertical scale.

B-8.

On a straight air track (negligible friction) gliders of mass m_1 and m_2 are attached to two opposite walls by springs of stiffness k_1 and k_2, respectively, and are also attached to one another by a spring of stiffness k. (See the figure.) Write down the equations of motion of the two gliders. Let

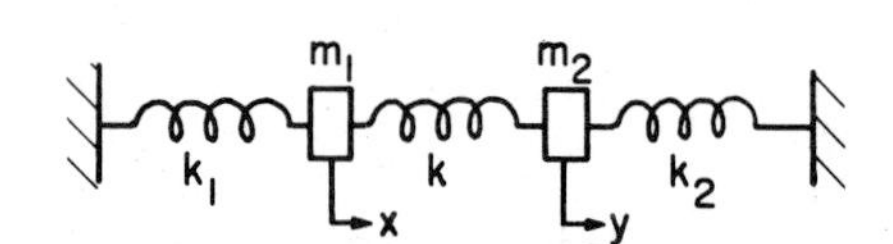

$$k_1/m_1 = k_2/m_2 = \omega_0^2$$

Substitute $x = Ae^{i\omega t}$ and $y = Be^{i\omega t}$ into the above equations and find the frequencies and amplitudes of the two normal modes of vibration.

B-9.

Three pendulums, all of length ℓ, are symmetrically arranged as shown in the figure. The center bob, of mass 2m, is connected by ideal springs of force constant k to the outer bobs, each of mass m. What are the frequencies and relative displacements of the pendulums when they are vibrating in each of the three normal modes of the system? Consider only vibrations in the plane of the figure. (Caution: A little physical insight will save a lot of algebra in this problem.)

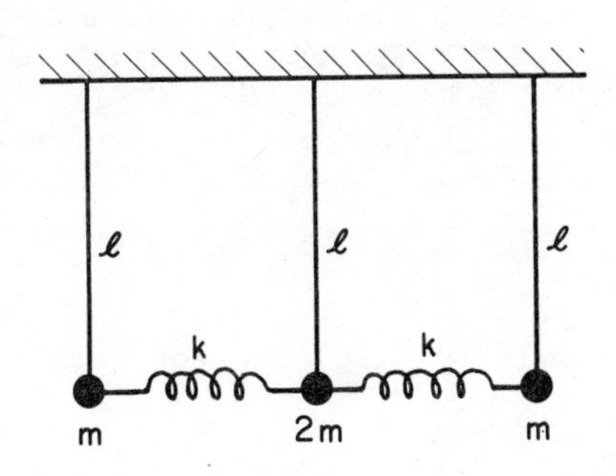

B-10.

Two identical cylinders of moment of inertia I are hung by identical wires of torsion constant K. No pendulum-like motion is allowed. How many modes of oscillation are there and what are their periods?

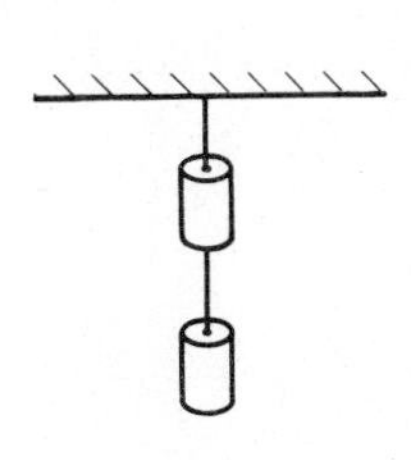

B-11.

Two identical masses m are suspended in identical springs with force constant k, as shown. Find the frequencies of the normal modes. No pendulum-like motions are allowed.

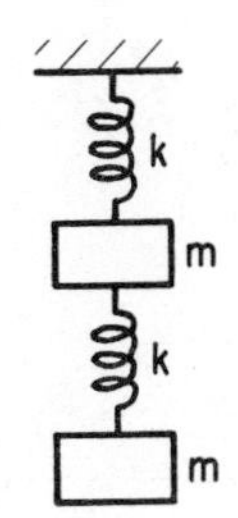

B-12.

A thin rod of mass M, length L, moves on a frictionless horizontal table. Its CM is constrained to move on the straight line a - a'. Two identical springs (spring constant K) are connected to the endpoints of the rod, and operating parallel to a - a'. For small amplitudes, find the fundamental modes of oscillation and their frequencies. Describe the motion.

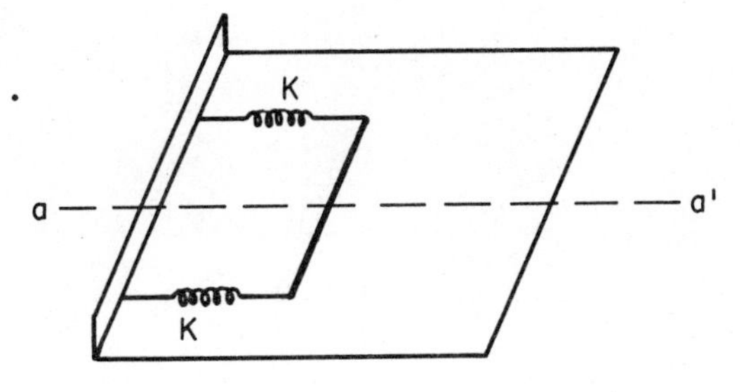

C-1.

In a standing wave on a stretched string, which can be described by $y = A \sin Kx \cos \omega t$, each element of mass σdx along the wave can be treated as an infinitesimal harmonic oscillator undergoing oscillations about $y = 0$. Determine the total energy contained in one wavelength of the standing wave.

C-2.

A nonrelativistic electron with mass m is confined between two plates separated by a distance L.

a) Estimate the minimum possible kinetic energy, using the uncertainty principle.

b) Calculate this energy, using the condition that the wave function describing the electron is a standing sine wave with nodes at the boundaries.

c) What is the average momentum of the electron? (Careful: consider magnitude and direction.)

CHAPTER 36

Fourier Analysis of Waves

Refer to The Feynman Lectures on Physics, Vol. I, Ch. 50.

A-1.

Give the Fourier expansions of the functions

a) $y = \text{const.}$

b) $y = \sin x \quad (0 \le x \le 2\pi)$.

B-1.

Starting from the Fourier analysis of the square wave,

$f(x) =$ 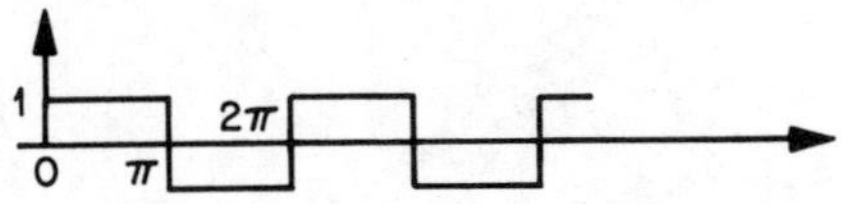

$$= \frac{4}{\pi}\left(\sin x + \frac{1}{3}\sin 3x + \frac{1}{5}\sin 5x + \dots\right)$$

Show that

a) $1 - \frac{1}{3} + \frac{1}{5} - \frac{1}{7} + \dots = \pi/4$

b) $1 + \frac{1}{9} + \frac{1}{25} + \frac{1}{49} + \dots = \pi^2/8$

c) $1 + \frac{1}{4} + \frac{1}{9} + \frac{1}{16} + \frac{1}{25} + \dots = (4/3)\left(1 + \frac{1}{9} + \frac{1}{25} + \frac{1}{49} + \dots\right) = \pi^2/6.$

B-2.

a) Analyze the function

$g(x) =$ 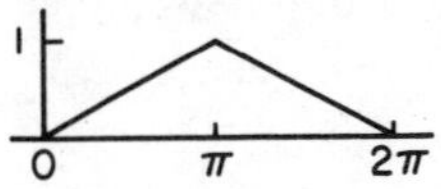

into its Fourier components and show that your result agrees with the result obtained by integrating the function of problem 36-B-1.

b) Use this result to show that

1) $1 + 1/3^4 + 1/5^4 + 1/7^4 + \dots = \pi^4/96$

2) $\sum_{n=1}^{\infty}(1/n^4) = \frac{2^4}{2^4 - 1}(1 + 1/3^4 + 1/5^4 + \dots) = \pi^4/90$

B-3.

In Chapter 45 of Vol. I of The Feynman Lectures on Physics one needs to evaluate $\int_0^\infty \frac{x^3\,dx}{e^x - 1}$. You can now do this by multiplying numerator and denominator by e^{-x} and expanding

$$\frac{1}{1 - e^{-x}} = (1 + e^{-x} + e^{-2x} + \ldots)$$

and carrying out the integrals term by term. Thus you should obtain

$$\int_0^\infty \frac{x^3\,dx}{e^x - 1} = \int_0^\infty u^3 e^{-u}\,du\,[1 + 1/2^4 + 1/3^4 + \ldots]$$

$$= 6 \times \pi^4/90 = \pi^4/15.$$

Try it.

B-4.

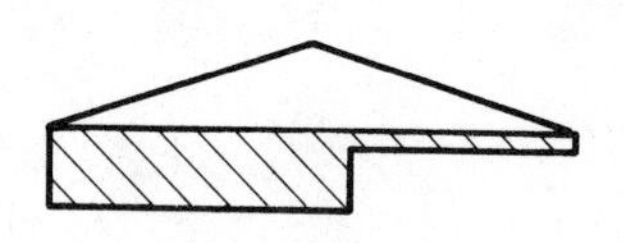

A guitar string is plucked at the center of its length. Calculate the amplitude (relative to the fundamental) of the first 3 harmonics.

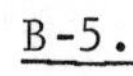

B-5.

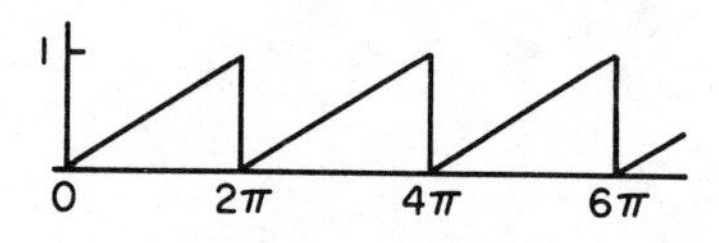

Find the Fourier series which represents the sawtooth function used in the horizontal sweep circuit of an oscilloscope:

B-6.

A string of length L cm has a mass density of σ gm cm^{-1} and is under tension S dynes. At time t = 0, the shape is given by

$$y(x) = 3 \sin \frac{\pi x}{L} + 1 \sin \frac{3\pi x}{L} \quad \text{(in cm)}$$

a) What is the period of oscillation T?

b) What is the shape at one-half period? (t = T/2)

C-1.

A full-wave rectifier is a device which transforms a sine wave of amplitude V_0 into the form shown in the figure:

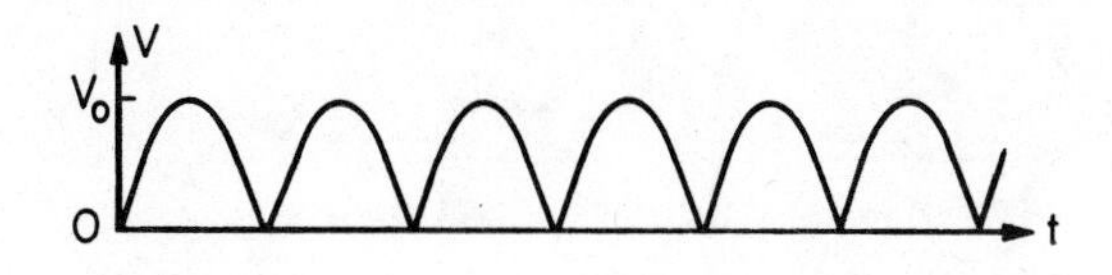

a) Evaluate the average value of V(t). This will be the DC output voltage.

b) Find the amplitude of the second harmonic component of the output voltage.

C-2.

A certain transformer yields an output voltage proportional to

$$V_{out} = V_{in} + \epsilon(V_{in})^3$$

Analyze the effect introduced by the cubic term upon:

a) an input sine wave

b) two or more input sine waves of different frequency added together.

APPENDIXES

APPENDIX A

Units and Dimensions

Units and Dimensions	Symbol	Value	Remarks
MASS [M]			
kilogram	kg	1 kg	MKSA unit of mass
gram	g	10^{-3}kg	cgs unit of mass
pound	lb	0.4536 kg	
LENGTH [L]			
meter	m	1 m	MKSA unit of length
centimeter	cm	10^{-2}m	cgs unit of length
millimeter	mm	10^{-3}m	
micron	μ	10^{-6}m	
Angstrom	Å	10^{-10}m	
kilometer	km	10^{3}m	
inch	in	2.54 cm	Exact
foot	ft	0.30480 m	
mile	mi	1.6093 km	
astron. unit	A.U.	1.497×10^{8} km	Dist. of ⊕ from ☉
light year	l.y.	9.5×10^{12} km	
parsec	pc	206265 A.U.	3.263 l.y., or 31×10^{12} km
TIME [T]			
second	s	1 s	MKSA unit of time, cgs unit of time
millisecond	ms	10^{-3}s	
microsecond	μs	10^{-6}s	
nanosecond	ns	10^{-9}s	
minute	^{m} or min	60 s	^{m} used as a superscript: $1^{m} = 60^{s}$
hour	^{h} or hr	3600 s	^{h} used as a superscript: $1^{h} = 60^{m}$
day (solar)	^{d} or d	8.64×10^{4} s	^{d} used as a " $1^{d} \equiv 86400^{s}$
year	^{y} or y	3.16×10^{7} s	^{y} used as a " $1^{y} = 365^{d}.25$

Units and Dimensions

Units and Dimensions	Symbol	Value	Remarks
CURRENT $[QT^{-1}]$			
ampere	A	1 A	MKSA unit of current
milliampere	mA	10^{-3}A	
microampere	μA	10^{-6}A	
VELOCITY $[LT^{-1}]$			
$m\ s^{-1}$	$m\ s^{-1}$	$1\ m\ s^{-1}$	MKSA unit
$mi\ hr^{-1}$	$mi\ hr^{-1}$	$22/15\ ft\ s^{-1}$	
ACCELERATION $[LT^{-2}]$			
$m\ s^{-2}$	$m\ s^{-2}$	$1\ m\ s^{-2}$	MKSA unit
FORCE $[MLT^{-2}]$			
newton	N	$1\ kg\ m\ s^{-2}$	MKSA unit
dyne	dyne	10^{-5}N	cgs unit
ENERGY WORK $[ML^2T^{-2}]$			
joule	J	$1(kg\ m^2\ s^{-2})$	MKSA unit
erg	erg	10^{-7} J	cgs unit
electron volt	eV	1.602×10^{-19}J	
MOMENTUM IMPULSE $[MLT^{-1}]$			
$kg\ m\ s^{-1}$	$kg\ m\ s^{-1}$	1 N s	MKSA unit
POWER $[ML^2T^{-3}]$			
watt	W	$1\ J\ s^{-1}$ 1 VA	MKSA unit
CHARGE [Q]			
coulomb	C	1 A s	MKSA unit
electron charge	q_e	1.602×10^{-19}C	

Units and Dimensions

Units and Dimensions	Symbol	Value	Remarks
POTENTIAL $[ML^2T^{-2}Q^{-1}]$			
volt	V	$1\ JC^{-1}$	MKSA unit
RESISTANCE $[ML^2T^{-1}Q^{-2}]$			
ohm	Ω	$1\ VA^{-1}$	MKSA unit
INDUCTANCE $[ML^2Q^{-2}]$			
henry	H	$1\ V\ s\ A^{-1}$	MKSA unit
CAPACITANCE $[M^{-1}L^{-2}T^2Q^2]$			
farad	F	$1\ C\ V^{-1}$	MKSA unit
microfarad	μF	$10^{-6}F$	
picofarad	pF or μμF	$10^{-12}F$	
ELECTRIC FIELD $[MLT^{-2}Q^{-1}]$			
volt per meter	$V\ m^{-1}$	$1\ N\ C^{-1}$	MKSA unit
MAGNETIC FIELD $[MT^{-1}Q^{-1}]$			
weber m^{-2}	$Wb\ m^{-2}$	$1\ N\ m^{-1}sec\ C^{-1}$	MKSA unit
gauss	G	$10^{-4}\ Wb\ m^{-2}$	
gamma	γ	10^{-5} gauss	

APPENDIX B

I. Physical Constants and Values
(Rounded values)

Refer e.g. to: C.W. Allen, Astrophysical Quantities, The Athlone Press, 1963.

E.R. Cohen, Nuovo Cimento, Supp. Vol. VI, Ser. X, 1957.

Physics Today, Vol. 17 , No. 2, 1964.

1. Astrophysical and Geophysical

Sun:

Mass ($m_\odot$)	1.99×10^{30} kg
	$= 3.33 \times 10^5\ m_\oplus$
Equatorial radius	6.96×10^8 m
Mean density	$1.41\ g/cm^3$

Earth:

Mass ($m_\oplus$)	5.98×10^{24} kg
Equatorial radius	6.38×10^6 m
Mean density	$5.52\ g/cm^3$
Angular velocity	7.29×10^{-5} rad. s^{-1}
Mean orbital speed	29.77 km s^{-1}
Land area	$1.48 \times 10^{14}\ m^2$
	$\approx 29\%$ of surface
Ocean area	$3.63 \times 10^{14}\ m^2$
	$\approx 71\%$ of surface
Mean ocean depth	3770 m

Moon:

Mass ($m_☽$)	7.34×10^{22} kg
	$= 1/81.31\ m_\oplus$
Equatorial radius	1.74×10^6 m
Mean density	$3.34\ g/cm^3$

Sun-Earth distance:

Mean	1.50×10^{11} m = 1 A.U.
r_P	1.47×10^{11} m
r_A	1.52×10^{11} m

Earth-Moon distance:

Mean	3.84×10^{8} m
r_p	3.63×10^{8} m
r_A	4.06×10^{8} m
Speed of light:	$c = 2.9979 \times 10^{8}$ m s^{-1}
Universal gravitational constant	$G = 6.670 \times 10^{-11}$ N m^{2} kg^{-2}
Solar constant at 1 A.U.	1374 W m^{-2}
Acceleration of gravity (at earth's surface, varies with latitude and altitude)	$g = 9.81$ m s^{-2}

2. <u>Atomic and Nuclear</u>

Planck's constant	$h = 6.626 \times 10^{-34}$ J-s
	$= 4.135 \times 10^{-15}$ eV-s
	$\frac{h}{2\pi} = \hbar = 1.0544 \times 10^{-34}$ J-s
	$= 6.58 \times 10^{-16}$ eV-s
Bohr radius $= \dfrac{4\pi\epsilon_0\hbar^2}{m_e q_e^2} = \dfrac{\hbar^2}{m_e e^2}$	$a_0 = 5.29 \times 10^{-9}$ cm
	$= .529$ Å
Classical electron radius $= \dfrac{e^2}{m_e c^2} = \alpha^2 a_0$	$r_0 = 2.82 \times 10^{-15}$ m
	$= 2.82$ fermi
Fine structure constant $= \dfrac{e^2}{\hbar c}$	$\alpha = \dfrac{1}{137}$
$-E_0$ for hydrogen $= \dfrac{e^2}{2a_0}$	13.6 eV
Nuclear "radius"	$\approx 1.3 \times 10^{-13} A^{1/3}$ cm
	$\approx 1.3 \times 10^{-5} A^{1/3}$ Å
Atomic "radius"	≈ 1 Å
Molecular "radius"	≈ 1.5 Å
Electron rest mass	$m_e = 9.11 \times 10^{-31}$ kg
	$m_e c^2 = 0.51$ MeV
Proton rest mass	$m_p = 1.67252 \times 10^{-27}$ kg
	$= 1836\ m_e$
	$m_p c^2 = 938.26$ MeV

Neutron rest mass	$m_n = 1.67482 \times 10^{-27}$ kg
	$m_n c^2 = 939.55$ MeV
Atomic mass unit ($\equiv \frac{1}{12}$ mass of C^{12})	1 amu = 1.66×10^{-27} kg
	(1 amu) $\times c^2 = 931$ MeV
Compton wavelength for electron ($\lambda_{c_e} = 2\pi\alpha a_0 = \frac{h}{m_e c}$)	$\lambda_{c_e} = 2.43 \times 10^{-12}$ m
Free electron scattering cross section	$\frac{8\pi}{3} r_0^2 = 6.65 \times 10^{-29}$ m^2

3. Macroscopic

ϵ_0	8.854×10^{-12} F m^{-1}
$1/4\pi\epsilon_0$	9.00×10^9 m F^{-1}
μ_0	$4\pi \times 10^{-7}$ H m^{-1}
$\mu_0 \epsilon_0 c^2$	1
$1/\epsilon_0 c$	377 Ω
Resistivity of copper	$\approx 10^{-8}$ Ω cm
Refractive index	
n_{water}	1.33
n_{glass}	≈ 1.5
n_{air}	1.0003
Speed of sound (air at STP)	331 m s^{-1}
Density of air (STP = 0^oC at 1 atm)	1.293 kg m^{-3}
	$\approx 10^{-3}$ g cm^{-3}
Standard atmosphere	1 atm = 1.013×10^5 N m^{-2}
	= 760 mm Hg
	≈ 14.7 lbs in^{-2}
Density of water (20^oC)	1.00×10^3 kg m^{-3}
Avogadro's number	$N_0 = 6.025 \times 10^{23}$ molecules/mole
Boltzmann's constant	$k = 1.38 \times 10^{-23}$ J/^oK
	$= 8.62 \times 10^{-5}$ eV/^oK
Gas constant	$R = 8.31$ J/g-mole ^oK

Molar volume at STP 22.41×10^3 cm^3/mole

Stefan-Boltzmann constant $= \frac{\pi^2}{60} \frac{k^4}{\hbar^3 c^2}$ $\sigma = 5.67 \times 10^{-8}$ $W/m^2(^oK)^4$

kT = 1 eV for T = 11,600 ^oK

$\simeq \frac{1}{40}$ eV at room temperature

1 eV/atom = 9.652×10^4 J/mole = 23.1 K cal/mole

1 hp = 746 W

II. Numerical Constants

$1^o = 1.745 \times 10^{-2}$ rad.

$1' = 2.9089 \times 10^{-4}$ rad.

$1'' = 4.8481 \times 10^{-6}$ rad.

$e = 2.71828....$

$\pi = 3.14159....$

$\log_{10} e = 0.434$

$\ln 2 = 0.693$

ANSWERS TO PROBLEMS

ANSWERS

CHAPTER 1

B-3.

a) $n_G \sim 10^{19}\ cm^{-3}$

$n_L \sim 10^{22}\ cm^{-3}$

b) $m \sim 10^{-23} g$

c) $\ell \sim 10^{-5} cm$

d) $P \sim 10^{-7}$ atm.

B-4.

$A \approx 1.4 \times 10^{-14}\ cm^2$

B-5.

6.02×10^{23} molecules/mole

B-6.

a) $\approx 2.7 \times 10^{19}$ atoms cm^{-3}

b) $\approx 6.1 \times 10^{23}$ molecules/mole

C-1.

$\sim 10^{24}$ molecules/mole

C-2.

$N_g \sim 0.7 \times 10^{19}$ molecules/cm^3

CHAPTER 2

A-1.

$W = \frac{3}{\sqrt{2}}$ kg-wts

A-2.

$F_P = \frac{1}{\cos\alpha}$ kg-wt

$F_W = \tan\alpha$ kg-wt

A-3.

$W_2 = 0.25$ kg-wts

A-4.

$A = \left(\frac{1}{2} + \frac{\sqrt{3}}{2}\right)$ kg-wts

$B = \sqrt{\frac{3}{2}}$ kg-wts

A-5.

$T_1 = T_2 = \frac{50}{\sqrt{2}}$ lb-wts

A-6.

a) downward

b) $T = W\frac{y}{x}$

A-7.

$$F = W\frac{\sqrt{h(2R - h)}}{R - h}$$

A-8.

a) $F = 0$ (except gravity)

b) $\tau = FD$

c) $\tau = FD$

A-9.

$F = 20.7$ N, 45°

.34 m L of 0

A-10.

$$v = \sqrt{2gD\frac{W_1 - W_2}{W_1 + W_2}\sin\theta}$$

A-11.

$$v = \sqrt{gD(\sin\varphi - \sin\theta)}$$

B-1.

a) $a = -\frac{1}{2}\left(1 - \frac{1}{\sqrt{2}}\right)g$

b) M_2

$$t_1 = \sqrt{\frac{2H}{g\left(1 - \frac{1}{\sqrt{2}}\right)}}$$

c) No

B-2.

$$T = \frac{L}{x}\left(W + \frac{w}{2}\right)\tan\theta$$

B-3.

a) 45 lb-wts

b) 45 lb-wts, 90 lb-wts

B-4.

$\theta = 30^{\circ}$

B-5.

$\alpha = 30^{\circ}$

B-6.

$F = 0.6\ W$

B-7.

2 ton-wts

B-8.

$T = 265$ g-wts

$\alpha = 79^{o}.1$

B-9.

$T = \frac{\sqrt{3}}{4} W$

B-10.

$\theta = 30^{o}$

B-11.

$T = \frac{Wh}{2\pi r}$

B-12.

$W = \frac{4w}{\sin\theta}$

B-13

$F_1 = \frac{W}{3}$

$F_2 = \frac{2W}{3}$

$F = \frac{4W}{3\sqrt{3}}$

B-14.

a) AC, CE, EG, BC, EF, ED

b) $BD = \frac{W}{2}$

$DE = \frac{5}{12} W$

B-15.

$W = \frac{3}{4} w$

B-16.

$V = 196 \text{ cm s}^{-1}$

B-17.

$v = \sqrt{2gH}$

C-1.

$\theta = \tan^{-1} \frac{1}{3\sqrt{3}} = 10^{o}.9$

C-2.

$W = \frac{wr}{R - r}$

C-3.

$A = 5$ m

$B = 11$ m

$T_{max} \approx 34 \times 10^{3}$ kg-wts

C-4.

a) $F = W \frac{L}{h}$

b) $|\vec{F}_A| = W\sqrt{1 + \left(\frac{L}{h}\right)^2}$

$\theta = \tan^{-1}\left(\frac{h}{L}\right)$

CHAPTER 3

A-1.

$t \approx 1.6$ hr

A-2.

1.033

A-3.

$1.6 \text{ m s}^{-2} \simeq \frac{g_\oplus}{6}$

A-4.

a) $\sim$ 35.2 A.U.

b) 59

A-5.

$\sim 5.9 \, R_E$

B-1.

a) $\lambda = 0$

b) $r_s = \frac{1}{9} r_{\oplus☽}$

B-2.

a) $\frac{M_\odot}{M_\oplus} = 3.33 \times 10^5$

b) $\frac{M_4}{M_\oplus} = 318$

B-3.

$m_a + m_b = \frac{R^3}{T^2} \, m_\odot$

B-4.

II : unchanged

III : $T^2 = \frac{4\pi^2}{GM} R^{(3 + a)}$

C-1.

$\frac{\Delta g}{g} = 7 \times 10^{-6}$

C-2.

$M = 1.02 \times 10^{-7} \, TV^3 \, M_\odot$

C-3.

a) $R_c = 1.88 \times 10^6$ km

b) $a = \frac{R_p^{\,2}}{2R_p - R_c} = 8.33 \times 10^6$ km

c) $T_c = \frac{2\pi a\sqrt{aR_c}}{vR_p} \approx 4.8$ days

C-4.

$T^2 = \frac{4\pi^2}{G} \, \frac{(R + r)^3}{(M + m)}$

C-6.

a) $\sim 3.1 \, m_\odot$

CHAPTER 4

A-1.

a) $t = 1843.8$ s

b) $v \approx 1385$ ft s^{-1}

A-2.

≈ 155 s

A-3.

down

A-4.

$v \approx 465$ m s^{-1}

$\omega \approx 7.3 \times 10^{-5}$ s^{-1}

$\frac{a}{g} \approx 3.5 \times 10^{-2}$

B-1.

b) 46 mi.

c) 2.7×10^{2} s

B-2.

$e \approx 0.98$

B-3.

a) $H_{max} = \frac{v^2}{2g} \sin^2\theta$

$R = \frac{v^2}{g} \sin 2\theta$

b) $\theta = \pi/4$

B-4.

$$V = \frac{L}{\cos\theta}\sqrt{\frac{g}{2(L\tan\theta - h)}}$$

B-5.

a) $v \approx 48$ ft s^{-1}

b) $R \approx 8.5$ ft

B-6.

$x = Vt - R\sin\frac{Vt}{R}$

$y = R(1 - \cos\frac{Vt}{R})$

$v_x = V(1 - \cos\frac{Vt}{R})$

$v_y = V\sin\frac{Vt}{R}$

$a_x = \frac{V^2}{R}\sin\frac{Vt}{R}$

$a_y = \frac{V^2}{R}\cos\frac{Vt}{R}$

B-7.

14.8 m s^{-1}

C-1.

a) $\theta = \tan^{-1}3$

b) $x = 14$ m

c) $V = 19.8$ m s^{-1}

C-2.

≈ 202 ft

C-3.

a) 52.5 mi hr^{-1}

b) 2.75 ft s^{-2}

C-4.

$a_J = \frac{8}{9} a_R$

CHAPTER 5

a)

A-1.

b) $a = \frac{2}{5} g$

$T_1 = \frac{2}{5}$ kg-wts

$T_2 = \frac{6}{5}$ kg-wts

A-2.

$T = 8.8 \times m$ N

A-3.

$T = 25$ N

B-1.

$F = \frac{M_2}{M_1} (M + M_1 + M_2) g$

B-2.

$F = 392$ N

B-3.

$a = \frac{g}{9}$ upward

$T = 222$ g-wts

B-4.

a) $M = \dfrac{(M_a + M_b) \frac{D}{4} - \frac{M_b}{2} L \cos\theta}{L \cos\theta - \frac{D}{4}}$

b) $t = \sqrt{\dfrac{8L \sin\theta}{g}}$

B-5.

$g = \dfrac{v^2 (2M + m)}{2mh}$

B-6.

a) $a = \dfrac{F - (M_1 + M_2) g}{M_1 + M_2}$

b) $T = \dfrac{M_1}{M_1 + M_2} F$

c) $a = \frac{F}{M_2} - g$

$a' = -g$

d) $t = \sqrt{\dfrac{2M_2 s}{F}}$

C-1.

$\Delta t = 0.9$ s

C-2.

2.7 kg-wt

C-3.

a) $a_{up} = g/3$

b) 280 lb

C-4.

$m_B \simeq 5.8$ kg

b)

C-1.

$x_{max} = 1$

C-4.

$h_{max} \approx 5 \times 10^3$ ft

$R \approx 1.6 \times 10^4$ ft.

CHAPTER 6

A-1.

$m_2/m_1 = 3$

A-2.

$E' = 0.71\ E$

A-3.

a) $v_E = 8.4 \times 10^{-22} \text{m s}^{-1}$

b) $\frac{T_E}{T_p} = 1.7 \times 10^{-24}$

B-1.

$V_F = 3.66 \text{ m s}^{-1}$

B-2.

a) Yes

b) To the N

c) $V = 5 \times 10^{-4} \text{m s}^{-1}$

B-3.

$$a_1 = \frac{(m_1 - m_0)g + r_0(v_0 + gt)}{m_1 + m_0 - r_0 t} \quad \text{(downward)}$$

$$0 < t < \frac{m_0}{r_0}$$

B-4.

$a = 4.0 \text{ m s}^{-2}$

B-5.

$F = \mu v(v + gt)$

C-1.

$$V = \frac{m + M}{m} \times \sqrt{\frac{g}{L}}$$

C-2.

b) $\tau_0 = 2L \sqrt{\frac{Mm}{2T(M + m)}}$

C-3.

$\Delta v \approx v \frac{f}{4}$

C-4.

a). $a = \frac{r_0 V_0}{M_0}$

b) $r_0 = 490 \text{ kg s}^{-1}$

c) $V = - V_0 \int_{M_0}^{M} \frac{dM}{M}$

C-5.

$F_R = 5.1 \times 10^{-3}$ N

$F_R \alpha - v^2$

CHAPTER 7

A-1.

$\vec{r}(t) = \vec{r}_0 + \vec{v}_0 t + \frac{1}{2}\vec{g}\, t^2$

A-2.

a) $5\vec{i} + \vec{j}$

b) $\vec{i} + 3\vec{j} - 2\vec{k}$

c) 3

d) 3

e) 3

f) $15\vec{i} - 18\vec{j} + 9\vec{k}$

A-3.

c) $\rho \approx 4.6$ m (if $\vec{r}$ in m)

A-4.

a) 14.5^o west of north

b) 53.9 minutes

B-1.

a) From $40\overset{o}{.}5$ NE

b) From $35\overset{o}{.}6$ SE

B-2.

Method 2, by 4.0 min.

B-3.

a) $\frac{t_V}{t_A} \frac{V}{\sqrt{V^2 - R^2}}$

b) $\frac{t_A}{t_L} = \frac{t_V}{t_A}$

B-4.

$D = R \cos^{-1}[\sin \lambda_1 \sin \lambda_2 + \cos \lambda_1 \cos \lambda_2 \cos(\varphi_1 - \varphi_2)]$

B-5.

a) $\sim 3.2 \times 10^{-3}$ m s^{-2} towards sun

b) $\sim 7.2 \times 10^{-3}$ m s^{-2}

$\theta \sim 24^o$

c) $\sim 8.5 \times 10^{-3}$ m s^{-2}

towards sun

B-6.

a) a = 2g to right

b) $a' = g\sqrt{2}$ $\theta = 45^o$

c) 272 kg-wt

B-7.

$T = 2\pi \sqrt{\frac{H}{g}}$

C-1.

$t \le t_0$

$\vec{r}_a = (7 + 7t)\vec{i} + 3t\vec{j} + (4.9 - 4.9t^2)\vec{k}$

$\vec{r}_b = (49 - 7t)\vec{i} + 3t\vec{j} + (4.9 - 4.9t^2)\vec{k}$

$t \ge t_0$

$\vec{r} = 28\vec{i} + 3t\vec{j} + (4.9 - 4.9t^2)\vec{k}$

C-2.

a) due N

b) 0.17 hr

CHAPTER 8

B-2.

$\theta_{max} = \sin^{-1} \frac{m}{M}$

B-3.

$\theta_1 = \tan^{-1} 3$

$|\vec{v}_1'| = \frac{v}{4}\sqrt{10}$

$|\vec{v}_2'| = \frac{v}{4}\sqrt{2}$

B-4.

$\alpha = 120^o$

B-5.

a) $\vec{V}_{CM} = 4\vec{i} - 3\vec{j}$

b) $|U_1| = |U_2| = 5 \text{ m s}^{-1}$

c) $\vec{v}_1' = 4\vec{i} + 2\vec{j}$

B-6.

$|\vec{v}_1'| = \frac{v_0}{2}\sqrt{3}$ $\theta_1 = -30^o$

$|\vec{v}_2'| = \frac{v_0}{2}$ $\theta_2 = +60^o$

B-7.

a) $|\vec{v}_2'| = \sqrt{3} \times 10^6 \text{ m s}^{-1}$

b) $|\vec{v}_1'| = \sqrt{73} \times 10^6 \text{ m s}^{-1}$

$\theta_1 = 113^o$

c) $|\vec{U}_1| = 9 \times 10^6 \text{ m s}^{-1}$

$\alpha = 120^o$

B-8.

$|\vec{v}_1'| = 50\sqrt{7} \text{ cm s}^{-1}$

$\theta_1 = -\tan^{-1} \frac{\sqrt{3}}{2} = -41^o$

$|\vec{v}_2'| = 50 \text{ cm s}^{-1}$

$\theta_2 = +60^o$

B-9.

$\frac{\Delta T}{T}\Big|_{lab} = \frac{(1 - \alpha^2)m_2}{m_1 + m_2}$

B-10.

a) $\theta = \tan^{-1}\sqrt{\frac{M - m}{M + m}}$

b) $\theta = \tan^{-1}\sqrt{\frac{\alpha^2 M^2 - m^2}{(M + m)^2}}$

B-11.

$\frac{M}{m_p} = 9$

B-12.

a) $\sqrt{5} \text{ m s}^{-1}$

$\tan^{-1} \frac{1}{2}$ NW

b) $\frac{3}{4}$

c) 90°

B-13.

a) $\vec{v} = 2\vec{j} + 2\vec{k} \text{ m s}^{-1}$

b) $T_{CM} = 30 \text{ J}$

CHAPTER 9

A-1.

$F = -108$ N

A-2.

$a = -\frac{g}{8}$

A-3.

see 9-1

B-1.

$x = \mu h$

B-2.

$x = 32$ cm

B-3.

$\mu_{min} = \frac{1}{2}(\cot\theta - 1)$

B-4.

a) $\Delta T = \mu T \Delta\theta$

b) $\frac{T_2}{T_1} = e^{\mu\alpha}$

B-5.

$v_0 = 595$ m s^{-1}

B-6.

51.8 MPH

B-7.

$t = 2.2$ sec

B-8.

a) .68 m

b) 1.1 s

c) 2.3 J

B-9.

a) 75 cm s^{-2}

b) 200 g-wts

B-10.

$x < x_0$: $v = V_0$

$x_0 \leq x \leq x_0 + L$: $v(x) = V_0 - \frac{k}{m}(x - x_0)$

$x > x_0 + L$: $v(x) = V_0 - \frac{k}{m} L$

if $\frac{k}{m} L < V_0$

B-11.

$\epsilon = \frac{R}{4} \Delta P$

$\left| \frac{\sigma}{\epsilon} \right| = 1$

B-12.

Accelerating

$a = \frac{g}{\sqrt{3}}$ m s^{-2}

B-13.

$R = \frac{mv}{qB}$

$T = \frac{2\pi m}{qB}$

C-1.

a) $W = 600$ g-wts

b) $T = 800$ g-wts

c) $\theta = \pi/2$

C-2.

$F = \frac{1 + \mu}{1 - \mu} m g$

C-3.

a) $\sqrt{3}\, W \sin\alpha$

b) $\varphi = 60^o$

C-4.

$R = 4.9 \times 10^{-5}$ cm

C-5.

a) $F_x = q v_y B$

$F_y = q(E - v_x B)$

$F_z = 0$

b) $F_x' = q v_y' B$

$F_y' = -q v_x' B$

c) cycloidal

CHAPTER 10

A-1.

$x_0 - x = x_0 - v_0\sqrt{\frac{m}{k}}$

A-3.

Anywhere

A-4.

$v_\infty \approx 3.9$ mi s^{-1}

A-5.

1.4×10^3 V

A-6.

$Q = 5.6 \times 10^{-5}$ C

A-7.

$\varphi = 310$ kV

B-1.

a. 1) 3.0 m s^{-1}

2) 2.5 m s^{-2}

3) 45 W

b. 1) 4.5 m s^{-1}

2) 2.5 m s^{-2}

3) 67.5 W

B-2.

a) $\vec{F}(t = 0) = 4.5\vec{i} + 12\vec{j} - 2.6\vec{k}$ N

b) $\vec{a}(t = 0) = 4.5\vec{i} + 12\vec{j} - 2.6\vec{k}$ m s^{-2}

c) $T(t = 0) = 2.5$ J

d) $\frac{dT}{dt}(t = 0) = 21.4$ W

B-3.

$\vec{r} = 2.00\vec{i} + 3.02\vec{j} + .01\vec{k}$ m

$\vec{v} = .045\vec{i} + 2.12\vec{j} + .97\vec{k}$ m s^{-1}

$T = 2.71$ J

B-4.

a) $W = 0$

b) $W = 0$. Yes.

B-5.

$H = \frac{1}{2} R$

B-6.

a) $x = H \sin^2\theta + R \cos^2\theta - R \cos^3\theta$

b) $F = mg\left(\frac{2H}{R} + 1\right)$

B-7.

$d = \frac{mg}{k} - \frac{R}{5}$

B-8.

$v = \sqrt{\frac{gL}{2}}$

B-9.

$\frac{R}{3}$

B-10.

$\theta = \sin^{-1} 0.27$

B-11.

7.2 m s^{-2}

B-12.

≈ 625 J

≈ 570 J

≈ 330 J

B-13.

$r \leq R$: $\varphi = -\frac{GM}{2R^3}(3R^2 - r^2)$

$\vec{a} = -\frac{GM}{R^3}\vec{r}$

$r > R$: $\varphi = -\frac{GM}{r}$

$\vec{a} = -\frac{GM}{r^3}\vec{r}$

B-14.

$$\vec{a} = -\frac{4\pi}{3}\rho G\left[\frac{R^3}{(R + x)^2} - \frac{(R/4)^3}{(\frac{5}{4}R + x)^2}\right]$$

B-15.

$y > \frac{d}{2}$: $a_y = -2\pi\rho dG + \frac{4\pi}{3} r^3 \rho \frac{G}{y^2}$

$\frac{d}{2} > y > r$: $a_y = -4\pi\rho Gy + \frac{4\pi}{3} r^3 \rho \frac{G}{y^2}$

$r > y \geq 0$: $a_y = -4\pi\rho G y + \frac{4\pi}{3}\rho Gy$

B-16.

$E = \frac{-GmM}{2a}$

B-17.

a) $T^2 = \frac{4\pi^2}{GM} a^3$

b) $T^2 = \frac{\pi^2 G^2 M^2}{2(E/m)^3}$

C-1.

19.2 cm

C-2.

25 kw

C-3.

4.60×10^4 atm.

C-4.

$$W \geq GMm_1\left(\frac{1}{R} - \frac{1}{D - r}\right)$$

$$+ Gm\, m_1\left(\frac{1}{D - R} - \frac{1}{r}\right)$$

C-5.

Escape on parabolic orbits

C-6.

$v_0 > 11.8$ mi s^{-1}

$v_0 < 47.1$ mi s^{-1}

C-7.

$v_0 = 40.8$ km s^{-1}

$\alpha = 40^{\circ}.9$ w.r. to earth-sun line

CHAPTER 11

A-1.

a) MT^{-2}

b) ML^2T^{-2}

c) ML^2T^{-2}

d) MT^{-2}

e) 1

f) $ML^{-1}T^{-1}$

g) LT^{-2}

h) $MLT^{-2}Q^{-1}$

i) $MT^{-1}Q^{-1}$

j) LT^{-1}

A-2.

377 Ω

A-3.

$$v' = \frac{\lambda}{\tau} v$$

$$a' = \frac{\lambda}{\tau^2} a$$

$$F' = \frac{\mu\lambda}{\tau^2} F$$

$$E' = \frac{\mu\lambda^2}{\tau^2} E$$

A-4.

$$T \propto \sqrt{\frac{\ell}{g}}$$

B-1.

$4\pi^2$

B-2.

T indep. of k

B-3.

$$T \propto \sqrt{\frac{m}{k}}$$

B-4.

$$T \propto \frac{mv^2}{\ell}$$

$$a \propto \frac{v^2}{\ell}$$

B-5.

$$R \propto \frac{v^2}{g} f(\theta)$$

$$T \propto \frac{v}{g} f'(\theta)$$

B-6.

$$T \propto \sqrt{\frac{m}{\sigma}}$$

B-7.

$$v \propto \frac{1}{\ell}\sqrt{\frac{T}{\sigma}}$$

B-8.

$$v \propto \sqrt{g\lambda}$$

C-1.

$$p \propto \frac{mv^2}{V} f(N)$$

C-2.

$[GM] = L^3T^{-2} = \text{const.}$

CHAPTER 12

A-1.

$x = \gamma(x' + \beta ct')$

$y = y'$

$z = z'$

$t = \gamma(t' + \frac{\beta}{c} x')$

A-2.

$$v_x = \frac{v_x' + V}{1 + \frac{V}{c^2} v_x'}$$

$$v_y = \frac{v_y' \sqrt{1 - \frac{V^2}{c^2}}}{1 + \frac{V}{c^2} v_x'}$$

A-3.

$$v_x' = \frac{v_x - V}{1 - \frac{Vv_x}{c^2}}$$

$$a_x' = \frac{a_x \left(1 - \frac{V^2}{c^2}\right)^{3/2}}{\left(1 - \frac{Vv_x}{c^2}\right)^3}$$

A-4.

$L' \simeq 4.5$ m

$\theta' \simeq 33.7^\circ$

A-5.

$\Delta t = 16.8\ \mu$ s

$\Delta t' = 2.37\ \mu$ s

$L' = 0.71$ km

B-1.

$$F = \frac{m_0 c^2}{b}$$

B-2.

a) $M \simeq 42$ kg/year

b) HDO: $\sim 2\ cm^3 s^{-1}$

B-3.

$\sim 6.3 \times 10^8$ tons s^{-1}

C-1.

a) $g = 1.03$ l.y. y^{-2}

b) $x = 4.15$ l.y.

$v = .982\ c$

CHAPTER 13

A-2.

a) $pc = T\left(1 + \frac{2m_c^2}{T}\right)^{1/2}$

b) $\frac{v}{c} = \frac{\sqrt{3}}{2}$

A-3.

$\Delta t \approx 5^m$

B-1.

a) $pc(\text{MeV}) = 3 \times 10^{-2} BRZ(\text{Gm})$

b) $R = 6.8 \times 10^3$ km

B-2.

a) 1.8 m

b) 15 M Hz

c) 14%

B-3.

$$T_1 = c^2 \frac{(M - m_1)^2 - m_2^2}{2M}$$

$$T_2 = c^2 \frac{(M - m_2)^2 - m_1^2}{2M}$$

B-4.

$T_\mu = 4.1$ MeV

$T_\nu = 29.7$ MeV

$p_\mu = p_\nu = 29.7$ MeV/c

B-5.

$$E_\gamma = \Delta E\left(1 - \frac{\Delta E}{2mc^2}\right)$$

B-6.

a) $c/2$

b) $\frac{4}{\sqrt{3}} m_0$

B-7.

$T = 6\ m_p c^2$ (5.6 GeV)

B-8.

$T_e = 4004$ GeV

B-9.

$E_\gamma = 4\ m_p c^2$ (3.8 GeV)

C-1.

a) $T_p \approx 2mc^2$ (279 MeV)

b) $T_\pi \approx \frac{m^2c^2}{2M}$ (10.4 MeV)

C-2.

a) $$E_\gamma = \frac{m_\pi c^2 \sqrt{(1 - \beta^2)}}{2(1 - \beta \cos \theta)}$$

b) $$E_{max} = \frac{m_\pi c^2}{2} \frac{(1 + \beta)}{\sqrt{1 - \beta^2}} \qquad \theta = 0$$

$$E_{min} = \frac{m_\pi c^2}{2} \frac{(1 - \beta)}{\sqrt{1 - \beta^2}} \qquad \theta = \pi$$

c) $$\frac{\sqrt{1 - \beta^2}}{2}(E_{max} + E_{min}) = \frac{m_\pi c^2}{2} = E_\gamma^0$$

CHAPTER 14

A-1.

a) + 140 N m

b) 2.8 m

c) 14 N

A-3.

$\lambda' \sim 66.6^{\circ}$

A-4.

$V = 2\pi^2 R^3$

A-5.

$K.E. = \frac{M}{3}\omega^2 R^2$

B-1.

$x = R\left(\frac{2R}{L}\right) \sin\left(\frac{L}{2R}\right)$

$y = 0$

$x = \frac{4}{3}\frac{R}{\alpha}\sin\frac{\alpha}{2}$

B-2.

x = 1.7 cm

B-3.

$y = \frac{1}{2} x$

B-4.

a) F = 8.1 N

b) $x = \frac{3\sqrt{3}}{2}$ cm

B-5.

$\alpha = \tan^{-1}\frac{1}{6\sqrt{3}}$

B-6.

OP = 1.5 ft

B-7.

$h = \frac{a}{2}(3 - \sqrt{3})$

B-8.

$x = \frac{m_1 L}{m_1 + m_2}$ (from m_2)

B-9.

$P = 16\, m\mu\pi^3 f^3 r^2$

C-1.

n = a

C-2.

M = 4.0 lb

C-3.

$\Delta L = \frac{M\omega^2 L}{2K - M\omega^2}$

$2 > \frac{M\omega^2}{K}$

CHAPTER 15

A-1.

$$I = \frac{mL^2}{12}$$

A-2.

$$\omega = \sqrt{\frac{3g}{\ell}}$$

A-3.

$$a = \frac{mg}{m + \frac{M}{2}}$$

B-1.

a) $m \frac{L^2}{3}$

b) $\frac{mL^2}{12}$

c) mr^2

d) $m \frac{r^2}{2}$

B-2.

$$I = 22 \, Ma^2$$

B-3.

$$F = \frac{Mg}{4}$$

B-4.

$$W = 6m \, L^2 \omega_0^{\ 2}$$

B-5.

a) $V_0 = r \sqrt{\frac{2 \, Mgh}{I + Mr^2}}$

B-6.

$$a = 2g \sin \theta$$

B-8.

$$I = \frac{8}{15} \pi\rho \, (R^5 - r^5) = \frac{2}{5} M \frac{R^5 - r^5}{R^3 - r^3}$$

B-9.

$$\mu_0 = \frac{2}{7} \tan \theta$$

B-10.

b) $a = \dfrac{g}{1 + \dfrac{R^2}{2r^2}}$

B-11.

$$h = \frac{3d}{2} - 3r$$

B-12.

a) $v_2 = \frac{r_1}{r_2} \, v_1$

b) $W = \frac{1}{2} mv_1^{\ 2} \frac{r_1^{\ 2} - r_2^{\ 2}}{r_2^{\ 2}}$

c) $F = \frac{mv^2}{r}$

B-13.

a) $a = \dfrac{FR(R \cos \alpha - r)}{I + MR^2}$

B-14.

$$\frac{h}{r} = \frac{7}{5}$$

C-1.

$$r_3^{\ 2} + r_1^{\ 2} = r_2^{\ 2}$$

C-2.

$$\alpha_{max} = \frac{2g \cos \theta}{R}$$

C-3.

$$t = \frac{2}{3} \frac{\ell\omega_0}{\mu g}$$

C-4.

$$D = \frac{12\ V_0^2}{49\ \mu g}$$

$$V = \frac{5}{7} V_0$$

C-5.

a) $V_0 = \frac{2}{5} R\,\omega_0$

b) $V_0 = \frac{1}{4} R\,\omega_0$

C-6.

$$\ell = R\left(\sqrt{1 + \frac{M}{4m}} - 1\right)$$

C-7.

$$F_x' = F_x \cos\theta + F_y \sin\theta + 2\,m\omega\,\dot{y}' + m\omega^2 x'$$

$$F_y' = F_y \cos\theta - F_x \sin\theta - 2\,m\omega\,\dot{x}' + m\omega^2 y'$$

CHAPTER 16

A-1.

$V = 406$ units

A-4.

(e)

B-1.

a) before

b) $V_{CM} = \frac{\ell}{2}\omega_0 \quad \omega = \omega_0$

B-2.

$$\frac{v_{AC}}{v_{AB}} = -\frac{7}{2}$$

B-3.

$$v = \frac{1}{2}\left(\frac{M}{m} - 1\right) V - \frac{L^2\omega^2}{24V}$$

$$a = \frac{\omega L^2}{12V}$$

B-4.

$$V_{CM} = \frac{v}{2}$$

$$L = \frac{mvR}{2}$$

$$\omega = \frac{v}{3R}$$

$$K.E.)_1 = \frac{mv^2}{2}$$

$$K.E.)_2 = \frac{mv^2}{3}$$

B-5.

$$V_{CM} = \frac{v_0}{6}$$

$$\omega = \frac{2}{15}\ \frac{v_0}{a}$$

B-6.

a) $V_{CM} = \frac{J}{m}$

$$\omega = \frac{12\ Jr}{mL^2}$$

$$V_A = \frac{J}{m}\left(1 - \frac{6r}{L}\right)$$

b) $AP = \frac{2}{3} L$

c) $\ell = \frac{2}{3} L$

B-7.

a) $\frac{v}{2}$

b) $Mv\frac{L}{4}$

c) $\frac{6}{5}\frac{v}{L}$

d) 20%

B-8.

$$V_f = \frac{V}{2}$$

$$\omega_f = \frac{6V}{7L}$$

B-9.

$$V = \sqrt{8g\ L}$$

B-10.

a) $\omega_0 \frac{\ell}{2}$

B-11.

a) $I_0\omega_0$

b) $\dfrac{m\ R^2\omega_0^2}{R - r(1 + 20\pi)}$

B-12.

$$T_{max} = \omega^2 m\ell^2$$

B-13.

a) 45°

b) $\frac{M\ell^2}{24}\omega^2$

B-14.

$F = 89.8\ \mathrm{N}$

B-15.

$$\Omega = \frac{I_2}{I_1 + I_2 + M_2 r_2^2}\,\omega$$

B-16.

a) $R = \dfrac{V}{2\omega}$

b) $\varphi \approx \dfrac{2\omega R}{V}$

B-17.

$$\omega_f = \frac{2}{13}\,\omega_0$$

B-18.

$\Delta T \sim 1\ \mathrm{ms}$

B-19.

$$\frac{3GMm}{R^3}\, r^2 \sin 2\theta$$

C-2.

$$J = M\sqrt{\frac{\pi g L n}{3}}$$

n = integer

C-3.

a) $$\omega = \frac{I_0 + mR^2}{I_0 + mr^2}\,\omega_0$$

c) $$v = \omega_0\sqrt{\frac{I_0 + mR^2}{I_0 + mr^2}\,(R^2 - r^2)}$$

C-4.

a) $$\frac{M\omega^2 ab(a^2 - b^2)}{12(a^2 + b^2)^{3/2}}$$

b) $$\frac{M}{12}\,\omega^2\,\frac{a^2 b^2}{a^2 + b^2}$$

C-5.

$T \sim 27\ \mathrm{N\ m}$

C-6.

a) $$\frac{L_x}{L_z} = \frac{4mv_0}{MR\omega_0}$$

b) $$\frac{\omega_x}{\omega_0} = \frac{8mv_0}{MR\omega_0}$$

C-7.

a) $\vec{L}(\mathrm{J\,s}) = 20\,\hat{e}_x + .0119\,\hat{e}_y$

$\Omega_n = 154\ \mathrm{rad\ s^{-1}}$

$r = 1.77 \times 10^{-2}\ \mathrm{cm}$

b) $\Omega_p = 1.47 \times 10^{-3}\ \mathrm{rad\ s^{-1}}$

$L_p = 1.91 \times 10^{-4}\ \mathrm{J\,s}$

$T_p = 1.40 \times 10^{-7}\ \mathrm{J}$

$\Delta E \approx 2.8 \times 10^{-7}\ \mathrm{J}$

C-8.

$\tau_{☽} \approx 2.2\ \tau_{\odot}$.

C-9.

Best accepted values of these quantities are:

a) $8.11 \times 10^{37}\ \mathrm{kg\ m^2}$

b) $5.91 \times 10^{33}\ \mathrm{kg\ m^2\ s^{-1}}$

c) $2.16 \times 10^{29}\ \mathrm{J}$

d) 25,725 y.

CHAPTER 17

A-2.

$$T = 2\pi\left(\frac{3g}{2L} + \frac{3(K_1 + K_2)}{M}\right)^{-1/2}$$

A-3.

$$x = \frac{A}{\sqrt{2}}$$

A-4.

a) 2.18 cm

b) -49.4 cm s^{-1}

A-5.

$$T = \pi\sqrt{\frac{2L}{g}}$$

B-1.

$$T = \pi\sqrt{\frac{MR^2}{K}}$$

B-2.

$T \approx 1.4$ s

B-3.

a) $2\pi\sqrt{\frac{d}{g}}$; $2\pi\sqrt{\frac{I_c + Md^2}{Mgd}}$

b) $-\frac{g}{d}\sin\theta_0$; $-\frac{Mgd}{I_c + Md^2}\sin\theta_0$

c) $\sqrt{\frac{2g}{d}(1 \cos\theta_0)}$; $\sqrt{\frac{2\,Mgd}{I_c + Md^2}(1 - \cos\theta_0)}$

B-4.

$\omega_0 = 28 \text{ rad s}^{-1}$

B-5.

a) $\tan\theta_0 = \frac{1}{3}$

b) $\theta(t) = \theta_0 - \frac{J}{M}\frac{1}{\sqrt{g\ell}}\;4\sqrt{\frac{288}{125}}\sin\sqrt{\frac{g}{\ell}}\;4\sqrt{\frac{9}{10}}\;t$

B-6.

$T \approx 42$ min.

B-7.

$$T = 2\pi\sqrt{\frac{m}{k_1 + k_2}}$$

$$T = 2\pi\sqrt{\frac{m(k_1 + k_2)}{k_1 k_2}}$$

B-8.

$$A = \frac{v}{4}\sqrt{\frac{M}{2k}} \; ; \; T = 2\pi\sqrt{\frac{M}{2k}}$$

B-9.

a) d

b) $V_{CM} = \frac{d}{3}\sqrt{\frac{k}{m}}$

$A = \sqrt{\frac{2}{3}}\, d$

B-10.

$$v_1 = v_0 - x\sqrt{\frac{K}{M_1(1 + \frac{M_1}{M_2})}}$$

$$v_2 = v_0 + x\sqrt{\frac{K}{M_2(1 + \frac{M_2}{M_1})}}$$

B-11.

$$x_{max} = \frac{(m + M)}{k}\mu g$$

B-12.

a) 10^6 ergs

b) $7.8 \times 10^3 \text{ g s}^{-2}$

c) 16 cm

B-13.

a) $\nu = \frac{1}{2\pi}\sqrt{K\left(\frac{1}{I_1} + \frac{1}{I_2}\right)}$

b) $\frac{A_1}{A_2} = -\frac{I_2}{I_1}$

C-2.

a) $T = 2\pi\sqrt{\frac{\ell}{g}}$ b) $T = \frac{2\pi}{\sqrt{3}}\frac{L}{d}\sqrt{\frac{\ell}{g}}$

C-3.

$$T = \pi\sqrt{\frac{29a}{g}}$$

C-4.

$$m = \frac{KR}{2g}$$

C-5.

a) $T = 2\pi\sqrt{\frac{m_1 m_2}{K(m_1 + m_2)}}$

b) reduced mass

c) $E = \frac{1}{2} kA^2$

d) $\frac{E_1}{E_2} = \frac{m_2}{m_1}$

C-6.

$t \approx 5.3$ s

C-7.

$$\theta_0' = \sqrt{\frac{I}{I + ma^2}}\,\theta_0$$

C-9.

$T = 2\pi\sqrt{\frac{2A}{g}}$; $a = A\sqrt{2}$; $k = A(\sqrt{2} - 1)$

C-10.

49 cm.

CHAPTER 18

B-1.

$$y = \cos \frac{2k\pi}{n} + i \sin \frac{2k\pi}{n} \qquad k = 0,1,2,\ldots,n-1$$

C-1.

$\log_{11} 2 = 0.289$

$\log_{11} 7 = 0.811$

CHAPTER 19

A-2.

$\frac{10^4}{2\pi}$ Hz

A-3.

$\approx 377\sqrt{2}\ \Omega$

A-4.

$L \approx 71$ mH

A-5.

$C \approx 3.3 \times 10^{-3}$ μF

A-6.

a) $\hat{Z} = i(\omega L - \frac{1}{\omega C})$

b) $\hat{Z} = \frac{i\omega L}{1 - \omega^2 LC}$

A-7.

a) $\frac{1}{C} = \frac{1}{C_1} + \frac{1}{C_2}$

b) $C = C_1 + C_2$

A-8.

a) $L = L_1 + L_2$

b) $\frac{1}{L} = \frac{1}{L_1} + \frac{1}{L_2}$

A-9.

a) $\omega_0 = \frac{1}{\sqrt{3LC}}$

b) $\omega_0 = \frac{1}{\sqrt{3LC}}$

A-10.

$T = \frac{L}{R}$

A-11.

$Q \sim 10^4$

B-1.

c) $x = A e^{-\left(\frac{\gamma}{2} + \sqrt{\frac{\gamma^2}{4} - \omega_0^2}\right)t} + Be^{-\left(\frac{\gamma}{2} - \sqrt{\frac{\gamma^2}{4} - \omega_0^2}\right)t}$

d) $A = x_0$

$B = \frac{2v_0 + \gamma x_0}{\sqrt{4\omega_0^2 - \gamma^2}}$

B-2.

a) $v = v_0 e^{-\frac{\gamma}{m}t}$

b) $v = v_0 - \frac{\gamma}{m}(x - x_0)$

B-3.

a) $v_\infty = \frac{g \sin\theta}{\gamma}$

b) $v(t) = \frac{g \sin\theta}{\gamma}(1 - e^{-\gamma t})$

c) $x(t) = \frac{g \sin\theta}{\gamma}(t + \frac{e^{-\gamma t} - 1}{\gamma})$

B-4.

42.8 m

B-5.

A = 5.75 cm

B-6.

a) $5\frac{d^2x}{dt^2} + .693\frac{dx}{dt} + 20\pi^2 x = 0$

b) 1.00006 s

c) 20, 33

d) $\sim$ 1.1 W

B-7.

$V = V_0 e^{-\frac{t}{RC}}$

B-8.

Undamped, damped, overdamped oscillation.

B-9.

a) $Z_L = i\omega L$

b) $Z_C = \frac{1}{i\omega C}$

B-12.

a) $I_0 = \frac{1}{16}$ A

b) $\Delta = 0$

B-13.

$I_R = 0$

$I_{L_{max}} = V_0\sqrt{\frac{C}{L}}$

B-14.

a) $C_1 = \frac{1}{\omega^2 L}$

b) $C_2 = \frac{C_1}{1 - \omega RC_1}$

c) $\frac{I_1}{I_2} = \sqrt{2}$

B-15.

a) $\Delta E = \frac{1}{2}\frac{C_1 C_2}{C_1 + C_2} V_0^{\ 2}$

b) $V_1 = V_2 = \frac{C_1}{C_1 + C_2} V_0$

B-16.

a) $t \approx 16.1$ s

b) 0

B-17.

$V_{max} = \frac{V_0}{R}\sqrt{\frac{L}{C}}$

B-18.

$V_{max} = 10\sqrt{2}$

B-19.

$V_0' = V_0$

$|V_2'| \approx \frac{|V_2|}{7.6}$

B-20.

a) $A = \frac{1}{2}\frac{h}{(1 - 4\pi^2 \frac{L}{gT^2})}$

b) 1.3 ft

c) 106.3 ft

B-21.

a) $\omega_0 = \sqrt{\frac{k}{M}}$

b) $x = \frac{e\omega^2}{\omega_0^{\ 2} - \omega^2}$ in dir. of e.

c) $\omega_{cr} = \omega_0$

d) $\omega_{cr} = \omega_0$

e) CM on center line

C-1.

a) 1) $x = \frac{F_0}{k} + (x_0 - \frac{F_0}{k}) \cdot e^{-\frac{\gamma}{2}t}(\cos\omega_\gamma t + \frac{\gamma}{2\omega_\gamma}\sin\omega_\gamma t)$

$\omega_\gamma = \sqrt{\omega_0^{\ 2} - \frac{\gamma^2}{4}}$; $\omega_0^{\ 2} = \frac{k}{m}$

2) $x = \frac{J}{m\omega_\gamma} e^{-\frac{\gamma}{2}t} \sin\omega_\gamma t$

3) $x = \frac{F_0}{\gamma\sqrt{km}} \sin\omega_0 t$

$+ e^{-\frac{\gamma}{2}t}\left[x_0\cos\omega_\gamma t - \frac{1}{\omega_\gamma}\left(\frac{F_0}{m\gamma} - \frac{\gamma}{2}x_0\right) \cdot \sin\omega_\gamma t\right]$

b) $\omega^* = \sqrt{\omega_0^{\ 2} - \gamma^2/2}$

C-2.

a) $m\ddot{x} - mg\mu + kx = 0$

$$A_0 = \begin{cases} B \\ \dfrac{2m\mu g}{k} - B \end{cases}$$

$$A_1 = \begin{cases} \dfrac{2m\mu g}{k} + B \\ \dfrac{4m\mu g}{k} - B \end{cases}$$

$$A_2 = \begin{cases} \dfrac{4m\mu g}{k} + B \\ \dfrac{6m\mu g}{k} - B \end{cases}$$

etc.

C-3.

$$A = \frac{qE_0}{\omega^2\sqrt{m^2 + \alpha^2\omega^2}}$$

$$\triangle = \pi + \tan^{-1}\frac{\alpha\omega}{m}$$

C-4.

$v \approx 7.2\ s^{-1}$.

C-8.

a) 2A

b) 16.9 kV

c) 35 μs

C-9.

V = 46.5 mph

CHAPTER 20

B-1.

a) AK = 50 ft

b) t = 60.0 s

c) t = 60.1 s

B-2.

a) PP' = 0.0387 m

b) $\frac{\Delta t}{t_0} = 0.11$

B-3.

$\emptyset \approx 11.2^{\circ}$

B-7.

a) $x_0 = \frac{R}{2}$

b) $\frac{\Delta x_0}{x_0} = -0.02$

B-8.

x = 200 cm

D 1.86 cm

B-9.

a) 6.7×10^{-5} m

b) 8.5×10^{-2} m

B-10.

$$y = \pm\sqrt{2F\, x\,(1 - \frac{1}{n}) - x^2\,(1 - \frac{1}{n^2})}$$

or $$\frac{y^2}{F^2\,(\frac{n-1}{n+1})} + \frac{(x - \frac{Fn}{n+1})^2}{(\frac{Fn}{n+1})^2} = 1$$

B-11.

$d = \frac{d'}{n}$

B-12.

4 cm from center.

B-13.

y = 1.92 R

B-14.

d = 2.0 cm

B-15.

$M = \frac{F}{f}$

B-16.

$$\frac{1}{F} = \frac{1}{f} + \frac{1}{f'} - \frac{D}{ff'}\,;$$

$$\Delta = \frac{fD}{f + f' - D}$$ (toward L' from L);

$$\Delta' = \frac{f'D}{f + f' - D}$$ (toward L from L').

B-17.

a) $4\frac{1}{6} - 5$ cm

b) 6,5

B-18.

x = 5.2 cm

B-19.

r = 1.6 cm

B-20.

a) $d_2 > d_1$

b) away

c) $f = \frac{L_2 d_2}{D + d_2} = \frac{L_1 d_1}{D + d_1}$

C-1.

Case 1: $y^2 = \frac{4Dd}{(D - d)^2}\left[\left(x - \frac{D + d}{2}\right)^2 - \frac{(D - d)^2}{4}\right]$

hyperbola

Case 2: $(2d + D)^2 y^2 + 4d(d + D)(x - \frac{D}{2})^2$

$= 4d(d + D)\left[(d + D)d - \frac{D^2}{4}\right].$

ellipse

P = origin of coordinates.

C-2.

$f = \frac{g}{2\omega^2}$

CHAPTER 21

B-1.

$$\vec{E}(t) = \frac{q}{4\pi\epsilon_0 c^2} \frac{a\omega^2}{R} \left[\hat{e}_x \cos \omega(t - \frac{r}{c}) + \hat{e}_y \cos \omega(t - \frac{r}{c} - \frac{\pi}{2}) \cos \theta \right]$$

$$I(\theta = \frac{\pi}{2}) = \frac{1}{2} \left(\frac{q\ a\ \omega^2}{4\pi\epsilon_0 c^2 R} \right)^2$$

$$I(\theta = 0) = \left(\frac{q\ a\ \omega^2}{4\pi\epsilon_0 c^2 R} \right)^2$$

B-2.

$$P = \frac{3}{8\pi} \frac{\sin^2\theta}{R^2} P_{total}$$

$$P = 2.4 \times 10^{-11}\ Wm^{-2}$$

B-3.

S:I = .17 I_0

S 60°W:I = 3.0 I_0

W:I = 5.8 I_0

B-4.

$$I(\theta) = I_0 \frac{\sin^2[\pi(1 + \sin\theta)]}{\sin^2\left[\frac{\pi}{4}(1 + \sin\theta)\right]}$$

B-5.

a) $I = 2I_0 \left[1 + \cos\left(\pi \sin\theta\right)\right]$

b) $I = 2I_0 \left[1 + \cos\left(\frac{\pi}{2}(1 + 2\sin\theta)\right)\right]$

B-6.

$a = 2\lambda$

$b = \frac{2\lambda}{\sqrt{3}}$

B-7.

a) $\vec{E}(t) = 0$ (b) $\vec{E}(t) = \frac{\sqrt{2}\, q\omega^2 d}{4\pi\epsilon_0 c^2 R} \sin \omega\,(t - \frac{R}{c})$

B-8.

$$\frac{d\alpha}{dt} = -\frac{\cos\theta}{120}\ \text{Hz}$$

B-9.

C: $I = 5I_A$

$\theta = 26.5°$ w/r x-axis

D: $I = I_A$

left hand circular polarization

E: $I = I_A$

normal to (x,y) plane

B-10.

$$I = 2I_0 \left[1 + \cos\left(\frac{\pi}{2}(1 - \cos\theta)\right)\right] \cdot \frac{\sin^2\left(\frac{N\pi}{2}\sin\theta\right)}{\sin^2\left(\frac{\pi}{2}\sin\theta\right)}$$

B-11.

$$\vec{E}(t) = \frac{q}{2\pi\epsilon_0 c^2} \frac{\omega c}{R} \sin\left(\frac{L\omega}{2c}\cos\theta\right) \cos\omega \cdot \left(t - \frac{R}{c}\right)$$

CHAPTER 22

A-1.

$Q \sim 5.5 \times 10^6$

B-1.

9.1 km

B-2.

$x = 1.6$ mm

B-3.

$$I(Z) = \frac{1}{\alpha_1^2} + \frac{1}{\alpha_2^2} + \frac{2}{\alpha_1\alpha_2} \cos\left\{\frac{2\pi}{\lambda}(\alpha_1 - \alpha_2) + \pi\right\}$$

where $\alpha_1 = \sqrt{(Z - d)^2 + D^2}$

$\alpha_2 = \sqrt{(Z + d)^2 + D^2}$

B-4.

a) $r = \lambda\sqrt{10.25}$

b) $I \approx \frac{1}{4} I_{max}$

B-5.

a) $$\frac{I_\theta}{I_{max}} = \frac{\sin^2 \frac{\beta}{2}}{\left(\frac{\beta}{2}\right)^2} \frac{1 + \cos\varphi}{2}$$

where $\beta = 4\pi \sin\theta$

$\varphi = 8\pi \sin\theta$

b) 5; $\theta \simeq 0°, 14.5°, 30°, 48.5°, 90°$

c) $1, \frac{4}{\pi^2}, 0, \frac{4}{9\pi^2}, 0$

C-2.

$$\frac{I_t}{I_0} = \frac{T^4}{(1 - 2R^2\cos 2\varphi + R^4)} = \frac{T^4}{2R^2(1 - \cos 2\varphi) + T^4} \quad \text{where } \varphi = \frac{2\pi D}{\lambda}$$

C-3.

a) $h' = h\frac{F_2}{F_1}$

b) $\lambda_n(\text{Å}) = \frac{10^7}{nN}\left|\sin\theta_i - \sin\theta_d\right|$

c) $D(\text{mm}) = 10^{-7}\frac{n\,NF_2}{\cos\theta_d}$

d) $\omega' = \omega\frac{F_2}{F_1}\frac{\cos\theta_i}{\cos\theta_d}$

C-4.

a) $\theta = 51.9°$

b) $\lambda = 3750, 4370, 6560$

d) 5.6 mm Å^{-1}

e) 7×10^{-3} Å

CHAPTER 23

B-1.

$(1 - n) = 8.4 \times 10^{-6}$

B-2.

$\sim 10^{7}\ \mathrm{cm}^{-3}$

B-3.

$$I = I_0\, e^{-\frac{Nq^2}{\epsilon_0 m\gamma c}}$$

C-1.

a) $$P = \frac{q^2\omega^4 x_0^2}{12\pi\epsilon_0 c^3}$$

b) $$\gamma_R = \frac{q^2\omega^2}{6\pi\epsilon_0 mc^3}$$

c) $$\Delta\lambda = \frac{2\pi c}{\omega^2}\ \gamma_R = 1.2 \times 10^{-4}\ \text{Å}$$

CHAPTER 24

B-3.

$N_e \sim 10^7 \text{ cm}^{-3}$

B-4.

a) 1.5%

b) 9%

B-5.

a) $\sigma = \dfrac{N^2 \chi^2 q^2 \omega^4}{6\pi\epsilon_0^2 c^4} \left(\dfrac{E_{\parallel}}{E_0}\right)^2$

b) $\dfrac{\sigma_\theta}{\sigma} = \cos^2\theta$

CHAPTER 25

A-3.

$$I_t = \frac{I}{8} \sin^2 2\theta$$

B-1.

Intensity: see 21-B-1

a) circular polarization

b) linear

B-2.

$$\frac{I_t}{I_0} = \frac{1}{2} (\alpha^4 + \epsilon^4) \cos^2\theta + \alpha^2\epsilon^2 \sin^2\theta$$

B-3.

$\frac{I_R}{I_0} \sim 34.5^\circ$, and girl friend leaves in disgust!

B-5.

a) 17%

b) 67.4°

B-6.

$$I_t = I_0 \cos^{2n} \frac{\theta}{n}$$

B-7.

$$I_{max}/I_{min} = \cot^2\theta$$

B-9.

a) 1.67×10^{-2} mm

b) elliptical polarization

$$E_x = E_0 \cos\varphi \cos\omega t$$

$$E_y = E_0 \sin\varphi \cos(\omega t + 0.7 \times 2\pi)$$

where φ = dir. of polarization of incident light.

CHAPTER 26

A-6.

1.5×10^8 km

B-2.

$\nu_1 = 1.67\ \nu_0$

$\tan \theta_1 = 0.75$

B-3.

$$v = c\,\frac{\nu_0 - \nu'}{\nu_0 + \nu'}$$

B-4.

$\frac{v}{c} = 7.6 \times 10^{-6}$

B-5.

Approaching at 510 km s^{-1}

B-6.

$v/c \approx .8$

C-1.

a) $$\ddot{x}(t) = -\frac{v^2 x}{R^2}\,\frac{1 + \frac{vR}{cx}}{\left(1 + \frac{vx}{cR}\right)^3}$$

b) $$\frac{I_{max}}{I_{min}} = \frac{\left(1 + \frac{v}{c}\right)^4}{\left(1 - \frac{v}{c}\right)^4}$$

C-2.

$$\vec{E}_x(t,R_0) = -\frac{q_e}{4\pi\epsilon_0 c^2 R_0}\,\frac{\vec{a}\sin\theta}{(1 - \beta\cos\theta)^3} \quad \text{for } t \geq \frac{R_0}{c}$$

C-3.

a) $$F = \frac{I_0 A}{C}$$

b) $$F \approx .16\,\frac{I_0 A}{C}\left(1 - \cos\frac{6\pi d}{\lambda}\right)$$

c) $$F = \frac{I_0 A}{C}\left(1 - e^{-\frac{4\pi}{\lambda} n_2 d}\right)$$

C-4.

$F = 1.3 \times 10^{-2}$ N

C-5.

$\frac{dR}{dt} = 360$ m s^{-1}

C-6.

b) $R \approx \frac{6 \times 10^{-4}}{\rho}$ m $\quad [\rho] =$ kg m^{-3}

CHAPTER 27

A-2.

$\sin\theta = \frac{h}{p_0 w}$

A-3.

a) 1.8 Å

b) i) 0.39 Å

ii) 8.7×10^{-3} Å

c) 1.3×10^{-25} Å

d) x-ray.

A-4.

6150 Å

A-5.

910 Å, UV

A-6.

2.6×10^{-3} Å

A-7.

$E = h\sqrt{\frac{\beta}{m}}$

A-8.

$\tau \sim 8 \times 10^{-10}$ s

A-9.

620 MeV

A-10.

5×10^{-13} cm

A-13.

a) 11.3 eV

b) 3.3×10^{15} Hz.

B-1.

a) $7^\circ.1$

b) 21.6 m

c) 1.9, 2.7, 3.3, 4.3 m

B-2.

$15^\circ.7$, $22^\circ.2$, $27^\circ.4$, $32^\circ.2$, $36^\circ.5$

B-3.

6560 Å, 4860 Å, 18840 Å.

B-4.

33 eV

B-5.

a) $\theta \simeq \frac{\pi}{4}$

b) 2.1×10^{-21} J

B-6.

a) 3°, $.3^\circ$.

C-1.

a) 8.3×10^{-4} Å

b) $3\sqrt{2}$ m

c) 2.46 eV

C-2.

a) $$r_n = \frac{4\pi\epsilon_0 n^2 \hbar^2}{me^2}$$

$$\omega = \frac{me^4}{(4\pi\epsilon_0)^2 n^3 \hbar^3}$$

b) $$T_n = \frac{me^4}{2(4\pi\epsilon_0)^2 n^2 \hbar^2}$$

$$U_n = -\frac{me^4}{(4\pi\epsilon_0)^2 n^2 \hbar^2}$$

$$E_n = -T_n$$

c) $$\Delta E \propto \left(\frac{1}{n_f^2} - \frac{1}{n_i^2}\right)$$

CHAPTER 28

B-1.

$P^{\gamma-1}/T^{\gamma}$ = const.

$TV^{\gamma-1}$ = const.

B-2.

a) $P_A = 3.17\ P_0$

$P_b = 2.64\ P_0$

b) 1.1

B-3.

$$P_f = \frac{P_1 + P_2}{2}$$

$$T_f = \frac{T_1 T_2 (P_1 + P_2)}{P_1 T_2 + T_1 P_2}$$

B-4.

$P = P_0\ e^{-\mu gh/RT}$

B-5.

1.82×10^5 J

B-6.

173°C

B-7.

20 cm Hg

B-8.

842 mm Hg

B-9.

a) 1740°K

b) 5.8

C-1.

a) $T_f = T_0$

$P_f = \frac{P_0}{2}$

b) $T_f = \frac{T_0}{2^{\gamma-1}}$

$P_f = \frac{P_1}{2^{\gamma}}$

C-2.

$$\frac{dT}{dh} = - \frac{\gamma - 1}{\gamma} \frac{\mu g}{R}$$

$\approx -\ 0.01°/\text{m}$

C-3.

$$\omega^2 = \left(\frac{P_0 A}{L_0} + K\right)/m$$

C-4.

31%

CHAPTER 29

A-3.

$C_V = \frac{5}{2}$ R/mole

B-1.

a) 3/2 R

b) 5/2 R

B-2.

$h_\oplus = 8.8$ km

$h_\odot = 113$ km

B-3.

$$P(h = 0) = \frac{Nmg}{A} \frac{e^{mgL/kT}}{e^{mgL/kT} - 1}$$

$$P(h = L) = \frac{Nmg}{A} \frac{1}{e^{mgL/kT} - 1}$$

B-4.

a) $f = \dfrac{m_1}{m_1 + m_2 e^{-(m_1 + m_2)gh/kT}}$

b) $1 - e^{-m_1/m_2}$

B-6.

$$F(E)dE = A\sqrt{\frac{2E}{m^3}}\; e^{-E/kT}\, dE$$

B-7.

a) $k = \dfrac{2N}{V^2}$

b) $\langle v \rangle = \dfrac{2V}{3}$

$v_{rms} = \dfrac{V}{\sqrt{2}}$

B-8.

a) 0.55

b) 0.06

B-9.

$$P_1/P_2 = \sqrt{\frac{T_1}{T_2}}$$

B-10.

a) $A\,\frac{n}{4}\,vf(v)dv,\; f(v) = \frac{4}{\sqrt{\pi}}\left(\frac{m}{2kT}\right)^{3/2} \cdot v^2 e^{-\frac{mv^2}{2kT}}$

b) $v_{rms}^{(e)} = \sqrt{\dfrac{4kT}{m}}$

$v_{rms}^{(0)} = \sqrt{\dfrac{3kT}{m}}$

C-1.

$\Delta\lambda \approx 0.012$ Å

C-2.

1.2×10^{5} °K

C-3.

$\approx 10^{-9}$

C-4.

$F = \frac{\pi}{3}\sqrt{\frac{2\pi m}{kT}}$ (depends on approx. used.)

C-5.

1. a) $v' = -\dfrac{P}{(\gamma - 1)\rho v} + \sqrt{\left(\dfrac{P}{(\gamma - 1)\rho v} + v\right)^2 + \dfrac{2W}{\rho v A}}$

b) $T' = \dfrac{T}{v}\, v'$

c) $F = \rho v A\, (v' - v)$

2. $F \approx 5.3 \times 10^4$ N

CHAPTER 30

A-1.

a) $11,600^{\circ}K$

b) 1/40 eV

c) 12400 Å

A-2.

96,520 J/g-mole

B-1.

~ 100%

B-2.

$\approx 10^{-5}$

C-3.

$$C_V = \frac{3N_0 k \left(\frac{\Delta E}{kT}\right)^2 e^{\Delta E/kT}}{(3 + e^{\Delta E/kT})^2}$$

CHAPTER 31

A-2.

1.8×10^3 cm

B-1.

$\ell \sim 10^{-7}$ m

$\tau \sim 0.2 \times 10^{-9}$s

B-2.

a) 11×10^{-4} mm Hg

b) 1

B-3.

$$\mu = \frac{\mu_a \mu_b}{\mu_a + \mu_b}$$

B-6.

$$\frac{dE}{dt} = \frac{1}{4} \frac{n_0 \bar{v} k \Delta T}{\gamma - 1}$$

$$\frac{F}{A} = \frac{1}{4} n_0 \bar{v} m \Delta U$$

C-1.

$L = 56\ell$ (= $\ell \ln 2N$ for 50% chance)

C-4.

a) $V_D = \frac{d^2}{\ell ce} \frac{\sqrt{3mc^2 kT}}{t}$

b) $t_e = 4 \times 10^{-7}$s electrons are essential

$t_I = 8 \times 10^{-5}$s

CHAPTER 32

A-1.

1.4 J

A-2.

1/9 J

A-3.

He-engine

A-4.

66%

B-1.

a) $T_i = \dfrac{4(P + Mg/A)V_1}{NR}$

$T_f = \dfrac{8(P + Mg/A)V_1}{NR}$

b) $(P + Mg/A)V_1$

c) $\frac{3}{2}(P + Mg/A)V_1$

d) $\frac{5}{2}(P + Mg/A)V_1$

B-2.

b) 101 J

c) $1200^\circ K$

d) $\dfrac{2\gamma + 1}{\gamma - 1}\, n\, RT_0$

e) $\dfrac{\gamma + 1}{\gamma - 1} \times 0.23\ J/^\circ K$

B-3.

a) $1.1 \times 10^3 J$

b) $600^\circ K$

c) $6.8 \times 10^3 J$

d) $9.1 \times 10^3 J$

e) 7%

f) 66%

B-4.

b) $27.8\ J/^\circ K$

B-5.

a) $V_b = 8.8\ \ell$

$V_d = 12.3\ \ell$

b) $1.25 \times 10^3\ J$

c) $0.95 \times 10^3\ J$

d) 25%

e) $0.11\ J/^\circ Kg$

B-6.

$\gamma = 1.57$

$\Delta s = -1.4\ cal/^\circ K$

B-7.

$$\Delta W = p_0 V_0 \left\{ \frac{2^{\gamma-1} - 1}{\gamma - 1} - \ln 2 \right\}$$

B-9.

day: 10.9 KW

night: 24.6 KW

B-10.

b) $W = C_p\ (T_1 + T_2 - 2T_f)$

B-11.

$11 \times 10^3\ J/^\circ K$

C-1.

a) $\dot{W} = \dot{N}R \dfrac{\gamma}{(\gamma - 1)} [T_c + T_A - T_c p^{-(1-1/\gamma)} - T_A p^{-(1-1/\gamma)}]$

b) $p_m = \left(\dfrac{T_c}{T_A}\right)^{\frac{\gamma}{2(\gamma - 1)}}$

c) $\dot{W}m = \dot{N}R \dfrac{\gamma}{(\gamma - 1)} (\sqrt{T_c} - \sqrt{T_A})^2$

d) $\epsilon = 1 - \sqrt{\dfrac{T_A}{T_c}}$

e) $\dot{V}_A = 2.8 \ m^3 s^{-1}$

f) $\epsilon = 50\%$

g) $p_m = 11.3$

CHAPTER 33

A-3.

$C_v = \frac{16\sigma}{c} VT^3$

A-4.

a) .85 cal/°K

b) .85 cal/°K

B-2.

-2.9 °K/km

B-3.

$\frac{dz}{dt} = \frac{K}{L\rho}\left(\frac{\Delta T}{z}\right)$

z(t = 1 h) = 2.1 cm.

B-4.

1. a) ~ 16 J/°K
   b) 0
   c) ~ 16 J/°K
2. 0,0,0

B-5.

a) $(\Delta S)_T = \frac{16\sigma}{3c} T^3 \Delta V$

b) $(\Delta S)_V = \frac{16\sigma}{3c} V(T_2{}^3 - T_1{}^3)$

$S(V,T) = S(V_0,T_0) + \frac{16}{3}\frac{\sigma}{c}(VT^3 - V_0T_0{}^3)$

B-6.

122°C

B-7.

≈ 270°K

B-8.

f = 1

B-9.

$T = T_0 e^{-\frac{3Ac}{16R}t}$

B-10.

a) F = 64

b) larger

B-11.

F = 4

B-12.

a) 1.95×10^{-4} J s^{-1}

b) 0.06 °K s^{-1}

B-13.

$P_G = 1.7 \times 10^{16}$ Nm^{-2}

$P_R = 7.2 \times 10^{12}$ Nm^{-2}

C-4.

$F = \frac{R^2}{R^2 + r^2}$

CHAPTER 34

A-1.

$$v \propto \sqrt{\frac{M}{\rho}}$$

A-2.

$$\sqrt{\frac{1}{2}}$$

A-3.

0.77

A-4.

$99^{o}C$

B-2.

$$\frac{\partial^2 y}{\partial x^2} = \frac{\sigma}{T} \frac{\partial^2 y}{\partial t^2}$$

B-3.

a) $\nu = \frac{1}{2\pi} \sqrt{\frac{T}{m} \frac{\ell}{x(\ell - x)}}$

b) $y(t) = A \cos \sqrt{\frac{T}{m} \frac{\ell}{x(\ell - x)}}\ t$

c) $\nu_{max} = \infty$

$\nu_{min} = \frac{1}{\pi} \sqrt{\frac{T}{m\ell}}$

B-4.

a) $P = P_0 - \frac{\omega^2 \xi_m}{k} \sin(\omega t - kx)$

b) $K.E. = \frac{1}{4} \rho_0 A \lambda \omega^2 \xi_m{}^2$

B-5.

a) $x_m = 1.05 \times 10^{-2}$ cm

b) $\Delta T = 2.18 \times 10^{-2}\ {}^{o}K$

C-1.

2.95

C-3.

a) 8.7×10^{-7} kg m^{-3}

b) 3.6×10^{-8} m

c) 1.1×10^{-5} W m^{-2}

CHAPTER 35

A-1.

$v_{ph} = v_g = c$

A-3.

$v_{ph} = 39.5 \text{ m s}^{-1}$

$v_g = 19.7 \text{ m s}^{-1}$

A-4.

6 modes

A-5.

$$u(x,y,t) = Ae^{i\omega t} \sin \frac{\pi}{a} x \sin \frac{\pi}{b} y$$

$$\omega = c\sqrt{\frac{\pi^2}{a^2} + \frac{\pi^2}{b^2}}$$

B-2.

$$v_g = \frac{1}{2}\left[v_{ph} + \frac{\frac{4\pi T}{\rho\lambda}}{v_{ph}}\right]$$

B-3.

a) 24.4 cm s^{-1}

b) 18.3 cm s^{-1}

B-4.

$\lambda_{min} = 1.7$ cm

$\nu_{min} = 13.6 \text{ s}^{-1}$

B-5.

a) 1.6 s^{-1}

b) 0.03 s

c) 363 m s^{-1}

B-6.

$\sim 10 \text{ s}^{-1}$

B-7.

b) $\omega_0 = \frac{7}{6} \frac{v\pi}{a}$

B-8.

a) $$\frac{d^2x}{dt^2} + \omega_0^2 x + k(x - y)/m_1 = 0$$

$$\frac{d^2y}{dt^2} + \omega_0^2 y + k(y - x)/m_2 = 0$$

b) $\omega_1^2 = \omega_0^2 \quad A/B = 1$

$\omega_2^2 = \omega_0^2 + k/m_1 + k/m_2 \quad A/B = -\frac{m_2}{m_1}$

B-9.

1) $\omega_1 = \sqrt{g/\ell} \quad (x_1 = x_2 = x_3)$

2) $\omega_2 = \sqrt{\frac{g}{\ell} + \frac{k}{m}} \quad (x_1 = -x_3;\ x_2 = 0)$

3) $\omega_3 = \sqrt{\frac{g}{\ell} + \frac{2k}{m}} \quad (x_1 = x_3;\ x_2 = -\frac{(x_1+x_3)}{2} = -x_1)$

B-10.

$$T_1 = \frac{T_0}{\sqrt{2.62}}$$

$$T_2 = \frac{T_0}{\sqrt{.38}} \quad ; \quad T_0 = 2\pi\sqrt{\frac{I}{K}}$$

B-11.

$$\omega_1 = \sqrt{\frac{0.38\ k}{m}}$$

$$\omega_2 = \sqrt{\frac{2.62\ k}{m}}$$

B-12.

$$\omega_1 = \sqrt{\frac{2k}{m}}$$

$$\omega_2 = \sqrt{\frac{6k}{m}}$$

C-1.

$\frac{\sigma\omega^2 A^2}{4} \lambda$

C-2.

a) $\frac{h^2}{2mL^2}$

b) $\frac{h^2}{8mL^2}$

c) $\langle p \rangle = 0$

CHAPTER 36

B-2.

a) $g(x) = 1/2 - \frac{4}{\pi^2}(\cos x + \frac{1}{9}\cos 3x + \frac{1}{25}\cos 5x + \ldots)$

B-4.

$\frac{A_1}{A_0} = 1$

$\frac{A_2}{A_0} = 0$

$\frac{A_3}{A_0} = \frac{1}{9}$

B-5.

$h(x) = \frac{1}{2} - \frac{1}{\pi}(\sin x + \frac{1}{2}\sin 2x + \frac{1}{3}\sin 3x + \ldots)$

B-6.

a) $T = 2L\sqrt{\frac{\sigma}{s}}$

b) $y(T/2) = -y(0)$

C-1.

a) $\langle V(t) \rangle = \frac{2V_0}{\pi}$

b) $\frac{4}{15}\frac{V_0}{\pi}$

C-2.

a) $V_{out} = \left(1 + \frac{3}{4}\epsilon\right)\sin x - \frac{\epsilon}{4}\sin 3x$